Orbitals *in* Atoms *and* Molecules

Orbitals *in* Atoms *and* Molecules

CHR. KLIXBÜLL JØRGENSEN

Cyanamid European Research Institute
Cologny, Geneva, Switzerland

ACADEMIC PRESS
LONDON and NEW YORK · 1962

ACADEMIC PRESS INC. (LONDON) LTD.
BERKELEY SQUARE HOUSE
BERKELEY SQUARE, LONDON, W.1

U.S. edition published by
ACADEMIC PRESS INC.
111 FIFTH AVENUE
NEW YORK 3, NEW YORK

Library of Congress Catalog Card Number: 62–18531

Printed in Great Britain by
W. & J. Mackay & Co Ltd, Chatham

Preface

This book attempts to point out various common features in the description of many-electron systems both in atomic spectroscopy and in the case of less complicated polyatomic molecules. The latter has been the subject of considerable research during recent years, the energy levels of transition group complexes involving a partly filled shell now being much better understood than in 1950. The art of the application of group theory and the avoidance of certain exaggerated conclusions makes up the main part of this present work. The degenerate orbitals with identical one-electron energies occurring in certain high symmetries such as the spherical and octahedral permit various unifying generalizations to be made.

In an interdisciplinary topic somewhere between physics and chemistry, it is inevitable that the nomenclature will appear unusual to some of the readers. Thus Roman numerals in parentheses as in Cr (III) and Ir (IV) are used for oxidation numbers of atoms involved in molecular formation, as also Ni (0) and Cl ($-$I). On the other hand, gaseous ions are denoted Fe^{++} and U^{+4} and not, as frequently done by atomic spectroscopists, by Roman numerals one unit higher, FeIII and UV. Polyatomic entities are written with their usual chemical formula, $Mn(H_2O)_6^{++}$ and $PtBr_6^{--}$, etc.

It is a pleasure to acknowledge many valuable discussions with my old colleague, Dr. Claus Schäffer, now at the Laboratory of Inorganic Chemistry, University of Copenhagen, and with Professor Jannik Bjerrum who is now Director of this laboratory. I have also received most useful encouragement with various parts of this book resulting from discussions with Dr. Richard Trees, National Bureau of Standards, Washington, D.C., and with Dr. Richard E. Watson and Dr. R. K. Nesbet. Also Professor Robert Satten was most helpful in connection with Chapter 11 on f shells. Finally, I would once more express my gratitude to Professor Per-Olov Löwdin, for his invitation to deliver lectures to his Quantum Chemistry Group in Uppsala in February 1958. Although originally I was a sort of inorganic chemist (or inorganic physicist, as has been suggested) this offer had a most beneficial catalytic effect, and but for this opportunity this book could not have been written.

Chr. Klixbüll Jørgensen

May, 1962

v

Contents

Contents

1. Well-defined Electron Configurations

The fundamental idea most useful for the description of many-electron systems, i.e. atoms, molecules, and solids, is the *electron configuration*. As we shall elaborate, the assumption of one-electron wavefunctions, *orbitals* ψ, occupied by zero, one or at most two electrons (in the latter case with opposite spin direction) is only an approximation to the total wavefunction Ψ of the many-electron systems. In most cases, it is a fairly good approximation, but our main reason for accepting it is that, at present, any other, more sophisticated representation is much too complicated to be handled for more than some four or six electrons, restricting our field to isolated atoms such as carbon or molecules such as BeH_2. Actually, quantum mechanics in its most strict sense has only been applied to two-electron systems such as He and H_2, and, with some approximation, to Li, Be, and LiH. This is not as surprising when compared to classical mechanics, where a general solution was not found of the motion of three particles under their mutual gravitational attraction, whereas the solution (of great astronomical interest) of two particles is completely known. Both in quantum and classical mechanics, the difficulty is the same: the appropriate equations are very clear-cut, but they cannot be explicitly solved at present.

However, there are many reasons to be much more optimistic regarding electron systems of importance to atomic spectroscopy and chemistry, rather than regarding nuclei. Though the nuclei most definitely show evidence of shell structure in the same way as atomic electron systems, the interactions between the neutrons and protons are not known at present with any degree of accuracy. On the other hand, the *only potentials of importance in electron systems are electromagnetic*. Running the usual risk of conservative minds, we may even affirm that there is good evidence that, if any other interaction was of importance in electron systems, it would already have been discovered. (We may recall that the gravitational potential is 10^{40} times weaker than the electromagnetic interaction between charged elementary particles.) In addition by far the greater part of the interaction in electron systems is *purely electrostatic*. The rest are called electrodynamic or relativistic effects and they are only important for electrons coming close to nuclei with high atomic number Z.

In this chapter, we shall restrict ourselves to the electrostatic effects. Following Mulliken, we use capital letters for quantities related to total systems and small letters for one-electron quantities. The virial theorem for an isolated atom relates the total energy $-T$, the sum of the electrostatic potential energy E_{pot} and the kinetic energy of the electrons E_{kin} by the equations

$$E_{pot} = -2T \text{ and } E_{kin} = T. \tag{1.1}$$

In systems with more than one nucleus, i.e. molecules, eq. (1.1) is only valid when the nuclei are at their equilibrium distances (or at very large mutual distances).

In the following, we write equations in atomic units, with the length unit 1 bohr$=a_0=0.528$ Å (1 Å$=10^{-8}$ cm) and the energy unit 1 rydberg$=109.7$ kK, representing the ionization energy T of a hydrogen atom with a very heavy nucleus. Many authors prefer the atomic unit 2 rydbergs ($=e^2/a_0$, where the electronic charge is $-e$). When indicating numerical results, we usually apply the rather convenient *kilokayser* kK, which is a unit of wavenumber of radiation, but also an energy unit when combined with Bohr's equation from 1913

$$E = h\sigma c, \tag{1.2}$$

the frequency ν of the radiation in sec^{-1} being the product of the wavenumber σ and the velocity of light *in vacuo* c, and h being Planck's constant. The relations between kK and some other energy units are:

$$
\begin{aligned}
&1 \text{ kK} = 1000 \text{ K} = 1000 \text{ cm}^{-1} \\
&1 \text{ eV} = 8.06 \text{ kK} \\
&1 \text{ kcal/mole} = 0.351 \text{ kK/molecule} \\
&1 \text{ joule/mole} = 8.4 \times 10^{-5} \text{ kK/molecule.}
\end{aligned}
\tag{1.3}
$$

For our purposes, we need only to consider real (and not complex) one-electron wavefunctions ψ. This restriction is essentially refraining from considering the effect of external magnetic fields on our system. The electron density in the usual three-dimensional space is then given simply by ψ^2.

One of the rather queer things about quantum mechanics is the relation between the kinetic energy e_{kin} and ψ^2, being dependent on the Laplace operator involving the second differential coefficient of ψ with respect to the Cartesian co-ordinates

$$e_{kin} = \int \frac{h^2}{4\pi^2 m} \left[\frac{\partial^2 \psi}{\partial x^2} + \frac{\partial^2 \psi}{\partial y^2} + \frac{\partial^2 \psi}{\partial z^2} \right] \psi \, d\tau. \tag{1.4}$$

The constant of nature $h^2/(4\pi^2 m)$ is adapted to be 1 in atomic units, and the integration with the differential $d\tau$ in the end symbolizes all ranges of the appropriate co-ordinates, here x, y, z between limits entirely including the region where ψ is different from zero. The wavefunction ψ is normalized when

$$\int \psi^2 d\tau = 1. \tag{1.5}$$

Two normalized wavefunctions ψ_1 and ψ_2 have an overlap integral

$$S_{12}=\int\psi_1\psi_2d\tau. \tag{1.6}$$

If the overlap integral is zero, ψ_1 and ψ_2 are said to be *orthogonal.*

The potential energy, expressing the attraction of the electron in ψ by the nuclei with charges $+Z_1e, +Z_2e, \ldots, +Z_qe$, has a much simpler formulation than eq. (1.4), *viz.*

$$e_{nuc}=-\sum_k\int\frac{Z_k}{r_k}\psi^2d\tau. \tag{1.7}$$

where r_k is the distance of the electron from the nucleus Z_k. Equation (1.7) is the same expression as in classical electrostatic theory for the potential energy of a charge distribution ψ^2 in the potential $U(x, y, z)=\Sigma_k(Z_k/r_k)$. In many cases, quantum-mechanical quantities Q are obtained by the integration of $Q\psi^2$ over $d\tau$, and it is therefore practical to introduce the bracket $<Q>$ as notation for the result, and to consider this bracket as the "average value" of Q for ψ^2. For instance, in an atom or gaseous ion with only one nucleus, it is reasonable to put the origin of the co-ordinate system at the nucleus and to define the unique distance r between the nucleus and the electron by

$$r^2=x^2+y^2+z^2 \tag{1.8}$$

in which case one can define average values of r^n for a given ψ^2

$$<r^n>=\int r^n\psi^2d\tau. \tag{1.9}$$

It is seen that eq. (1.7) reduces to $-Z<r^{-1}>$ for the nuclear charge Z. However, eqs. (1.7), (1.10), (1.11), (2.27), (2.29) and (2.45) have the energy unit 2 rydbergs.

The electrostatic energy of the total system is not a simple addition of the nuclear-electronic interaction e_{nuc} from eq. (1.7), but contains also a positive *interelectronic repulsion energy*, and if the system is a molecule, the internuclear repulsion energy which has a fairly simple expression:

$$E_{nuc}=\sum_{a\neq b}\frac{Z_aZ_b}{r_{ab}}, \tag{1.10}$$

each pair of nuclei taken once, involving only their distance r_{ab} and not the electronic wavefunctions. Unfortunately, nobody can maintain that the effects of interelectronic repulsion are simple, and we only begin to foresee the difficulties when regarding the approximation on which this book is based, the well-defined electron configuration of orthogonal ψ.

The total kinetic energy E_{kin} is here the summation of the one-electron energies e_{kin} of eq. (1.4), the nuclear-nuclear and nuclear-electronic contributions to the potential energy are given by eqs. (1.10) and (1.7) respectively, and the interelectronic repulsion energy can (in this simplified case) be written as sums of Coulomb integrals J(a, b) [in special cases J(a, a)] and "exchange" integrals K(a, b) defined by integrations over two electrons (in the orbitals ψ_a and ψ_b) at the time, with the mutual distance r_{12}:

$$J(a,\ b) = \int\int \frac{1}{r_{12}} \psi_a^2 d\tau_1 \psi_b^2 d\tau_2$$

$$K(a,\ b) = \int\int \frac{1}{r_{12}} \psi_a \psi_b d\tau_1 \psi_a \psi_b d\tau_2 \qquad (1.11)$$

where $J(a, b)$ represent the classical interaction between two extended charge distributions ψ_a^2 and ψ_b^2. This quantity would also occur in the classical theory, whereas $K(a, b)$ would have no place there. The latter quantity is the electrostatic interaction between the charge distribution $\psi_a\psi_b$ and itself, and still calculated according to classical formulae.

The interelectronic repulsion energy of the system is calculated by taking each pair of electrons, in their orbitals ψ_a and ψ_b (which must be identical or orthogonal), and reckon $J(a, b) - K(a, b)$ if their spins are parallel [i.e. $m_s(a) = m_s(b)$ where m_s can assume the values $+\frac{1}{2}$ or $-\frac{1}{2}$) and $J(a, b)$ if their spins are opposite $(m_s(a) = -m_s(b))$].

A common example is a configuration with a series of orbitals ψ_a, ψ_b, ... ψ_q all filled, i.e. occupied each by two electrons. We will denote such a configuration by the spectroscopic symbol $a^2 b^2$ . . . q^2 writing the number of electrons in each orbital as an exponent to the name of the orbital.

We saw above that the total electronic energy of this system can be written

$$E_{kin} = T = 2\sum_{k=a}^{q} e_{kin}(k)$$

$$E_{pot} = -2T = -2\sum_{k=a}^{q} e_{nuc}(k) + \sum_{k=a}^{q} J(k, k) + 4\sum_{a \neq b} J(a, b) - 2\sum_{a \neq b} K(a, b). \qquad (1.12)$$

The ionization energy of removing one electron from the orbital ψ_m can be calculated *assuming no rearrangement of the orbitals in the new configuration* $a^2 b^2$ . . . m^1 . . . q^2, being

$$I_m = e_{nuc}(m) - e_{kin}(m) - J(m, m) - 2\sum_{a \neq m} J(a, m) + \sum_{a \neq m} K(a, m). \qquad (1.13)$$

The assumption of no rearrangement of the orbitals has a close connection with Koopman's theorem that the ionization and excitation energies of a given configuration are very nearly the same, either making two different calculations of the total energy of the excited state and the ground state, or using eq. (1.13).

There is a certain appeal in the idea of expressing the total energy of a system as a sum of one-electron energies, but it is not easy to define these quantities in a consistent way. In a many-electron system, the genuine one-electron operator quantities $e_{nuc}(m) - e_{kin}(m)$ are usually much larger, frequently by a factor of ten for the loosest bound electrons, than I_m, the two-electron quantities (J and K integrals) cancelling most of the contribution from the two first terms. On the other hand, the sum of the ionization energies I_m (one electron taken at the time from the undamaged original system) is not equal to -1 times the total energy either, but is $-\Sigma J(k, k)$ too small. It might therefore seem proper to define one-electron energies as

$$i_m = I_m + \tfrac{1}{2}J(m, m) + \underset{a \neq m}{\Sigma J(a, m)} - \underset{a \neq m}{\tfrac{1}{2}\Sigma K(a, m)} \qquad (1.14)$$

which would make $T = \Sigma i_m$ and actually make the virial theorem for the system, eq. (1.1) valid for the individual one-electron energies:

$$-e_{kin}(m) = \tfrac{1}{2}[e_{nuc} - \tfrac{1}{2}J(m, m) - \underset{a \neq m}{\Sigma J(a, m)} + \underset{a \neq m}{\tfrac{1}{2}\Sigma K(a, m)}]. \qquad (1.15)$$

From the virial theorem for the system, it can be demonstrated that

$$T = \Sigma i_m = -\Sigma f_1 - \Sigma g_{12} = \Sigma I_m + \Sigma g_{12} \qquad (1.16)$$

the two-electron quantities g_{12} being taken twice in the summation of I_m, while the one-electron quantities f_1 are correctly taken into account. Of course, the sum of the *consecutive* ionization energies, gradually leading to the removal of all electrons from the nuclei, equals T.

There is no doubt, however, that the quantities i_m defined in eq. (1.14) have very little practical interest to chemists, the arithmetic mean i_m of I_m and the frequently much larger $f_1 = e_{nuc}(m) - e_{kin}(m)$ being much larger than I_m in many cases. These considerations mainly serve to demonstrate how difficult it is to define one-electron energies in both a consistent and satisfactory way.

We admit an expansion of our definition of "well-defined electron configuration" in the case of *degenerate sets of orbitals*. These sets of orbitals, having the same energy (in the sense of identical f_1 and certain conditions on the g_{12}), are extremely important in high symmetries, as we shall see, and are called *shells* in monatomic entities and *subshells* in molecules. If a number e of orbitals are degenerate, each subshell or shell in a well-defined configuration contains 0, 1, 2, 3, 4, . . . or $2e$ electrons, though it may not always be possible to assign an integral number of electrons to each definite orbital in the degenerate set.

Very frequently, the e orbitals ψ can be written in such a way that only three different parameters of interelectronic repulsion occur, *viz.* J(a, a), J(a, b), and K(a, b) where a and b are two different cases of the degenerate orbitals. Usually J(a, b) is much larger than K(a, b). This can be understood from eq. (1.11), since the charge density $\psi_a\psi_b$, being a product of two orthogonal wavefunctions, firstly has alternant positive or negative sign in various points of the space; secondly, K(a, b) has only positive contributions from places where the "squared overlap" $\psi_a{}^2\psi_b{}^2$ is positive. For these two reasons

$K(a, b)$ may be rather small, while $J(a, b)$ would not vanish even if ψ_a and ψ_b were separated at some distance. The difference between $J(a, a)$ and $J(a, b)$ has the same order of magnitude as $K(a, b)$.

We may consider a very simplified example for showing two important differences between interelectronic repulsion in classical and quantum mechanics. If q electrons occur in a set of degenerate orbitals, and if we make the approximation that all J integrals are identical, the classical value would be $\frac{1}{2}q^2J$, while eq. (1.12) indicates $\frac{1}{2}q(q-1)J$, that is $-\frac{1}{2}J$ less for each electron. In other words, the electron is a self-coherent particle, though for all practical purposes it functions as a charged cloud ψ^2 in a stationary state. Therefore, there is no repulsion between the electron and itself, or rather, this repulsion is taken care of in its rest mass energy. A "classical" hydrogen atom with a cloudy electron would have the ionization energy decreased $\frac{1}{2}J = \frac{5}{8}$ rydberg for this reason.

Secondly, eq. (1.12) suggests a decreased interelectronic repulsion energy for electrons having parallel spin, as expressed by the K integrals with negative coefficients. This entirely nonclassical phenomenon is caused by the action of Pauli's principle on the total wavefunction Ψ, which for a well-defined configuration can be written as an antisymmetrized Slater determinant according to rules given in Condon and Shortley's book.

These sentences have some chance of soon becoming obsolete for the following reasons. Ψ for a system with q electrons has 4q variables, that is 3q continous space variables and q spin variables, each assuming only one of two possible values. It is very difficult to have an intuitive idea of the wavefunction of a bismuth atom or the complex FeF_6^{---} containing 83 electrons being represented in a space with 249 ordinary dimensions. Actually, there are good reasons for believing that the 249 dimensions are superfluous to the physical description, and that six (or possibly rather five) continuous and two spin variables would suffice. As we saw above, in electron systems there is no trace observed of three- or more-particle interactions; one- and two-electron operators are all that is needed. As pointed out by Löwdin, this would make second-order density matrices having as variables the co-ordinates of only two electrons $(x_1, y_1, z_1, m_{s1}, x_2, y_2, z_2, m_{s2})$ a valid substitute for the much more complicated Ψ. Actually, Ψ would already now have been rejected for the same reason as the special relativistic theory abandoned the classical Galilei-space-time; that is, the description contains more information than can be obtained from experiments, if it were not for an annoying fact: there exists a definite rule, the variation principle, that the application of the Hamiltonian operator (expressing the various contributions of kinetic and potential energy discussed above) on an arbitrary trial wavefunction Ψ never gives an energy lower than the actual, observed energy. Unfortunately, one can construct seemingly decent second-order density matrices which give a more negative energy than the actual value. We have not yet found a criterion for "permissible" second-order density matrices corresponding to possible Ψ and obeying the variation principle.

It is reasonable to hope for such a criterion to be found, and there is little doubt that Ψ has only received a provisional acquittal. Especially, we know now that the interelectronic repulsion energy is only a question of $<\frac{1}{r_{12}}>$ of such a second-order density matrix.

[The allusion to five rather than six independent space variables of the second-order density matrix was made because, generally, a nondegenerate state has a Ψ which has no lower symmetry than the Hamiltonian operator. Therefore, it is expected that second-order density matrices can be written as functions of $(x_1, y_1, z_1, r_2, r_{12}, m_s 1, m_s 2)$, since the interelectronic repulsion is spherically symmetric and dependent on r_{12} only.]

REFERENCES

Many books treat the analogies and differences between classical and quantum mechanics much more profoundly than is possible here. Thus,

Kauzmann, W., "Quantum Chemistry", Academic Press, New York, 1957;

Margenau, H., and Murphy, G. M., "The Mathematics of Physics and Chemistry", 2 ed., D. Van Nostrand, Princeton, N.J., 1956.

It must be realized that the study of quantum mechanics for its own purpose can be pursued much longer than needed for the chemical applications. A useful "chemical" book is

Eyring, H., Walter, J., and Kimball, G. E., "Quantum Chemistry", John Wiley, New York, 1944.

2. Degenerate Orbitals in High Symmetry

The highest possible symmetry in Euclidean three-dimensional space is the spherical symmetry with centre of inversion, where the physical quantities depend only on one space variable, the distance r [eq. (1.8)] from the origin of the co-ordinate system. Arguments from spherical symmetry can be used for isolated atoms and monatomic ions, while all conceivable molecules have lower symmetry, as we see in Chapter 4.

In spherical symmetry, the individual orbitals ψ have the exceptional property of being separable in a product of an angular function A_l and a radial function R/r:

$$\psi = A_l(x, y, z) \cdot R(r)/r. \tag{2.1}$$

We divide here by r to make R^2 express the charge density of ψ^2 per spherical shell ("between r and r+dr"), but many authors prefer to use R/r for the radial function.

In eq. (2.1) we meet for the first time a group-theoretical quantum number, the non-negative integer l characterizing the angular function A_l. For historical reasons, spectroscopists introduced trivial names for the various values of l, viz.

$$
\begin{array}{cccccccccccc}
l = 0 & 1 & 2 & 3 & 4 & 5 & 6 & 7 & 8 & 9 & 10 & \ldots \\
s & p & d & f & g & h & i & k & l & m & n & \ldots
\end{array}
\tag{2.2}
$$

and, after the development of quantum mechanics, it was discovered that l had something to do with the orbital angular momentum of the electron being equal to $\sqrt{l(l+1)}h/2\pi$.

The angular function A_l can be written as a linear combination of homogeneous polynomials A_p in Cartesian co-ordinates:

$$A_p = x^a y^b z^c / r^l \qquad a + b + c = l. \tag{2.3}$$

Many authors prefer to write A_p in a polar co-ordinate system with trigonometric functions of angles substituting x, y, and z. This is a little confusing and not suitable for our purpose, because our favourite example of a molecular symmetry will be the octahedral, to which the Cartesian co-ordinates are particularly adapted.

It is seen that only one A_p exists for $l=0$. Since we neglect the normalization factors [satisfying eq. (1.5) on a spherical surface], we can write this s-electron angular function as the constant 1.

It is also obvious that three A_p exist for $l=1$; we may write them as x/r, y/r, and z/r, respectively.

One might expect that six A_l would subsist for $l=2$. Among the six A_p possible

$$xy/r^2 \quad xz/r^2 \quad yz/r^2 \quad x^2/r^2 \quad y^2/r^2 \quad z^2/r^2 \qquad (2.4)$$

something is wrong with the three last ones. They are not linearly independent, as can be seen from the fact that the sum of the last three A_p $(x^2+y^2+z^2)/r^2$ is another way of writing 1 according to eq. (1.8). In other words, the six A_p of eq. (2.4) correspond to five d orbitals A_2 and one s orbital A_0. One way of making A_2 orthogonal is to write the last two

$$(x^2-y^2)/r^2 \quad (2z^2-x^2-y^2)/r^2. \qquad (2.5)$$

In the same way, ten A_p exist for $l=3$, but three A_l are to be separated out because they represent p orbitals A_1 and not f orbitals A_3. This is a general mechanism for orthogonalization of ψ in spherical symmetry. Two orthogonal ψ_1 and ψ_2 are orthogonal either because they have different A_l values (and they would be orthogonal even if they had identical radial functions R) or because they have the same l value but orthogonal radial functions.

Among the valid forms of A_3 is evidently $(xyz)/r^3$, but the other six f orbitals have quite complicated forms, due to the singling out of the three p characteristics. Bethe and Von der Lage studied these A_l under the name of "Cubic Harmonics" and indicated as a possible choice of the residual six A_3:

$$\begin{array}{ll} (x^3-\tfrac{3}{5}xr^2)/r^3 & x(z^2-y^2)/r^3 \\ (y^3-\tfrac{3}{5}yr^2)/r^3 & y(x^2-z^2)/r^3 \\ (z^3-\tfrac{3}{5}zr^2)/r^3 & z(x^2-y^2)/r^3. \end{array} \qquad (2.6)$$

Among the A_4, one is relatively simple, $(x^4+y^4+z^4-\tfrac{3}{5}r^4)/r^4$. In general, from the $(l+1)(l+2)/2$ possible A_p for a given value of l, only $(2l+1)$ genuine A_l appear, the rest corresponding to all previous l values smaller than the l value considered, and of the same parity. We introduce here the word *parity* in a very straightforward fashion, l being even for 0, 2, 4, 6 . . . and odd for 1, 3, 5, 7. . . . Actually, parity is a much more fundamental concept. The orbitals ψ and total wavefunctions Ψ in spherical symmetry and in any other symmetry having a *centre of inversion* can be classified according to odd or even parity by substitution of the "inverted" co-ordinates $(-x, -y, -z)$:

$$\begin{array}{l} \psi_{odd}\,(-x, -y, -z) = -\psi_{odd}\,(x, y, z) \\ \psi_{even}\,(-x, -y, -z) = \psi_{even}\,(x, y, z). \end{array} \qquad (2.7)$$

It is customary to use the German abbreviations u ($=$ ungerade) for odd and g ($=$ gerade) for even functions. An odd and an even function are necessarily orthogonal, because the contributions to the integration eq. (1.5) always cancel from opposite sides of the co-ordinate system. It is obvious that an arbitrary function ψ^* cannot necessarily be ascribed even or odd parity. However, it can always be written as the sum of two (non-normalized) functions ψ_{even} and ψ_{odd} defined by

$$\psi_{even}=(\psi^*(x, y, z)+\psi^*(-x, -y, -z))/2$$
$$\psi_{odd} \ =(\psi^*(x, y, z)-\psi^*(-x, -y, -z))/2 \qquad (2.8)$$

Whereas the angular functions of eq. (2.1) can be expressed in a definite form, the radial functions depend heavily on the *central field* $U(r)$, the electrostatic potential to be put into Schrödinger's equation. In spherical symmetry, the kinetic energy of an orbital ψ can be divided into two parts, *radial kinetic energy*, similar to eq. (1.4) being an integration of

$$e_{rad\ kin}=\int \frac{h^2}{4\pi^2 m}\frac{d^2R}{dr^2}\cdot R\ dr \qquad (2.9)$$

while the *angular kinetic energy* has the fixed form (in atomic units, the energy unit $1ry=e^2/2a_0$):

$$e_{ang\ kin}=\int \frac{l(l+1)}{r^2}\psi^2 dr=l(l+1)<r^{-2}> \qquad (2.10)$$

$d\tau$ being dr between the limits $r=0$ and $r=\infty$ (or larger than such r that ψ^2 has become negligible). In eq. (2.10) we can talk about a pseudo-potential of "centrifugal forces", vanishing for $l=0$.

Schrödinger's equation for R then becomes

$$\frac{h^2}{4\pi^2 m}\frac{d^2R}{dr^2}+\left[w-U(r)-\frac{h^2}{4\pi^2 m}\frac{l(l+1)}{r^2}\right]R=0 \qquad (2.11)$$

and the solutions for negative energy w are sought. For a positive w there exists a continuous infinity of solutions, called the *continuum*, corresponding to ionized states of the system (because the zero point of w is the energy of an electron very far away from the nucleus and the other electrons, if present) and not fulfilling the virial theorem eq. (1.1), since both e_{kin} and e_{pot} are positive. For negative w there exist only a discrete set of *stationary* states, fulfilling the virial theorem and having radial functions R which vanish exponentially at large r (expressing the fact that the electron is bound to the rest of the atom). However, for all values of l, and for all monatomic entities being either neutral or positively charged, there exist an infinite number of these stationary states, queueing very densely up for w being just below zero.

We shall concentrate our attention on the lowest stationary ψ of a given *symmetry type l*. Neglecting the behaviour of R at $r=0$ and $r\to\infty$, we can talk about the number of nodes of R, values of r where $R=0$. The lowest energy is found by an orbital having no nodes [this is mainly a question of d^2R/dr^2 of eq. (2.9) necessarily being much larger when nodes occur]. The following orbital with the same l can only be made orthogonal to the first one by having one node (because R_1R_2 must be positive for some r and negative for some other interval of r values). The third orbital must have two nodes for being orthogonal on both R_1 and R_2, and so on. We define a *principal quantum number* n such that the number of nodes of R is $n-l-1$. This has not the same direct physical significance as l, but is essentially a file number.

In a one-electron system with spherical symmetry, as represented by H, He$^+$, Li^{++}, . . . with a nucleus of the atomic number Z, eq. (2.11) can be solved completely with $U = -2Z/r$ (the factor 2 arising from the choice of one rydberg as unit of energy).

The lowest solution for each l can be demonstrated by substitution in eq. (2.11) to be

$$R = r^{l+1} \exp(-Zr/(l+1)) \tag{2.12}$$

again neglecting normalization constants, and the corresponding energy is

$$w = -Z^2/(l+1)^2 = -Z^2/n^2. \tag{2.13}$$

A very special property of $U = -2Z/r$ occurring in one-electron systems is that the higher solutions with nodes in R, though having widely different radial functions, have the same energy as the last term in eq. (2.13), i.e. $-Z^2/n^2$ independent of l. It is interesting to note various values of $<r^q>$ [cf. eq. (1.9)] calculated for the "hydrogenic" radial functions:

$$
\begin{aligned}
<r^{-3}> &= Z^3/(n^3(l+1)(l+\tfrac{1}{2})l) \\
<r^{-1}> &= Z/n^2 \\
<r> &= (3n^2 - l(l+1))/2Z \\
<r^2> &= n^2(5n^2 + 1 - 3l(l+1))/2Z^2.
\end{aligned}
\tag{2.14}
$$

The potential energy $-2T$ of a hydrogenic system being proportional to $<r^{-1}>$, eq. (2.13) corresponds to a l-independent value of the latter quantity.

In many-electron systems, the radial function R is *not hydrogenic*. The central field U(r) can take care of nearly all, but not all, the effects of interelectronic repulsion, because the latter turns out to have spherical symmetry to a great extent in the actual atom. The Hartree-Fock self-consistent functions (HFSCF) R of the various shells of a definite atom minimizes the energy given in eq. (1.12) and adapts therefore the behaviour of the individual n, l shells mutually, as described in Hartree's book. This is a fairly complicated calculation, done by repeated iteration and usually by analytical approximations to R, but it is not impossible with modern computing machines and has been done for a variety of atoms. Recently, Watson (1959, 1960) has performed such calculations for iron group atoms and ions with Z=21 to 30, and Watson and Freeman (1961) for the group Z=13 to 18 and Z=31 to 36.

A fairly good approximation to the HFSCF radial functions without nodes can be written

$$R = r^{l*+1} \exp(-\alpha r) \tag{2.15}$$

where l_* and α are two fractional constants. In literature, reference is frequently made to Slater's hydrogenic radial functions, having α equal to the ratio Z_*/n_* between an effective charge Z_* and an "effective principal quantum number" n_*. In nearly all cases, l_* is assumed to be equal to l of the n, l shell. However, for many purposes this is a quite unsatisfactory approximation. There are good reasons for believing that a much smaller value of l_*, say 0.5 or 0.7, is a much better approximation, and eqs. (2.16) and (2.17) show some justification for eq. (2.15) directly from Schrödinger's radial equation (2.11).

The central field U(r) in a many-electron system with the ionic charge $+(Z_0-1)e$ is $-2Z_0/r$ for large r, while it is approximately $-2Z/r$ for small values of r, close to the nucleus. Since the central field increases from Coulomb behaviour with Z_0 at large r to Coulomb behaviour with Z at small r (neglecting the small effects of external screening), it is possible to expand U in a Taylor series of r^{-1}, starting with the central field outside the atom at large r.

$$U = -\frac{2Z_0}{r} - \frac{Z_2}{r^2} - \ldots \quad (2.16)$$

Correspondingly, the energies w are situated somewhere in the interval $-Z^2/n^2$ and $-Z_0^2/n^2$, the internal shells with small $\langle r \rangle$ being close to the former, more negative limit, and very external orbitals with large $\langle r \rangle$ being close to hydrogenic behaviour with Z_0.

If we restrict our Taylor expansion eq. (2.16) to the two first terms, we can directly give the solution in the Schrödinger equation (2.11), because Z_2 cancels a part of the pseudo-potential $l(l+1)/r^2$ of angular kinetic energy, eq. (2.10), and the resulting solution R has the form eq. (2.15) with the constants given by

$$\begin{aligned} \alpha &= Z_0/(l_*+1) \\ Z_2 &= l(l+1) - l_*(l_*+1) \\ w &= -\alpha^2 = -Z_0^2/(l_*+1)^2. \end{aligned} \quad (2.17)$$

It is seen how, for a definite Z_2, the higher values of l correspond to larger l_* and therefore less negative values of the energy w. This argument is generally valid without the specific approximation expressed in eq. (2.16) for any central field becoming more negative for small r than $-2Z_0/r$, and gives the definite order of n, l shell energies w:

$$\begin{aligned} 1s &\ll 2s < 2p \\ &\quad 3s < 3p < 3d \\ &\quad 4s < 4p < 4d < 4f \\ &\quad 5s < 5p < 5d < 5f < 5g \\ &\quad \ldots \ldots \end{aligned} \quad (2.18)$$

Rydberg was the first (in 1906–13) to relate facts of atomic spectroscopy to the structure of the periodic table of elements; and N. Bohr further connected

Moseley's determination of the atomic numbers Z with the evidence from the alkali metal spectra [indicating empirically eq. (2.18)] demonstrating the composition of the closed-shell configurations corresponding to inert gases in the periodic table:

$$
\begin{aligned}
&\text{He}(Z=2): \quad 1s^2 \\
&\text{Ne}(Z=10): \quad 1s^2 2s^2 2p^6 \\
&\text{Ar}(Z=18): \quad 1s^2 2s^2 2p^6 3s^2 3p^6 \\
&\text{Kr}(Z=36): \quad 1s^2 2s^2 2p^6 3s^2 3p^6 3d^{10} 4s^2 4p^6 = [\text{Ar}]3d^{10}4s^2 4p^6 \quad\quad (2.19) \\
&\text{Xe}(Z=54): \quad [\text{Kr}]4d^{10}5s^2 5p^6 \\
&\text{Em}(Z=86): \quad [\text{Xe}]4f^{14}5d^{10}6s^2 6p^6 \\
&\quad\quad (Z=118): [\text{Em}]5f^{14}6d^{10}7s^2 7p^6
\end{aligned}
$$

where we denote the previous closed-shell configurations [Ar], etc., for saving space. It is worth noting the absence of inequality signs in eq. (2.18) between (given n, high l) and $(n+1$, low l). The relative order of such two orbitals depends on the detailed nature of $U(r)$ and in particular on the ionic charge Z_0-1. Thus, in practice, there is never any doubt that 2p has lower energy than 3s, though it was not proved from eq. (2.17). On the other hand, for neutral atoms with $Z_0=1$, 4s has *lower* energy than 3d at the point, $Z=19$ (potassium), where these orbitals become important for the electron configuration of the ground state. Actually, $4s<3d$ only in an interval starting around carbon ($Z=6$) and finishing at copper ($Z=29$), while $3d<4s$ for smaller Z (approaching the behaviour in hydrogen) and for Z larger than 30 (where both 3d and 4s are internal shells). If one considers ionic charges $+e$, the interval for $3d<4s$ is much more narrow, and for $Z_0=3$, it is reduced to near coincidence in silicon ($Z=14$) and phosphorus ($Z=15$). For ionic charges higher than $+2e$, the orbital 3d is always more stable than 4s. Hence, we have seen that the question whether 3d has lower energy than 4s does not have a clear-cut answer, if we do not specify the ionic charge and the atomic number.

Similar difficulties arise with the sets of orbitals 5f, 6d, and 7s for more than 86 electrons, which tend to arrange in the hydrogenic order $5f<6d<7s$ for high ionic charges (say Th^{+++} or U^{+4}) and in the opposite order $7s<6d<5f$ in neutral Ra, Ac, and Th.

We may use eq. (1.12) to construct a model of this behaviour at the beginning of each transition group. We say a model, because we neglect the effects of rearrangement of orbitals with consequent changes of the pertinent parameters (see page 4) and we make the approximation that the interelectronic repulsion energy in the configuration $[\text{Ar}]3d^a 4s^b$ can be written

$$
a(a-1)J(3d, 3d)/2 + ab\,J(3d, 4s) + b(b-1)J(4s, 4s)/2 \quad\quad (2.20)
$$

and we avoid thinking too much about the problem of one-electron energies [see eq. (1.14)] and define energies $-\varepsilon_{3d}$ and $-\varepsilon_{4s}$ of a single electron moving in the central field of the closed-shell configuration [Ar]. If we consider the element vanadium ($Z=23$), appropriate numerical values of the parameters are $\varepsilon_{3d}=500$ kK, $\varepsilon_{4s}=350$ kK, $J(3d, 3d)=120$ kK, $J(3d, 4s)$ $=J(4s, 4s)=70$ kK, and we obtain the following energies in kK compared to the closed-shell ion V^{+5}:

q=	$3d^q$	$3d^{q-1}4s$	$3d^{q-2}4s^2$	
1	-500	-350	—	
2	-880	-780	-630	(2.21)
3	-1140	-1090	-990	
4	-1280	-1280	-1230	
5	-1300	-1350	$-1350.$	

There is no doubt that the radial functions in V^{+5} and V^0 are so different that the assumption of invariant ε and J parameters is not entirely fulfilled. However, eq. (2.21) shows something very important for the understanding of the energy levels in the beginning of a transition group: though the 3d orbital in the whole series of ionic charges considered is attracted 150 kK by the [Ar] core than the 4s orbital, the ground configuration of V^0 is $3d^34s^2$ and of V^+ $3d^4$ but very nearly coincident with the lowest terms of $3d^34s$, whereas it is $3d^3$ of V^{++} and $3d^2$ of V^{+++}. In other words, the relative size of the interelectronic repulsion parameters $J(3d, 3d)$ compared to $J(3d, 4s)$ and $J(4s, 4s)$ may have as a consequence that the 4s electrons are needed for the stability of the ionic charges 0 and $+1$, but *removed at first by ionization*, leaving $[Ar]3d^q$ as the lowest configuration for ionic charges at least $+2$.

This also shows how difficult it is to give a sensible definition of *experimentally determined orbital energies*. Slater has proposed considering the baricentres of the configurations which are split into more energy levels. This is very reasonable, but leads to some rather peculiar but unavoidable consequences. Before considering this problem, we must explain several features of the *multiplet term structure* of configurations involving *partly filled shells*.

The number of states of a configuration is the number of orthogonal wavefunctions Ψ it is possible to write. This number is one, if all the shells or subshells (i.e. the sets of degenerate orbitals) are fully occupied. If one shell or subshell with the degeneracy number e contains only one electron, the number of states is $2e$, but they are degenerate, forming one *energy level*, if we continue to neglect electrodynamic and relativistic effects. The same is true for $(2e-1)$ electrons in a single partly filled shell, that is one electron less than the maximum number possible. If q electrons occur in a single partly filled shell or subshell, the number of states is

$$\binom{q}{2e} = \frac{(2e)!}{q!(2e-q)!}. \tag{2.22}$$

This binomial expression is symmetric with respect to q and $(2-q)$. It is a much more fundamental rule, Pauli's hole equivalence, that not only the number of states but also the symmetry types occurring of the energy levels, and their number, are identical for q electrons and q "holes" in a set of degenerate orbitals.

As long as we only consider electrostatic, and not electrodynamic effects we have the approximation of Russell-Saunders coupling, and the symmetry types of the total Ψ are of two types: the total spin S and the symmetry type L in spherical symmetry or Γ_n in lower symmetries. In analogy to eq. (2.2), the values of L have trivial names, $viz.$

$$L = \begin{matrix} 0 & 1 & 2 & 3 & 4 & 5 & 6 & 7 & 8 & 9 & 10 \ldots \\ S & P & D & F & G & H & I & K & L & M & N \ldots \end{matrix}$$
(2.23)

and it has become customary to write $2S+1$ as left-hand superscript to the name of L or Γ_n. Thus, ^3F means a term with $L=3$ and $S=1$. S assumes integral non-negative values in systems with an even number of electrons and has then trivial names related to $2S+1$ and pronounced singlet ($S=0$), triplet (1), quintet (2), septet (3), . . ., whereas systems with an odd number of electrons have S equal to a positive number being the sum of an integer and a half. The trivial names are doublet ($S=1/2$), quartet (3/2), sextet (5/2), octet (7/2), ... The number of states participating in a multiplet term is $(2S+1)(2L+1)$. The term consists of one or more energy levels, which, in the latter case, can be separated by electrodynamic effects in the atom. An energy level is a number of absolutely degenerate states that can only be separated by interaction with an external electric or magnetic field decreasing the symmetry of the system, or by similar fields arising from the properties of the nucleus (hyperfine structure).

It is worth remarking that even or odd parity is also a symmetry type, and may be combined with both even or odd values of L. Many spectroscopists mark the terms of odd parity with a small circle, e.g. $^4S°$ and $^2P°$ of the configuration p^3 to be discussed below. For well-defined configurations, it is simply the parity of the sum of the l values which count.

One electron or one hole, i.e. $4l+1$ electrons, in the n, l shell produce the unique term $^2(l)$ as mentioned above. Two electrons or two holes produce $2l+1$ different terms, $viz.$:

$$^1S, {}^3P, {}^1D, {}^3F, {}^1G, {}^3H, \ldots, {}^3(2l-1), {}^1(2l).$$
(2.24)

Three electrons or three holes are somewhat more complicated:

$$\begin{aligned} p^3: \quad & {}^4S, {}^2D, {}^2P \\ d^3, d^7: \quad & {}^4F, {}^4P, {}^2G, {}^2P, {}^2H, {}^2D, {}^2F, {}^2D' \\ f^3, f^{11}: \quad & {}^4I, {}^4F, {}^4S, {}^4G, {}^4D, {}^2H, {}^2G, {}^2K, {}^2D, {}^2P, {}^2I, {}^2L, {}^2H', {}^2D', {}^2F, {}^2G', {}^2F' \end{aligned}$$
(2.25)

and it is noted that they frequently produce more than one term of the same symmetry type L, S. Hund's rule indicates that the lowest term has the maximum value of S combined with the highest value of L compatible with this condition. Hund's rule does not indicate the order of the other terms, which at first sight seems somewhat irregular. Equation (2.25) attempts to arrange the L values of a given S according to increasing energy.

This is not the place to outline exactly how eq. (2.25) has been found, or how the similar results are obtained in general for a partly filled shell. We shall restrict ourselves to a list of the one or two lowest S values and the highest L among the following S values:

$$
\begin{aligned}
&d^4, d^6: && ^5D, {}^3P, {}^3F, {}^3H, {}^1I, \ldots \\
&d^5: && ^6S, {}^4G, {}^4P, {}^4D, {}^4F, {}^2I, \ldots \\
&f^4, f^{10}: && ^5I, {}^5F, {}^5S, {}^5G, {}^5D, {}^3M, \ldots \\
&f^5, f^9: && ^6H, {}^6F, {}^6P, {}^4M, {}^4I, {}^4K, {}^4L, {}^4F, {}^4G, {}^4H, {}^4P, {}^4D, \ldots \\
&f^6, f^8: && ^7F, {}^5D, {}^5L, {}^5G, {}^5H, {}^5I, {}^5F, {}^5K, {}^5H', {}^5G', {}^5D', {}^5P, \ldots \\
&f^7: && ^8S, {}^6P, {}^6I, {}^6D, {}^6G, {}^6F, {}^6H, {}^4N, \ldots.
\end{aligned}
\tag{2.26}
$$

Before returning to the actual calculation of interelectronic repulsion energy in simpler cases, such as p^q, we need not only the diagonal element of this energy, eq. (1.11) et seq., but also the rules for some simple non-diagonal elements. We do not treat here the general principles of perturbation theory and secular determinants, which can be seen in many books, even in "Absorption Spectra . . ." by the present writer.

If we have two different configurations which differ in more than two electrons, say Cabc and Cdef, where C is the common part of the two configurations, the nondiagonal element of the two-electron operator $1/r_{12}$ vanishes identically. If two configurations Cab and Ccd differ in two *spin orbitals* (i.e. orbital *and* spin characteristics), the nondiagonal element is

$$
\pm \left[\int\int \frac{1}{r_{12}} \psi_a \psi_c d\tau_1 \psi_b \psi_d d\tau_2 - \int\int \frac{1}{r_{12}} \psi_a \psi_d d\tau_1 \psi_b \psi_c d\tau_2 \right]
\tag{2.27}
$$

where the sign of the nondiagonal element depends on the choice of the phase of the wavefunctions. The integration of each of the two terms vanishes very frequently, one necessary condition for

$$
\int\int \frac{1}{r_{12}} \psi_w \psi_x d\tau_1 \psi_y \psi_z d\tau_2 \neq 0 \text{ is } m_s(w) = m_s(x) \text{ } and \text{ } m_s(y) = m_s(z).
\tag{2.28}
$$

Another necessary condition is that the two products $\psi_w \psi_x$ and $\psi_y \psi_z$ have the same group-theoretical symmetry type Γ_n.

If two configurations differ by only the occupation of one spin orbital, Ca and Cb, the nondiagonal element is no longer as given in eq. (2.27), but is a summation over all spin orbitals ψ_k occurring in the common part C, *viz.*

$$
\pm \left[\sum_k \left(\int\int \frac{1}{r_{12}} \psi_a \psi_b d\tau_1 \psi_k^2 d\tau_2 - \int\int \frac{1}{r_{12}} \psi_a \psi_k d\tau_1 \psi_b \psi_k d\tau_2 \right) \right]
\tag{2.29}
$$

again with the conditions of eq. (2.28). This summation is in a certain sense an effective one-electron quantity, correcting the various orbitals ψ_k, and it is a very small contribution if the orbitals are self-consistent.

We meet often the Heisenberg determinant with two identical diagonal elements and a nondiagonal element E_{12}

$$\begin{vmatrix} E_{11}-E & E_{12} \\ E_{12} & E_{11}-E \end{vmatrix} =0 \text{ with the eigenvalues } E=E_{11}\pm E_{12}. \qquad (2.30)$$

For instance, the configuration of one l electron and one s electron consists of two terms, $^3(l)$ and $^1(l)$. If we denote the spin-orbital configurations with $+$ and $-$ according to the sign of m_s of each electron, we have the following four states:

$M_s=1$. One state: (s^+l^+). $J(s, l)-K(s, l)$
$M_s=0$. Two states (s^+l^-) and (s^-l^+) both with the diagonal element
$\qquad$ $J(s, l)$ and the nondiagonal element $K(s, l)$ [eq. (2.27)] $\qquad$ (2.31)
$\qquad$ and hence the eigenvalues $J(s, l)\pm K(s, l)$ [eq. (2.30)]
$M_s=-1$. One state: (s^-l^-) $J(s, l)-K(s, l)$.

Consequently, the three states belonging to $^3(l)$ has the interelectronic repulsion energy $J(s, l)-K(s, l)$ and the eigenvalue corresponding to the singlet state has $J(s, l)+K(s, l)$. If we form the baricentre, i.e. the average energy weighted by the relative degeneracy numbers $(2S+1)(2L+1)$, it is for the configuration s^1l^1:

$$J(s, l)-\tfrac{1}{2}K(s, l). \qquad (2.32)$$

If we now consider the configuration p^2, we have according to eq. (2.22) totally $6\times5/2=15$ different states. Let us call the three p orbitals x, y, and z (page 9) and hence the six spin orbitals x^+, x^-, y^+, y^-, z^+, and z^-. It is evident that the parameters of interelectronic repulsion fall into three classes, viz.:

$$\begin{aligned} J(x, x) &= J(y, y) &= J(z, z) \\ J(x, y) &= J(x, z) &= J(y, z) \\ K(x, y) &= K(x, z) &= K(y, z). \end{aligned} \qquad (2.33)$$

We have three states with $M_s=1$, i.e. both spin directions positive. As discussed by the present writer (1959, 1961), they have essentially different symmetry types, (x^+y^+), (x^+z^+), and (y^+z^+), and therefore do not have nondiagonal elements of the type given in eq. (2.27). They represent hence three eigenvalues of the form

$$^3\Gamma_4 : J(x, y)-K(x, y). \qquad (2.34)$$

The meaning of the group-theoretical quantum number $^3\Gamma_4$ will become clearer in Chapter 4. The same result is obtained for each of the three states with $M_s=-1$, i.e. (x^-y^-), (x^-z^-), and (y^-z^-).

The nine states with $M_s = 0$ fall into four classes. Six states form three Heisenberg determinants of second degree, e.g. the two states

$$(x^+y^-) \text{ and } (x^-y^+) : J(x, y) - K(x, y)(^3\Gamma_4) \text{ and } J(x, y) + K(x, y)(^1\Gamma_5). \quad (2.35)$$

The three last states, (x^+x^-), (y^+y^-), and (z^+z^-), form a Heisenberg determinant of the *third degree*

$$\begin{vmatrix} J(x, x) - E & K(x, y) & K(x, y) \\ K(x, y) & J(x, x) - E & K(x, y) \\ K(x, y) & K(x, y) & J(x, x) - E \end{vmatrix} = 0 \quad (2.36)$$

having as eigenvalues $E =$

$$J(x, x) - K(x, y) \text{ twice } (^1\Gamma_3) \text{ and } J(x, x) + 2K(x, y) \text{ once } (^1\Gamma_1). \quad (2.37)$$

For p orbitals, the three types of parameters from eq. (2.33) have the following interrelation:

$$J(x, x) = J(x, y) + 2K(x, y) \quad (2.38)$$

which can most easily be proved from the fact that

$$\psi_w = \sqrt{2}(\psi_x + \psi_y)/2 \quad (2.39)$$

is itself a new p orbital, only turned $45°$ in the xy plane. It follows that

$$J(x, x) = J(w, w) = \tfrac{1}{4}J(x, x) + \tfrac{1}{4}J(y, y) + K(x, y) + \tfrac{1}{2}J(x, y) \quad (2.40).$$

giving eq. (2.38) when compared with eq. (2.33) and remembering that $\psi_x \psi_y$ do not interact with ψ_x^2 or ψ_y^2 because they are of different symmetry type. (In this case, it is quite evident that $\psi_x \psi_y$ is as often positive as it is negative at a definite distance r.)

Equation (2.38) demands that the eigenvalues $^1\Gamma_5$ of eq. (2.35) and $^1\Gamma_3$ of eq. (2.37) coincide. We have now found the interelectronic repulsion energy of the three terms of p^2 in eq. (2.24), *viz.*:

$$\begin{array}{ll} ^1S \,(^1\Gamma_1) & J(x, y) + 4K(x, y) \\ ^1D \,(^1\Gamma_3 \text{ and } ^1\Gamma_5) & J(x, y) + K(x, y) \\ ^3P \,(^3\Gamma_4) & J(x, y) - K(x, y). \end{array} \quad (2.41)$$

Going through very similar arguments for p^3, the term energies can be found:

$$\begin{array}{ll} ^2P(^2\Gamma_4) & J(x, x) + 2J(x, y) \\ ^2D(^2\Gamma_5) & J(x, x) + 2J(x, y) - 2K(x, y) \\ (^2\Gamma_3) & 3J(x, y) \\ ^4S \,(^4\Gamma_1) & 3J(x, y) - 3K(x, y) \end{array} \quad (2.42)$$

where $^2\Gamma_5$ and $^2\Gamma_3$ again coincide in virtue of eq. (2.38). The baricentres of the two configurations are found at

$$p^2 : J(x, y) \quad (2.43)$$
$$p^3 : 3J(x, y).$$

A direct calculation for p^6 from eq. (1.12) and (2.33) gives the energy of the unique state ^{1}S

$$3J(x, x)+12J(x, y)-6K(x, y)=15J(x, y) \qquad (2.44)$$

creating the expectation, fulfilled by actual calculation, that the baricentre of the configuration p^q is situated at $q(q-1) J(x, y)/2$.

This treatment could in principle be continued for the configurations such as d^q, and f^q, but much more powerful methods have been elaborated by Slater, Condon, and Shortley, and particularly by Racah. The three former authors pointed out that the integration over the various angular functions A_l in expressions like eq. (1.12) and (2.27) produce the coefficients $f_2, f_4, \ldots f_k$ to parameters F^k which are obtained by integration of the radial functions R

$$F^k=\int_0^\infty \left[\int_0^{r_2} \frac{r_1^k}{r_2^{k+1}} R^2 dr_1 + \int_{r_2}^\infty \frac{r_2^k}{r_1^{k+1}} R^2 dr \right] R^2 dr_2. \qquad (2.45)$$

If a partly filled l^q shell is considered, the coefficient f_0 to the integral F^0 is always $q(q-1)/2$ and is hence of no importance for the relative term distances in a configuration. Only l further parameters occur, i.e. the integrals $F^2, F^4 F^6, \ldots, F^{2l}$. It is convenient to divide the F^k integrals by certain denominators D_k producing parameters F_k. The values are for

$$
\begin{array}{llll}
\text{p orbitals} & D_2=25 & & \\
\text{d orbitals} & D_2=49 & D_4=441 & \\
\text{f orbitals} & D_2=225 & D_4=1089 & D_6=7361.64.
\end{array} \qquad (2.46)
$$

In the new parameters of interelectronic repulsion energy, F_k, the integrals of eq. (2.33) are for p^q configurations:

$$
\begin{aligned}
J(x, x) &= F^0+4F_2 \\
J(x, y) &= F^0-2F_2 \\
K(x, y) &= 3F_2.
\end{aligned} \qquad (2.47)
$$

The energies of interelectronic repulsion energy in d^2 are:

$$
\begin{aligned}
^1S &: F^0+14F_2+126F_4 \\
^1G &: F^0+4F_2+F_4 \\
^3P &: F^0+7F_2-84F_4 \\
^1D &: F^0-3F_2+36F_4 \\
^3F &: F^0-8F_2-9F_4.
\end{aligned} \qquad (2.48)
$$

Racah (1942, 1943) pointed out that other linear combinations of the parameters F_k are very useful for d^q configurations,

$$A=F^0-49F_4 \quad B=F_2-5F_4 \quad C=35F_4 \qquad (2.49)$$

rewriting eq. (2.48) for d^2:

$$^1S : A+14B+7C$$
$$^1G : A+4B+2C$$
$$^3P : A+7B \qquad (2.50)$$
$$^1D : A-3B+2C$$
$$^3F : A-8B.$$

The results are for d^3

$$\left.\begin{matrix} ^2D' \; 3A+7B+7C \\ ^2D \; 3A+3B+3C \end{matrix}\right\} \text{ with the nondiagonal element } 3\sqrt{21}B$$
$$^2F \; 3A+9B+3C$$
$$^2P, ^2H : 3A-6B+3C \qquad (2.51)$$
$$^2G \; 3A-11B+3C$$
$$^4P \; 3A$$
$$^4F \; 3A-15B.$$

As a further example, we may mention the sextet ground state of d^5 and the four quartets, and one of the eleven doublets:

$$^2I \; : \; 10A-24B+8C$$
$$^4F \; : \; 10A-13B+7C$$
$$^4D : \; 10A-18B+5C \qquad (2.52)$$
$$^4P : \; 10A-28B+7C$$
$$^4G : \; 10A-25B+5C$$
$$^6S \; : \; 10A-35B.$$

One of many advantages in Racah's notation eq. (2.49) is that energy differences between terms with maximum value of S in a given d^q configuration are multiples of B only. As we shall see in Chapter 4, this is particularly important for the partly filled shell in complexes of lower, e.g. octahedral, symmetry.

Racah (1949) also found a similar notation for the parameters in f^q configuration,

$$E^0 = F^0 - 10F_2 - 33F_4 - 286F_6$$
$$E^1 = (70F_2 + 231F_4 + 2002F_6)/9$$
$$E^2 = (F_2 - 3F_4 + 7F_6)/9 \qquad (2.53)$$
$$E^3 = (5F_2 + 6F_4 - 91F_6)/3$$

where E^3 now has the role of B in d^q configurations. Thus, the energies are in f^2:

$$^1S : \; E^0 + 9E^1$$
$$^3P : \; E^0 + 33E^3$$
$$^1I : \; E^0 + 2E^1 + 70E^2 + 7E^3$$
$$^1D : \; E^0 + 2E^1 + 286E^2 - 11E^3 \qquad (2.54)$$
$$^1G : \; E^0 + 2E^1 - 260E^2 - 4E^3$$
$$^3F : \; E^0$$
$$^3H : \; E^0 - 9E^3.$$

while the five quartets and a few of the doublets of f^3 have the following energies:

$$
\begin{aligned}
&^2P : 3E^0 + 3E^1 - 11E^3 \\
&^2K : 3E^0 + 3E^1 - 135E^2 - 11E^3 \\
&^2H : 3E^0 + 3E^1 + 21E^2 - 24E^3 \text{ (lowest diagonal element)} \\
&^4D : 3E^0 + 33E^3 \\
&^4G : 3E^0 + 12E^3 \\
&^4F, \,^4S : 3E^0 \\
&^4I : 3E^0 - 21E^3.
\end{aligned}
\tag{2.55}
$$

Some regularities become very conspicuous by a closer study of the inter-electronic repulsion energies in p^q, d^q, and f^q configuration. Thus, a physical significance can be found of the concept of *spin-pairing energy* considering the baricentre of the terms with a definite value of S of a given configuration.

However, we must first discuss the *seniority number* v. This quantum number equals q of a given term of a l^q configuration, if none of all the previous configurations l^{q-2}, l^{q-4}, l^{q-6}, . . . have presented a term with the same combination of L and S. If one such term has occurred previously, and the first time in l^k, the seniority number $v=k$ is assigned to one similar term in all the following configurations l^{k+2}, l^{k+4}, . . . on two conditions, however: that such similar terms with the same combination of L and S do indeed exist; and that a lower seniority number $k-2$ is not menaced by extinction, i.e. the terms of a given l^{k+m} are preferably assigned the lowest v. These rules can be more clearly seen in actual operation:

$$
\begin{array}{lllll}
v= & 0 & 2 & & 4 \\
p^0 & ^1S \\
p^2 & ^1S & ^3P, \,^1D, \\
p^4 & ^1S & ^3P, \,^1D, \\
p^6 & ^1S \\
d^2, d^8 & ^1S & ^3P, \,^1D, \,^3F, \,^1G \\
d^4, d^6 & ^1S' & ^3P', \,^1D', \,^3F', \,^1G' & ^5D, \,^3P, \,^3D, \,^3F, \,^3G, \,^3H, \,^1S, \,^1D, \,^1F, \,^1G, \,^1I \\
\cdots
\end{array}
\tag{2.56}
$$

whereas the similar lists for odd v are:

$$
\begin{array}{lllll}
v= & 1 & 3 & & 5 \\
p^1 & ^2P \\
p^3 & ^2P & ^4S, \,^2D \\
p^5 & ^2P \\
d^1, d^9 & ^2D \\
d^3, d^7 & ^2D' & ^4P, \,^4F, \,^2P, \,^2D, \,^2F, \,^2G, \,^2H \\
d^5 & ^2D'' & ^4P, \,^4F, \,^2P, \,^2D', \,^2F', \,^2G', \,^2H & ^6S, \,^4D, \,^4G, \,^2I, \ldots \\
\cdots
\end{array}
\tag{2.57}
$$

Thus, the two diagonal elements of energy given for $^2D'$ and ^2D of d^3 in eq. (2.51) correspond to the two seniority numbers $v=1$ and $v=3$. It is remarked that, in such a case, v is not a good quantum number of the two eigenvalues produced. The two actual ^2D terms have a mixture of the properties of $v=1$ and $v=3$. However, it is generally true that the term energies tend to be arranged according to increasing v at lower energy. It is also noted that usually the largest part of the states of l^q belong to terms with the highest value of v possible, the lower values of v rather being exceptions.

Now, the regularity observed in the baricentres of the terms with a definite S is that if all terms are considered regardless of their v, the interelectronic repulsion energy can be written in one of two equivalent ways:

$$q(q-1)A_1/2+[<S(S+1)>-S(S+1)]D \qquad (2.58)$$

or

$$q(q-1)A_2/2-S(S+1)D \qquad (2.59)$$

where A_1 and A_2 are quantities closely related to Racah's A or to the integral F^0 while D is a *spin-pairing energy parameter*. The energy difference between the baricentre of the terms with the total spin S and the baricentre of the next, lower value $S-1$ is consequently $2SD$. The average value $<S(S+1)>$ of a configuration l^q can be shown to be

$$<S(S+1)>=\frac{q(q+2)}{4}-\frac{2l+2}{4l+1}\cdot\frac{q(q-1)}{2}=\frac{3}{4}q-\frac{3}{8l+2}\cdot\frac{q(q-1)}{2} \qquad (2.60)$$

while it would simply be $\frac{3}{4}q$ in a configuration $l_1l_2l_3 \ldots l_q$ where the Pauli exclusion principle did not operate.

It might seem very surprising that eq. (2.58) and eq. (2.59) can be made equivalent. However, it is seen from eq. (2.60) that the necessary condition is that the one-electron energy of the shell is made $\frac{3}{4}D$ less negative and that

$$A_2=A_1-3D/(8l+2). \qquad (2.61)$$

If only *terms with the highest value of the seniority number* ($v=q$ for l^q configurations with at most a half-filled shell, that is $q\leq 2l+1$) are considered, the spin-pairing expression from eq. (2.59) becomes

$$-\frac{2l+2}{2l+3}DS(S+1) \qquad (2.62)$$

indicating that, among baricentres of different S, $1/(2l+3)$ of the average excitation energy is caused by decreased seniority number, while the rest is caused by spin-pairing energy present for constant v. The values of A_1 and

D expressed as linear combinations of the previously defined parameters are for:

$$\begin{array}{cccc} & \mathrm{p^q} & \mathrm{d^q} & \mathrm{f^q} \\[2mm] A_1 & J(x, y) = F^0 - 2F_2 & A - \dfrac{14}{9}B + \dfrac{7}{9}C & E^0 \\[4mm] D & \dfrac{5}{4}K(x, y) = \dfrac{15}{4}F_2 & \dfrac{7}{6}\left(\dfrac{5}{2}B + C\right) & \dfrac{9}{8}E^1. \end{array} \qquad (2.63)$$

The coefficients 5/4, 7/6, and 9/8 of D in eq. (2.63) are a clear allusion to eq. (2.62).

Though D evidently is a parameter of atomic spectroscopy, it has an implication for the chemical behaviour of the elements: the stability of the half-filled d and f shells with $S=(2l+1)/2$ is expressed by the differences of $-DS(S+1)$, going from q to q+1, increasing linearly with q [i.e. the total expressions eqs. (2.58) or (2.59) being parabolic functions of q when the ground state with maximum value of S is considered] except at $q=2l+1$, where this difference suddenly makes a jump equal to $(2l+2)D$. This is called "the hump of ionization energies at half-filled shells".

REFERENCES

Condon, E. U., and Shortley, G. H. (1953), "Theory of Atomic Spectra", Cambridge University Press, 2 ed.

Hartree, R. D. (1957), "The Calculation of Atomic Structures", John Wiley, New York, describes how H.F.S.C.F. calculations are performed.

Jørgensen, C. K. (1958), *Acta Chem Scand*, **12**, 903.

Moore-Sitterly, C. (1949), "Atomic Energy Levels", National Bureau of Standards Circular 467, Vol. I (H to V), Washington; (1952), Vol. II (Cr to Nb); (1958), Vol. III (Mo to La and Hf to Ac); Vol. IV to consider the 4f and 5f elements.

Racah, G. (1942), *Phys. Rev.* **62**, 438; (1943), **63**, 367.

Racah, G. (1949), *Phys. Rev.* **76**, 1352 (f shell).

Slater, J. C. (1960), "Quantum Theory of Atomic Structure", Vols. I and II, McGraw-Hill, New York.

Watson, R. E. (1960), *Phys. Rev.*, **118**, 1036; (1960), **119**, 1934; "Iron-Series Hartree-Fock Calculations", Technical Report No. 12 from the Solid-State and Molecular Theory Group, M.I.T., Cambridge (Mass.), 1959.

Watson, R. E., and Freeman, A. J. (1961), *Phys. Rev.*, **123**, 521; (1961), **124**, 1117.

3. Correlation Effects

The Hartree-Fock calculations for monatomic many-electron systems are indeed quite successful. Thus, the ionization energies from eq. (1.13) agree with experimental values (obtained from X-ray absorption edges in the case of internal shells) within 1 or 2 per cent, with two exceptions, however: the shell 1s (and in very heavy atoms, also 2s and 2p) have a slightly higher ionization energy caused by the relativistic effects to be discussed in Chapter 10; and in the case of relatively external shells (say 3p in a first transition group atom) the uncertainty of some 50 kK in the position of the acceptor orbital in the X-ray absorption process (cf. Chapter 12) is significant, compared to the absolute size of the ionization energy.

The nature of these deviations leaves no doubt that the HFSCF represent an essential part of the truth. If we use the fundamental criterion for judgment of the quality of Ψ, the variation principle, we find that the *total energy usually is at least* 99 *per cent as negative as the observed value.* It may be added that total energies are very large. In a heavy atom, the two first electrons in their 1s orbital have each approximately the energy $-Z^2$ rydbergs, the two giving the contribution $\sim$ 220 Z^2 kK to the total energy. The next eight electrons in the 2s and 2p shells each have slightly less ionization energy than $-Z^2/4$ rydbergs. Taking interelectronic repulsion into account [eq. (1.14)], their contribution will be somewhat smaller than 220 Z^2 kK. In general, in a very heavy atom, the filled n, l shells with a given principal quantum number n contribute somewhat less negative than $-2Z^2$ rydbergs to the total energy. For an atom of the first transition group, say manganese with $Z=25$, these quantities have the order of magnitude 250,000 kK, while a lanthanide atom, such as neodymium with $Z=60$, is roughly 1.8 million kK and thorium with $Z=90$ roughly 5 million kK. It is evident that an error of 0.1 per cent in these energies, corresponding to 250 kK in Mn and 5,000 kK in Th would be much larger than the usual chemical bond energies, some 20 to 40 kK, or the quanta of visible light between 13 and 25 kK.

We know the main reason for these deviations, small compared to the total energy, but unfortunately large compared to the energy differences of interest to us. This is the fact that HFSCF only takes care of interelectronic repulsion in Schrödinger's equation for Ψ to the extent that it can be described as a spherically symmetric function, participating in the central field U(r). This is a very good approximation, but not a perfect one. The electrons prefer less frequently to be as close to each other as would be necessary in a HFSCF

Ψ'. The deviations of Ψ' produced are called correlation effects, and we define the *correlation energy* as the difference between the experimental energy (corrected for relativistic effects) and the nonrelativistic HFSCF total energy. Actually, the total energy is only known of atoms with up to ten electrons (it is determined from the sum of consecutive ionization energies found by spectroscopic studies in the far ultraviolet),while the HFSCF energy is known of many more atoms. Hence, we can only state that the correlation energy is (in kK)

$$
\begin{array}{llll}
2 \text{ He} & -9.2 & 4 \text{ Be} & -20.7 \\
2 \text{ Li}^+ & -9.5 & 4 \text{ B}^+ & -24.5 \\
2 \text{ Be}^{++} & -9.6 & 4 \text{ O}^{+4} & -34.1 \\
2 \text{ C}^{+4} & -9.7 & 10 \text{ F}^- & -86.3 \\
& & 10 \text{ Al}^{+3} & -88.7.
\end{array} \tag{3.1}
$$

It is seen to be roughly constant in the two-electron systems and also roughly constant and ten times larger in the ten-electron systems. Actually, there are good reasons to believe that, in systems with some 18 to 26 electrons, the correlation energy is about -400 kK, according to some of Watson's results. Hence, the amount of correlation energy per electron is not dramatically increasing with the atomic number.

Unfortunately for us, the correlation energy is roughly evenly distributed over the various shells according to their occupation number, and not, like the total energy, heavily concentrated in the inner shells. A transition group ion with some -50 kK or -100 kK correlation energy built in the 3d shell may distort the term distances [say of eqs. (2.50) and (2.51)] considerably, since the correlation energy has the same order of magnitude as the first-order interelectronic repulsion energy differences predicted by the HFSCF theory. Actually, the interelectronic repulsion parameters F^k (or B and C of d^q, or E^k of f^q) derived from experimental energy levels are *invariably smaller* than the parameters calculated by eq. (2.45) from HFSCF radial functions R.

This was known for many years regarding the term distances [eqs. (2.41) and (2.42)] in the $2p^q$ and $3p^q$ configurations, but the calculations of Watson (1960, cited at the end of Chapter 2) of $3d^q$ and $3d^q4s^2$ configurations made the phenomenon much more clear. For a given ionic charge z, the ratio between the semiempirical and the HFSCF parameters F^k is roughly $(z+2)/(z+3)$, the agreement being rather bad for neutral atoms with $z=0$. Tables 3.1 to 3.3 indicate a few of the characteristic features of Watson's remarkable results.

By a closer inspection of Watson's tables, the present writer (1962) found several regularities which may serve as a part consolation after the demonstration of the breakdown of the HFSCF method in predicting term distances. The most striking regularity is that, in an isoelectronic series d^q, the decrease of the excitation energy of a given L, S term above the ground term, relative to the HFSCF prediction of this energy difference, *is nearly independent of the ionic charge z*, and in addition usually *the larger, the smaller*

O.A.M.–B

L and S. Since the first-order interelectronic repulsion energy generally increases with decreased L and S, the latter part of the sentence is to a first approximation only a statement that all term distances are decreased from their HFSCF values by a proportional amount [$1/(z+3)$ as given above; this is roughly a constant energy in an isoelectronic series d^q, since the absolute HFSCF energy differences are proportional to $z+3$ or a similar quantity]. However, there do occur deviations from the HFSCF energy which are individual functions of the symmetry type L, S and which also are roughly independent of z. For reasons to be explained below, this phenomenon is called "deviation from the Slater ratios". For instance, ^2P and ^2H of d^3 should be degenerate in the HFSCF method [eq. (2.51)], but occur at the following distances in kK above ^4F of d^3 according to Moore-Sitterly's tables:

	Ti$^+$	V	V^{++}	Cr^{+3}	Mn^{+4}	Fe^{+5}	Fe$^+$
^2P	8.9	13.5	(11.0)	(13.7)	22.2	25.1	16.1
^2H	12.7	14.9	16.6	20.7	24.4	27.8	18.1
Watson	15.0	19.2	19.4	23.5	27.2	30.3	21.2.

$$(3.2)$$

The configurations $3d^34s^2$(V) and $3d^7$(Fe$^+$) with identical equations for the term distances as $3d^3$ are also considered. The energy of ^2P in V^{++} and Cr^{+3} is possibly erroneous, or is influenced by very special effects particular to these two ions.

It is seen that, excepting the latter levels, ^2P is situated some 2 kK below ^2H and ^2H some 2.8 kK below the position predicted for both levels by Watson's HFSCF. Actually, among the d^3 and d^7 terms, ^2H and ^2G are the least decreased (next to the ground state, ^4F, which serves as zero of comparison), while ^4P and ^2F are much more decreased and ^2P most. The similar decreases relative to ^3F of $3d^2$ and $3d^8$ are in kK:

$$^1D \quad 3.2 \quad ^3P \quad 3.8 \quad ^1G \quad 3.4 \tag{3.3}$$

whereas ^1S probably would be much more decreased if it were known. In $3d^4$ and $3d^6$, the decreases are, relative to ^5D:

$$^3H \ 2.6, \ ^3G \ 4.2, \ ^3D \ 6.6, \ ^1I \ 3.8, \ ^1F \sim 9 \tag{3.4}$$

and in $3d^5$ relative to the ground term ^6S:

$$^4G \ 5.2, \ ^4P \ 6.2, \ ^4D \sim 7, \ ^4F \ 8.7, \ ^2I \ 7.6, \ ^2H \ 10.8, \ ^2G \ 11.7. \tag{3.5}$$

It is possible to get an impression of the relative correlation energy of the ground states by comparing the observed ionization energies with those predicted by Watson. Before the half-filled shell, i.e., $d^q \rightarrow d^{q-1}$ with $q \leq 5$, they are about 10 kK larger, whereas for $q > 5$, they are about 20 kK larger than predicted. This can be interpreted as the effective one-electron energy of a new 3d electron falling 15 kK due to new possibilities of electronic correlation. The hump at the half-filled shell can be taken as evidence that the quantity

$6D$ (page 22) is 10 kK smaller than predicted by HFSCF. This is remarkably close to the difference, 9 kK, between Watson's value of $6D{\sim}15B{+}6C$ [eq. (2.63)] and the semiempirical value. Hence, the differences in correlation energy going from the $3d^0$ system Ca^{++} to the $3d^{10}$ system Zn^{++} is some 150 kK. The main observable effect is that all energy differences dependent on interelectronic repulsion parameters, i.e. term distances and the spin-pairing energy, are some 20 to 30 per cent smaller than the HFSCF values.

Seen from one point of view, this is a most definite proof that the actual Ψ of the gaseous atom or ion *is not* to any good approximation a Slater-antisymmetrized determinant. For the most strict conception of quantum mechanics, it can be concluded that the variation principle itself is no longer of any use for our approximate Ψ, because a series of Ψ_a becomes only necessarily a better approximation to the actual ground state Ψ_g by decreased energy, if Ψ_a already has a lower energy than the first excited state with the same symmetry type as the ground state. Since the correlation energy is larger than the ionization energy of M and M$^+$, there is an infinity of such states of the same symmetry below our HFSCF Ψ_a. (See Fig. 3.1.)

Seen from another point of view, however, the many regularities mentioned above inspire some confidence that some physical understanding can be

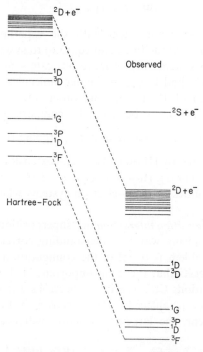

FIG. 3.1. Qualitative diagram of relative correlation energy. The symmetry types (L and S) of the lowest terms are indicated for the HFSCF and the actual wavefunctions.

achieved of the correlation effects. In particular, Watson's calculations have clearly demonstrated an important point: doing independent HFSCF calculations for two different terms of the same configuration $3d^q$ gives within some 2–3 per cent the same energy difference as calculated from the interelectronic parameters F^k obtained for one of the HFSCF solutions, or for a HFSCF of the baricentre of $3d^q$. Hence, it is seen that the rearrangement of orbitals [cf. eq. (1.13)] is not the main reason for the difference between the semiempirical and predicted values of F^k. It is interesting to note, however (Tables 3.1 and 3.2), that the ionization energies of internal shells and exchange integrals between two different internal shells are somewhat sensitive to the state of ionization of a given element.

The simplest physical model of the correlation effects is to introduce wavefunctions explicitly dependent on r_{12}, the interelectronic distance. This is very successful in the ground state of two-electron systems such as He, Li^+, . . . (and also the molecule H_2) where Ψ of a well-defined configuration ($1s^2$ of the monatomic entities) is written as a product of identical spatial orbital parts $\psi_1 \psi_2$ for the two electrons, the antisymmetrization being taken care of by the spin part of the orbitals. The well-defined configuration can now be abandoned by writing a correlation factor αr_{12}:

$$\Psi = \psi_1 \psi_2 (1 + \alpha r_{12}) \qquad (3.6)$$

obtaining a much better agreement with the experimental ground-state energy. It might seem obvious to extend eq. (3.6) to systems with more than two electrons and to systems with a more intricate symmetry type than ^1S. As a semiempirical method to use in simpler molecules, Julg (1960) recommended consideration of J integrals and other integrals of interrepulsion multiplied by a factor ~ 0.9 to be found by comparison with energy levels and ionization energies of the isolated atoms, arguing that $< \frac{1}{r_{12}} >$ has ~ 0.9 times the value predicted by HFSCF. This is an extension of Moffitt's idea of "atoms in molecules" (1951). However, as an *a priori* method, the correlation factors lead to difficulties in many-electron systems which are insurmountable at present.

It seems that *configuration interaction* or "superposition of configurations" is a much more promising way to understanding correlation effects. However, the difficult problem is to select the configurations to be considered. Equation (2.27) suggests that the main importance belongs to two-electron substituted configurations Cb^2, where two electrons a from the ground configuration Ca^2 have been replaced by two electrons b. From a second-order perturbation argument, the largest interaction will occur with such configurations having

$$\frac{E^2_{mn}}{E(Cb^2) - E(Ca^2)} \sim \frac{(K(a, b))^2}{2I(a) - 2I(b)} \qquad (3.7)$$

as large as possible. In the second part of eq. (3.7), the nondiagonal element E_{mn} between the two configurations, i.e. eq. (2.27), has been represented by the K integral between the two orbitals a and b, as is frequently true, and the energy difference between the two configurations in the denominator is approximated by twice the difference in ionization energy, $I(a) - I(b)$.

In the simplest case, He, Li^+, . . ., the $1s^2$ configuration might be expected to interact with excited configurations such as $2s^2$, $2p^2$, ... The quantities involved in eq. (3.7) are known from atomic spectroscopy, and the stabilization obtained by the interaction is much too insufficient to explain the difference between the ground-state energy observed and the HFSCF $1s^2$. However, we recall from eq. (2.11) that we not only have an infinity of discrete, stationary states with negative one-electron energy, but also an overall dense infinity of continuum states with positive energy. We are completely free to select continuum orbitals, or linear combinations of continuum and stationary orbitals, orthogonal on our ground state ψ, for use in the configurations eq. (3.7). However, if we consider more than one excited configuration, we must be very careful that the *virtual orbitals* we construct are indeed orthogonal; otherwise the perturbation treatment ends in a terrible chaos.

If we denote virtual orbitals (∞l) with the angular behaviour appropriate for a definite l value [eq. (2.3)] and a radial function not being a combination of stationary states only, Shull and Löwdin (1959) found that the two main contributions to the helium ground state, besides 99.19 per cent $1s^2$, are 0.38 per cent $(\infty s)^2$ and 0.39 per cent $(\infty p)^2$, the percentages expressing the contribution to Ψ^2. The radial function (∞p) looks very much like 1s, but only the symmetry type ^1S can be selected among the angular functions [cf. eq. (2.41)]. The nondiagonal element between the two configurations $1s^2$ and $(\infty p)^2(^1S)$ is $\sqrt{3}K(1s, \infty p)$. The radial function (∞s) has one node for being orthogonal on 1s, but does not look like 2s, which is much more extended. $<r>$ is roughly the same for 1s and (∞s). The nondiagonal element between $1s^2$ and $(\infty s)^2(^1S)$ is $K(1s, \infty s)$.

The other possible virtual configurations, such as $(\infty d)^2$, . . ., or involving orbitals having s or p angular behaviour and with radial functions orthogonal on 1s and (∞s), or on (∞p), contribute only to a very slight extent, altogether 0.04 per cent to the ^1S ground state [eq. (3.22)]. It is not accurate to think of the ground state of a helium atom obtaining some of the properties with regard to infinite radial extension, etc., as is usually connected with the idea of the continuum orbitals. Rather, we may regard the correlation effect as a sort of internal polarization of the charge cloud described by the HFSCF along the co-ordinates appropriate for the second-order density matrix. Figure 3.2 shows the density diagrams of the terms ^1S (and one ^3S) of configurations such as $1s^2$, $1s2s$, $2s^2$, $(\infty s)^2$, and a mixture of $1s^2$ with a little $(\infty s)^2$. Due to the spherical symmetry of the angular functions of all the orbitals involved here, only two (and not six) space variables are needed, i.e. r_1 and r_2. It is seen how the densities of ^3S and ^1S of 1s2s differ in the overlap region between 1s and 2s, and how the $\pm K(1s, 2s)$ of eq. (2.31) corresponds to the difference produced between $\langle r_{12}^{-1} \rangle$ in the two cases. In addition, it is seen how the admixture of a little $(\infty s)^2$ in $1s^2$ makes the density squeeze out in the two diagonally opposite corners with (small r_1, large r_2) and (large r_1, small r_2) with less density left where $r_1 \sim r_2$. The phenomenon shown in Fig. 3.2 is often called "radial correlation", whereas the influence of configurations such as $(\infty p)^2$ is called "angular correlation". The latter needs paper with a few more dimensions for its graphical representation.

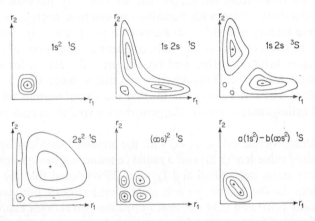

FIG. 3.2. Density of the spatial part of spherical symmetrical two-electron wave-functions with the variables r_1 and r_2. It is seen how the triplet wavefunction ^3S vanishes along the diagonal $r_1 = r_2$, and how the admixture of a small proportion of $(\infty s)^2$ to $1s^2$ decreases the density of ^1S close to this diagonal.

It may be useful to distinguish between continuum behaviour of Ψ of the many-electron system, as soon the energy is higher than the first ionization energy of the system (as is already the case of the states $2s^2$ and $2p^2$ of helium; frequently in atomic spectroscopy, such states may be fairly long-lived and observable, often with some tendency to auto-ionization) and continuum behaviour of the individual orbitals ψ.

Going from atoms with two electrons to the more general many-electron atoms, it is possible to make a rough distinction between correlation effects connected with *virtual orbitals* and with *near-orbital degeneracy*. The latter phenomenon does not occur in helium, but is very important in beryllium and other systems with four electrons as we shall see below. The relatively small energy difference between the 2s and 2p shells makes the interaction between the $1s^2 2s^2$ and the ^1S term of $1s^2 2p^2$ [having the nondiagonal element $\sqrt{3} K(2s, 2p)$] particularly strong. In gaseous atoms of the first transition group, near-orbital degeneracy effects between 3d and 4s occur, because $3d^{q-2}4s^2$ and $3d^{q-1}4s$ and $3d^q$ are nearly coincident. However, these effects disappear in the higher ionization states, because the overlap integral K(3d, 4s) is rather small, below 2 kK. With ionic charges at least two, the main correlation effects seem to be a near-orbital degeneracy of $3p^43d^{q+2}$ and the usual ground configuration $3p^63d^q$ (as discussed by Trees and Jørgensen, 1961) and virtual configurations $3d^{q-2}(\infty d)^2$, $3d^{q-2}(\infty f)^2$, $3d^{q-2}(\infty g)^2$, ... Of these, $(\infty f)^2$ is probably the strongest interacting, while $(\infty d)^2$ and $(\infty g)^2$ are somewhat weaker. Among these orbitals, (∞d) has one node in the middle of the 3d radial function, whereas (∞f), (∞g), . . . have no nodes and to some extent resemble 4f, 5g, . . . orbitals but having approximately the same $<r>$ as 3d. As pointed out by Trees, the situation is further complicated by the fact that configurations such as $3p^53d^q(\infty f)$ which at first glance seem to be one-electron substitutions of $3p^63d^q$ (and hence should be of minor importance), at closer analysis can be shown to be two-electron substitutions in the sense that different orbitals of the degenerate shell 3d are involved. Thus, $3p^53d^2$ (∞f) contains terms of the symmetry types occurring in the product of $3p^5(\infty f)$, *viz.* (^{1}D, ^{3}D, ^{1}F, ^{3}F, ^{1}G, ^{3}G) and the usual $3d^2$ terms (^{1}S, ^{3}P, ^{1}D, ^{3}F, ^{1}G) and always involve other 3d orbital combinations than the terms of $3d^2$ interacted with. Actually, these contributions can be shown to be of great importance in cancelling a large part of the effect on the parameters α and β in the linear theory (page 34) from the configurations $3p^63d^{q-2}(\infty f)^2$.

It is possible to make a qualitative estimate of the energies of these virtual orbitals. It may first be noted that, for a series of wavefunctions Ψ, e.g. in an isoelectronic series, a "scaling" of the distances by division with a factor $\eta=<r^{-1}>$ but keeping the same "shape" of all the orbitals, leads to a situation where all the potential energy (arising from electrostatic interactions) is proportional to η, whereas all the kinetic energy [as shown by a careful study of eqs. (2.9) and (2.10)] is proportional to $<r^{-2}>$, which for a definite shape of the wavefunction again is proportional to η^2. The total energy therefore can be written

$$+k_1\eta^2-k_2\eta. \tag{3.8}$$

If this expression is minimized with respect to η, the resulting value is

$$\eta=-k_2/2k_1 \text{ or } k_2\eta=2k_1\eta^2 \tag{3.9}$$

obeying the virial theorem. As Löwdin pointed out, the scaling procedure of eq. (3.8) is valuable for ameliorating approximate Ψ which do not already obey the virial theorem. In Hartree's book (1957) many examples are given of comparison between HFSCF of different atoms, where the radial functions (particularly at constant ionic charge) frequently are related by scaling with a parameter η closely related to $Z-Z_\sigma$ where Z_σ is a so-called screening constant.

To give an idea of how interelectronic repulsion acts in the central field to produce a certain scaling, let us consider $1s^2$ of a two-electron atom with atomic number Z and having the hydrogenic radial function [cf. eq. (2.12)]

$$R = r \exp(-\eta r). \tag{3.10}$$

The kinetic energy of each of the two electrons is $+\eta^2$ rydbergs and the nuclear attraction energy of each of the two electrons $-2Z\eta$. The interelectronic repulsion energy $J(1s, 1s)$ is $\frac{5}{4}\eta$ for radial functions of the type (3.10). The total energy of the two-electronic system is hence:

$$-T = 2\eta^2 + (-4Z + 5/4)\eta \tag{3.11}$$

which can be minimized with respect to η, giving

$$\eta = Z - 5/16 \text{ and } T = 2(Z - 5/16)^2. \tag{3.12}$$

For a helium atom with Z=2, the total energy

$$1458 \text{ rydbergs}/256 = 5.6953125 \text{ rydbergs} \tag{3.13}$$

compares favourably with the observed value, 5.8073 rydbergs, the difference being due in part to correlation energy and in part to the fact that eq. (3.10) does not exactly describe a HFSCF 1s radial function.

It is interesting to illustrate Koopman's theorem about slight effects on HFSCF energy quantities by rearrangement of orbitals by comparing the ionization energy calculated by two different methods. Subtraction of the ionization energy of the one-electron system, Z^2, from eq. (3.12) gives

$$Z^2 - \frac{5}{4}Z + \frac{50}{256}, \text{ for helium } \frac{434}{256} = 1.6953125 \text{ rydbergs} \tag{3.14}$$

while the ionization energy according to eq. (1.13), taking the parameters

$$-\eta^2 + 2Z\eta - \frac{5}{4}\eta \tag{3.15}$$

of the two-electron system gives with eq. (3.12)

$$Z^2 - \frac{5}{4}Z + \frac{75}{256}, \text{ for helium } \frac{459}{256} = 1.79296875 \text{ rydbergs.} \tag{3.16}$$

Incidentally, eq. (3.16) is much closer to the observed value than what seems to be the more careful and correct subtraction eq. (3.14)—*there is no* variation principle valid for energy differences.

Obviously, most ionization processes have much less radical effects in heavy atoms than the rearrangement of the orbitals in helium going from He to He⁺. Therefore, the 6 per cent difference between the ionization energies predicted in eqs. (3.14) and (3.16) is larger by far than what is usually produced by deviations from Koopman's theorem.

Returning to the virtual orbitals of helium, we would expect (∞s) to have roughly the same potential energy as 1s, i.e. $-2Z\eta$, because $<r>$ is roughly the same. On the other hand, the kinetic energy is four times larger, $+4\eta^2$, because the node causes $\dfrac{d^2R}{dr^2}$ of eq. (2.9) to vary four times more. The total energy of $(\infty s)^2$ is therefore about $+2T(1s^2)$.

The same analysis of (∞p) suggests the same potential energy, that is $-2\eta Z$, the same radial kinetic energy as 1s, i.e. $+\eta^2$, and angular kinetic energy which according to eq. (2.10) is expected to be close to $2\eta^2$, since the ratio $<r^{-2}>/<r^{-1}>^2$ is only slightly below one. In this case, therefore, the total energy of $(\infty p)^2$ is lower than of $(\infty s)^2$ and is only about $+T(1s^2)$.

The energy differences to (∞l) increases strongly with increasing l because of the angular kinetic energy $l(l+1)\eta^2$ and $(\infty l)^2$ will be situated approximately at $(l^2+l-1)T(1s^2)$. However, it might still be asked whether the whole process of configuration interaction would not be divergent, because the nondiagonal element between $1s^2$ and ^1S of $(\infty l)^2$ is $\sqrt{2l+1}$ $K(1s, \infty l)$. Consequently, the second-order perturbation sum eq. (3.7)

$$\sum_{l>0} \frac{(2l+1)(K(1s, \infty l))^2}{(l^2+l-1)T(1s^2)} \tag{3.17}$$

would diverge, go as a sum of $1/l$ for large l, if the K integrals were invariant. Fortunately, the K integrals decrease strongly with increasing l and make eq. (3.17) perfectly convergent.

In the transition group ions, the situation is much more complicated than in the helium atom. The relative proportion of radial and angular kinetic energy is not exactly known for the 3d orbital, but is certainly smaller than the ratio 1 : 2 suggested by the hydrogenic value $(n^2-l(l+1)) : l(l+1)$, and we call this ratio $R : l(l+1)$. We can write our 3d orbital energy

$$\underset{\text{central field}}{-<\frac{U}{r}>} \underset{\text{angular}}{+l(l+1)<r^{-2}>} \underset{\text{radial kinetic}}{+<Rr^{-2}>} \tag{3.18}$$

giving for the radial contribution parameter

$$<Rr^{-2}>=\tfrac{1}{2}<Ur^{-1}><r^{-1}>-l(l+1)<r^{-2}> \tag{3.19}$$

identifying, somewhat imprudently, $<r^{-1}>^2$ with $<r^{-2}>$.

The similar expression for (∞d) would be*

$$-<\frac{U}{r}>+l(l+1)<r^{-2}>+4<Rr^{-2}> \tag{3.20}$$

while for all excited (∞l) with $l>2$

$$-<\frac{U}{r}>+l(l+1)<r^{-2}>+<Rr^{-2}>. \tag{3.21}$$

* Actually, the potential energy will be slightly less negative. According to eq. (2.11), all radial functions must be proportional to r^{l+1} close to the nucleus.

For $\langle R \rangle$ somewhat below 3, these approximate expressions suggest that (∞d) and (∞f) have energies close to zero (or possibly a little bit negative, suggesting a strong participation of $4d$ and $4f$, respectively), (∞g) somewhat positive, and (∞h) some $+2T(3d)$. This shows clearly that we can expect nothing from the angular kinetic energy in preventing the ravage done to the configuration $3d^q$ by $3d^{q-2}(\infty l)^2$ with $l = 2$, 3, and 4. Our only hope is, as in eq. (3.17), that the nondiagonal elements are linear combinations of Condon and Shortley's parameters G^k with $k = l-2$, l, and $l+2$. Fortunately, G^k have a much more pronounced tendency than F^k to decrease as function of increasing k, and the correlation effects may perhaps become less important for $l > 4$. Another question, which is under study by Trees, Watson, and the writer, is to know to what extent the concept of second-order perturbation is valid, in other words, whether four-electron substitutions, six-, eight-, . . . are important. In the latter case, the situation is genuinely confusing.

We may also discuss the L, S dependence of the correlation energy. Trees (1951) originally suggested to add a term $+\alpha L(L+1)$ to the Slater-Condon-Shortley expressions for the interelectronic repulsion energy of d^q terms, and much better agreement was obtained with experimental values by assuming $\alpha \sim 0.08$ kK. A closer analysis by Racah and Trees (1960) showed that if α and a further parameter, β, connected with decreased seniority number v, are introduced, the treatment corresponds to Bacher and Goudsmit's *linear theory*. In this theory, the important parameters for the configuration l^q are the energies of the $(2l+1)$ different terms of l^2 as shown in eq. (2.24). These can be written as linear combinations of the $(l+1)$ integrals F^k which now become *phenomenological parameters* as well as l further parameters, all serving only to account for the $(2l+1)$ different energies of l^2. As the l further parameters can be used α in p^q and α and β in d^q. The energies of the terms of l^q can be found by combining the wavefunctions of l^2 *by coefficients of parentage*. It is then hoped that the correlation effects, introduced semiempirically in the description by consideration of the experimental values of l^2, turn out to be proportional also to the squares of the coefficients of parentage. This seems indeed to be the case to a good approximation, and the linear theory of atomic spectra has certainly a bright future before it, though it has not directly touched the problem of why all the parameters F^k so determined are smaller than the HFSCF values. One might hope also to get some physical understanding by considering the "model interactions" corresponding to parameters such as α, for instance dipolar polarization mutually between the orbitals. This may also be a slightly dangerous attempt, because as we said, we are intrinsically dealing only with linear combinations of experimental l^2 energies.

The seniority number v as discussed in eqs. (2.56) and (2.57) has a well-defined meaning inside the pure configuration l^q. However, it coincides with another interpretation: the possibility of interaction between $s^2 l^{q-2}$ and l^q.

For $q=2$, it is clearly seen that only the term ^1S can mix, and for $q=3$ the term $^2(l)$. These are exactly the terms with decreased v. We may generalize this aspect of the seniority number to the idea of *uncoupling of the l values* by interaction between $(l')^2 l^{q-2}$ and l^q. If $l' \geq l$, this uncoupling is possible for all L, S terms of l^q. If $l' < l$, it will usually only be possible for a part of the terms. For instance, $l'=1$ makes the interaction between p^2 and d^2 possible for ^3P, ^1D, and ^1S, but not for ^3F and ^1G. Hence, one might define a p-seniority number v_1 being zero for the three former terms and two for the two latter. Among the terms of d^3 only ^2H cannot interact with dp^2 and would hence have $v_1=3$, while all the other terms have $v_1=1$. Though one may argue that all terms of p^4 may interact with p^2s^2, or all terms of d^8 with d^6s^2, it is still true that the ^1S terms interact particularly strongly; and actually, the square of the nondiagonal element is as much larger than the squares of the non-diagonal elements for the other terms (^3P, ^1D, . . .) as indicated by the interaction between p^2 and s^2 and between d^2 and s^2, *viz.* $3(K(s, p))^2$ and $5(K(s, d))^2$.

The prominent examples of near-orbital degeneracy all belong to the seniority number type of explanation. It is not yet known whether the L, S dependence of virtual configuration interaction effects mainly depends on similar considerations, or whether the uncoupling to similar or larger l' values may introduce a strong selectivity with respect to symmetry type L, S of the term.

Löwdin introduced the concept of *natural spin orbitals* being appropriate for the clarification of correlation effects. We have not yet discussed the concept of Hartree-Fock calculations with spin orbitals with room for only one electron with specified m_s rather than orbitals (with room for two electrons with opposite m_s). It is quite evident from the variation principle that doubling the number of orbitals available can do nothing but ameliorate the energy. However, this amelioration does not seem very dramatic, and the calculations become much more lengthy. Thus, the ground state of a zinc atom ($Z=30$) involves seven different nl shells. If fourteen different radial functions of spin orbitals are admitted, the calculation is comparable to that of a mercury atom ($Z=80$) with fourteen different n, l shells. The situation is slightly different in systems with positive S, such as ^3F of [Ar]$3d^8$, Ni^{++}, where the ionization energies of the inner shell are larger for electrons that have m_s in the same direction as the most common m_s of the partly filled 3d shell than for the opposite spin direction, due to the K integrals. In this case, good agreement has been obtained by Freeman and Watson (1960) with various magnetic experiments by assuming the spin orbitals with opposite spin direction to have slightly different radial functions. However, this gives only a very small contribution to the deviation between the semiempirical and calculated parameters of interelectronic repulsion and does not produce essential changes in the total electronic density.

It is always somewhat dangerous to ameliorate the HFSCF by some refinement and then use the variation principle. For instance, the various M_s values of a given term, which are degenerate both in the HFSCF approximation [see eq. (2.31)] and in the actual Ψ', may very well become separated by uncritical approaches. The trouble with the so-called "unrestricted Hartree-Fock calculation" with spin orbitals is that, usually, a mixture of various S values are produced, which may then be separated by Löwdin's "projection operator" technique.

The unrestricted spin-orbital calculation of a system with $S=0$ still predicts different spin-orbital radial functions for the same shell in the HFSCF description. This does not mean, of course, that the two spin directions really become different, but simply that when one electron is put into a spin orbital, the other electron with opposite spin direction prefers a slightly different spin orbital, decreasing the interelectronic repulsion energy $<r_{12}^{-1}>$. In the special case of helium, the spin-orbital description (1s1s′) can be shown to be equivalent to the interaction between two orbital configurations $1s^2$ and $(\infty s)^2$, the orbital (∞s) having a radial function proportional to the difference $R(1s)-R(1s')$.

Now coming back to Löwdin's natural spin orbitals, they are (to a rather small extent) a function of the approximation admitted of a given system. The natural spin orbitals always have the symmetry types proper to the symmetry of the system* (in spherical symmetry hence well-defined l) but contrary to the orbitals we have been talking about, they do not necessarily have the occupation numbers 1 or 0 (for both spin directions 2, 1, or 0), but may assume real values between these limits. In the approximation of HFSCF, the orbitals combined with $m_s=\pm\frac{1}{2}$ are simply the natural spin orbitals. If we consider the approximation of three s orbitals (i.e. three pairs of identical spin orbitals with opposite m_s), the occupation numbers of the pair of the natural spin orbitals 1s is 0.995660, of (∞s) 0.004265, and of the pair $(\infty's)$ 0.000075. The interesting thing is that going to a large number of allowed orbitals, these occupation numbers seem very quickly to converge to fixed values. For instance, the numbers obtained for ten different orbitals, now allowing l to vary, are

$$0.991863 \text{ (1s)} \qquad 0.003896 \text{ (}\infty\text{p)} \qquad 0.000009 \text{ (}\infty\text{f)}$$
$$0.003840 \text{ (}\infty\text{s)} \qquad 0.000136 \text{ (}\infty'\text{p)} \tag{3.22}$$
$$0.000054 \text{ (}\infty'\text{s)} \qquad 0.000180 \text{ (}\infty\text{d)}$$

and probably quite near to the actual values from a natural-spin orbital analysis of Ψ' of the ^1S ground state of helium. The great virtue of the natural spin orbitals so defined is that only the configurations a^2, b^2, c^2, . . . participate in Ψ' and not the mixed configurations ab, ac, . . . which are much more numerous.

* However, Dr. Trees has pointed out to me that, in a nontotally symmetric term (i.e. not ^1S nor $^1\Gamma_1$), the interelectronic repulsion could produce mixtures of l in a definite natural spin orbital, e.g. in the configurations sp and dp interacting in ^3P.

It is expected that the natural spin orbitals of the ^1S ground state of neon consist of ten spin orbitals, i.e. $1s^2 2s^2 2p^6$ with population numbers just below 1, and some 26 spin orbitals with occupation numbers ~ 0.001, corresponding to the virtual shells $(\infty_1 s)$ (having the same $<r>$ as $1s$ but a node), $(\infty_1 p)$ (having the same $<r>$ as $1s$), $(\infty_2 s)$, $(\infty_2 p)$, and (∞d), all having roughly the same $<r>$ as $2s$ and $2p$, and hence participating in the two-electron substituted configurations

$$
\begin{array}{ll}
(\infty_1 s)^2 2s^2 2p^6 & 1s^2 (\infty d)^2 2p^6 \\
(\infty_1 p)^2 2s^2 2p^6 & 1s^2 2s^2 2p^4 (\infty_2 s)^2 \\
1s^2 (\infty_2 s)^2 2p^6 & 1s^2 2s^2 2p^4 (\infty_2 p)^2 \\
1s^2 (\infty_2 p)^2 2p^6 & 1s^2 2s^2 2p^4 (\infty d)^2.
\end{array}
\tag{3.23}
$$

However, such detailed studies have not been performed yet, though the qualitative ideas developed above on $3d^q$ strongly suggest that the natural spin orbitals indicated in eq. (3.23) have, on the average, larger population numbers than the following ones.

Some fundamental calculations have been performed recently for light atoms. Neglecting relativistic effects [which start off with a contribution $Z^4/(137)^2$ rydbergs] the electrostatic and kinetic energy can be exactly expanded in Z^2 multiplied by a Taylor series in Z^{-1}, viz.:

$$
-T = a_2 Z^2 + a_1 Z + a_0 + a_{-1} Z^{-1} + a_{-2} Z^{-2} + \ldots \tag{3.24}
$$

It can also be shown that the HFSCF energy $-T_{HF}$ of a given L, S term of a given configuration in an isoelectronic series can be written

$$
-T_{HF} = a_2 Z^2 + b_1 Z + b_0 + b_{-1} Z^{-1} + b_{-2} Z^{-2} + \ldots \tag{3.25}
$$

The coefficient a_2 is the same in both eqs. (3.24) and (3.25) and is the same as the coefficient valid for hydrogenic radial functions with the principal quantum number n,

$$
a_2 = -\Sigma n^{-2} \tag{3.26}
$$

because it can be found by consideration of an atom with very large Z, or rather, avoiding relativistic difficulties, a hypothetical atom where the electronic charge, and hence the interelectronic repulsion, becomes much weaker.

The J and K integrals between hydrogenic radial functions in this limiting case also give the coefficients b_1, e.g. the contribution $+5/4$ from $J(1s, 1s)$ as used in eq. (3.11). In the case of $1s^2$, $a_1 = b_1$. Thus, the actual energy of $1s^2$ of two-electronic atoms and the Hartree-Fock energy differ only in a_0 and the following coefficients:

$$
\begin{aligned}
-T &= -2Z^2 + 1.25Z - 0.31531 + 0.01707Z^{-1} - \ldots \\
-T_{HF} &= -2Z^2 + 1.25Z - 0.22201 - 0.00211Z^{-1} \ldots
\end{aligned}
\tag{3.27}
$$

This may be compared to eq. (3.12):

$$-T_{hydrogenic} = -2Z^2 + 1.25Z - 0.1953125. \tag{3.28}$$

The nearly constant correlation energy [eq. (3.1)] is hence mainly concentrated in the difference between the Z-independent coefficients $(a_0 - b_0)$. In general, however, for $n > 1$, the correlation energy also contains a quantity proportional to Z, being

$$T_{HF} - T = (a_1 - b_1)Z + (a_0 - b_0) + (a_{-1} - b_{-1})Z^{-1} + \ldots \tag{3.29}$$

Layzer (1959) and Linderberg (1961) pointed out that the coefficients a_1 can be calculated for hydrogenic radial functions, considering configuration interaction between configurations occupying the same principal quantum number to the same extent; e.g. between all $1s^2 2s^a 2p^b$ or between all $1s^2 2s^2 2p^6 3s^a 3p^b 3d^c$. Layzer even went so far as to suggest that the "complex" of all such configurations is a better entity to discuss for atomic spectroscopists than the individual configuration. In practice, this is a question whether or not near-orbital degeneracy actually occurs to a considerable extent. There is no doubt that, in thorium, the Layzer degeneracy $5s - 5p - 5d - 5f$ has a much smaller effect on the correlation effects observed than the actual near-degeneracy $5f - 6d - 7s$. On the other hand, the Taylor expansion in Z^{-1} makes a strong emphasis on the hydrogenic degeneracy and useful conclusions can be drawn.

Thus, the ground state ^1S of four-electron atoms has according to Linderberg

$$-T = -2.5Z^2 + 3.1186Z - \ldots$$
$$-T_{HF} = -2.5Z^2 + 3.1420Z - 1.6109 - 0.2662/(Z - 1.42). \tag{3.30}$$

As pointed out by Watson (1961), the $2s - 2p$ near degeneracy in this series contributes some $0.026Z$ rydberg to the stabilization of the ground state in calculations admitting two configurations, $1s^2 2s^2$ and $1s^2 2p^2$, while eq. (3.30) suggests a difference $0.0234Z$. Similar results have been obtained by Kibartas, Kavetskis, and Yutsis (1955).

The series Be, B^+, . . . is probably a rather exceptional case of exhibiting proportionally as much Z-dependent correlation energy. The discussion of correlation energy being either of the "virtual orbital" or of the "near-orbital degeneracy" type (page 30) is presumably more or less equivalent to the contributions in eq. (3.29) being of the type $(a_0 - b_0)$ or $(a_1 - b_1)Z$, respectively. It would have been very fortunate if atoms containing more than a few electrons had short Taylor series (eq. (3.24)). According to Linderberg and Shull's results for the Li and Be isoelectronic sequences, there is rather little hope for this state of affairs. Rather than to consider the non-negligible and rather irregularly varying $a_{-1}, a_{-2}, a_{-3}, \ldots$ it may possibly be a good idea to truncate eq. (3.25) to

$$-T \cong a_2 Z^2 + a_1 Z + a_0 + c/(Z - Z_c) \tag{3.31}$$

or a similar expression, as given in eq. (3.30).

In atomic spectroscopy, it has become useful to express various energy differences in a Taylor series, not directly in Z, but in an "effective" charge Z_* related to the concept of η proportional to $<r^{-1}>$ in eq. (3.8). Thus, Tables 3.1 to 3.3 give a strong impression of the semiempirical values as well as the HFSCF values of F^k integrals, and of the orbital energy difference 2s—2p and 3s—3p varying proportional to Z_* if defined as the sum $z+Z_c$ of the ionic charge z and a constant for a given isoelectronic series (cf. also Jørgensen, 1957). This is not the case for the exchange integrals between *different* shells G^k, which are not only dependent on $<r^{-1}>$ as F^k, but also on the "squared overlap" (see page 5) and are therefore roughly a measure of $<r^{-1}>\int\psi_1^2\psi_2^2 d\tau$.

TABLE 3.1. Ionization energies I(*nl*) and (nuclear attraction and kinetic energy) contributions $(-N+T)(nl)$ for Watson's HFSCF. The two kinds of quantities are denoted by H(*nl*) and K(*nl*) in Watson's papers. All in the unit kK here

	V^0	V^{++}	Cr^{+3}	Mn^{++}	Mn^{+4}	Fe^{+3}	Ni^0	Ni^{++}
	$[Ar]3d^5 4s^2$	$[Ar]3d^3$	$[Ar]3d^3$	$[Ar]3d^5$	$[Ar]3d^3$	$[Ar]3d^5$	$[Ar]3d^8 4s^2$	$[Ar]3d^8$
I(1s)	44230	44363	48710	52944	53280	57678	67069	67232
I(2s)	5238	5377	6102	6540	6888	7326	8318	8476
I(2p)	4393	4532	5208	5599	5944	6334	7224	7384
I(3s)	697	833	1052	985	1301	1218	1067	1226
I(3p)	441	578	775	693	1001	902	714	875
I(3d)	111	234	393	265	598	433	150	307
$(-N+T)$(1s)	58020	58020	63178	68554	68554	74150	86001	86001
$(-N+T)$(2s)	14134	14133	15417	16756	16756	18148	21098	21098
$(-N+T)$(2p)	13983	13984	15378	16608	16609	18001	20953	20953
$(-N+T)$(3s)	5361	5363	5926	6423	6506	7029	8185	8168
$(-N+T)$(3p)	4985	4995	5561	6032	6157	6637	7742	7745
$(-N+T)$(3d)	4015	4037	4758	4994	5470	5739	6518	6553

TABLE 3.2. Parameters of interelectronic repulsion for Watson's HFSCF in kK

	V^{++}	Cr^{+3}	Mn^{++}	Mn^{+4}	Fe^{+3}	Ni^{++}	Ni^{+4}
	$[Ar]3d^3$	$[Ar]3d^3$	$[Ar]3d^5$	$[Ar]3d^3$	$[Ar]3d^5$	$[Ar]3d^8$	$[Ar]3d^6$
F^0(1s, 1s)	3079	3216	3352	3352	3489	3763	3762
F^0(2s, 2s)	643	675	707	707	739	803	803
F^0(3s, 3s)	207	221	230	235	244	263	267
F^0(2p, 2p)	732	771	810	810	849	926	927
F^2(2p, 2p)	344	363	382	382	401	438	438
F^0(3p, 3p)	194.2	209.6	217.9	225.4	233.0	252.9	260.1
F^2(3p, 3p)	98.0	105.8	109.6	114.0	117.3	126.8	131.2
F^0(3d, 3d)	156.4	184.2	180.9	210.2	207.2	215.8	242.3
F^2(3d, 3d)	72.4	87.2	83.6	101.1	97.7	99.5	115.4
F^4(3d, 3d)	45.0	54.6	52.0	63.6	61.1	61.9	72.5

TABLE 3.3. Watson and Freeman's HFSCF for 3p-group elements. Notation as in Tables 3.1 and 3.2

	Al	Si	P	S	Cl	Cl⁻	Ar
I(1s)	12837	15100	17548	20190	23018	22937	26031
I(2s)	1077	1350	1647	1975	2327	2246	2704
I(2p)	705	933	1184	1466	1771	1690	2100
I(3s)	86	118	153	193	235	161	280
I(3p)	44	65	86	96	111	33	129
F^0(3p, 3p)	57.7	72.5	85.8	96.8	108.3	100.4	120.1
F^2(3p, 3p)	29.0	36.6	43.3	48.5	54.0	48.1	59.8

TABLE 3.4. Lisitzin's coefficients for use in eq. (3.32) in kK for the number q of electrons. The hydrogenic value of α is given in parentheses. β is a number, not an energy

q	α	β	γ
2	109.3 (109.7)	0.625	9.03
3	27.4 (27.4)	1.62	8.9
4	27.8 (27.4)	2.22	12.9
5	28.6 (27.4)	3.24	21.7
10	30.4 (27.4)	7.16	72.1
11	13.1 (12.2)	8.41	46.6
13	13.9 (12.2)	10.49	39.5
18	15.4 (12.2)	14.38	75
28	18.8 (12.2)	25.28	96
29	9.05 (6.86)	24.87	92
46	13.3 (6.86)	42.50	96
47	7.3 (4.39)	42.43	92
48	7.6 (4.39)	43.28	97
79	7.0 (3.05)	74.13	92

Lisitzin (1938) wrote *ionization energies* of an isoelectronic series

$$I = aZ^2 + bZ + c = \alpha(Z - \beta)^2 - \gamma \qquad (3.32)$$

with the parameters (cf. also Baughan, 1961):

$$\alpha = a \quad \beta = -b/2a \quad \gamma = (b^2/4a) - c \qquad (3.33)$$

of which some are given in Table 3.4. It is seen that eq. (3.32) formally can be derived from the difference between eq. (3.24) for the isoelectronic series and eq. (3.24) for the series with one electron less. However, if this were the only explanation (i.e. the variation of the coefficients a_{-k} in the two series were of no importance), α should be exactly $1/n^2$ according to eq. (3.26). Actually, the experimental values for low ionic charges z are indeed satisfactory with regard to $\alpha = n^{-2}$ for the electron numbers q=2 and 3. In the series q=4, 5, 6, . . .,

10, α slowly rises to a value 10 per cent larger than expected. The values in Table 3.4 are all some 8–95 per cent larger than the hydrogenic values, the strong deviations appearing at the end of the 3d shell (q=28) and 4d shell (q=46).

In the same way, we cannot with certainty identify differences in correlation energy such as given in eq. (3.3) to (3.5) with differences between values of a_0 in the individual series eq. (3.24) for each symmetry type L, S.

In the literature, it has often been argued that the old Hartree calculations without exchange (i.e. neglecting the K integrals of eq. (1.12), but taking the J integrals into account) and the HFSCF represent two extremes, between which the actual Ψ lies in some sense. That is with regard to radial extension, etc., because the variation principle indeed makes the energy necessarily decrease, Hartree functions without exchange >HFSCF > actual Ψ. It is argued that the antisymmetrization of the Slater determinant takes good care of the correlation of electrons with parallel spin, because the many-dimensional Ψ always have nodes at $(x_1, y_1, z_1)=(x_2, y_2, z_2)$ for two such electrons, which is not the general case for the Slater antisymmetrized Ψ for electrons with opposite spin direction.

However, there is no serious reason to believe that correlation effects are mainly a matter of ameliorating Ψ for electrons with opposite spin. It is seen from eqs. (3.3) and (3.5) that it is true that excited terms with lower S than the ground state always are depressed more by the correlation effects, partly compensating the high first-order interelectronic repulsion energy; but this is also true for excited terms with the same S as the ground state, e.g., ^3P of d^2 and d^8 and ^4P of d^3 and d^7. Actually, the Coulombic interaction being a "long-range" r^{-1} potential, there is no reason to believe that the correlation difficulties are localized very close to the coincidence of two electrons, since the total contribution to the energy from this local region is very low. It may be recalled that ψ of a hydrogenic 1s orbital passes a very strong singularity, the origin of the nuclear attraction $-2Z/r$ at $r=0$ without changing density, since R^2/r^2 [see eq. (2.12)] is roughly constant close to $r=0$. Only the pseudo-potential of angular kinetic energy, $+l(l+1)/r^2$, is strong enough to keep ψ away from the nucleus for positive l, R^2/r^2 now going as r^{2l}.

In this chapter we have only considered correlation energy in monatomic entities. In Chapter 5 we shall return to correlation effects in molecules. It is obvious that correlation effects will not be of concern to chemists (but they will be to atomic spectroscopists) if the effects are additive in a molecule from the constituent atoms. On the other hand, though small compared to the total energy of the molecule, correlation effects are very large compared to usual chemical energies, and if they vary to some extent, it will have terrifying consequences for the theory of chemical bonding. We may possibly be able to look back, in a few years' time, on this problem and consider it as much ado about nothing, if a general additivity theorem has been found. Until then, this is already enough to make *a priori* calculations of any but the simplest molecules impossible. The chemist who believes that he makes absolute predictions of total energies in a quantum-mechanical model may deceive himself, but he is distinctly wrong.

REFERENCES

Baughan, E. C. (1961), *Trans. Faraday Soc.*, **57**, 1863.
Freeman, A. J., and Watson, R. E. (1960), *Phys. Rev.*, **118**, 1168.
Fröman, A. (1958), *Phys. Rev.*, **112**, 870.
Julg, A. (1960), *J. Chim. Phys.*, **57**, 19.
Jørgensen, C. K. (1957), *J. Inorg. Nucl. Chem.*, **4**, 369
Kibartas, Kavetskis, and Yutsis (1955), *Zh. Eksp. Teor. Fiz.*, **29**, 623.
Layzer, D. (1959), *Ann. Phys., N.Y.*, **8**, 271.
Linderberg, J. (1961), *Phys. Rev.*, **121**, 816.
Linderberg, J., and Shull, H. (1960), *J. Molec. Spectr.*, **5**, 1.
Lisitzin, E. (1938), *Soc. Scient. Fennica Comm. Phys Mat.*, **10**, No. 4, Helsingfors.
Löwdin, P. O. (1957), *J. Phys. Chem.*, **61**, 55.
Löwdin, P. O. (1959), *Adv. Chem. Phys.*, **2**, 207.
Moffitt, W. (1951), *Proc. Roy. Soc. (London)*, **A210**, 224, 245.
Racah, G., and Shadmi, Y. (1960), *Phys. Rev.*, **119**, 156.
Shull, H., and Löwdin, P. O. (1959), *J. Chem. Phys.*, **30**, 617.
Trees, R. E. (1951), *Phys. Rev.*, **84**, 1089; (1958), *J. Opt. Soc. Am.*, **48**, 293.
Trees, R. E., and Jørgensen, C. K. (1961), *Phys. Rev.*, **123**, 1278.
Watson, R. E., and Freeman, A. J. (1960), *Phys. Rev.*, **120**, 1125 and 1134.
Watson, R. E. (1961), *Ann. Phys., N.Y.*, **13**, 250.

4. Octahedral Symmetry

We use octahedral symmetry as a suitable example of what happens when we degrade the symmetry from spherical to a lower one—when we go from atomic spectroscopy to molecular orbital (MO) theory.

The reasons for this choice of example are that the octahedral symmetry with centre of inversion O_h is a relatively very high one, showing many of the interesting consequences of degenerate orbitals, as already elaborated in Chapter 2; and that at present it is the best represented symmetry among the compounds whose energy levels have been identified. Actually, it is not only found in molecules MX_6, consisting of a central atom M surrounded by six *ligand* nuclei X at the apices of a regular octahedron, such as found in the gaseous IrF_6 or ions such as $MoCl_6^{---}$, $ReBr_6^{--}$, OsI_6^{--}, but it is also exemplified to a good approximation in complexes of ligand molecules X such as $Cr(H_2O)_6^{+++}$, $Ni(NH_3)_6^{++}$, $Cr(NCS)_6^{---}$, $Os(SCN)_6^{--}$, $Pt(OH)_6^{--}$ or bidentate ligands (en$=NH_2CH_2CH_2NH_2$; gly$^-=NH_2CH_2COO^-$; ox^{--} $=OOCCOO^{--}$) in Rh en$_3^{+++}$, Ni gly$_3^-$, Fe ox$_3^{---}$ or tridentate ligands (den $=NH_2CH_2CH_2NHCH_2CH_2NH_2$) in Co den$_2^{+++}$, which all strictly speaking have a lower symmetry, but where the energy levels very nearly have the same distribution as in O_h. In addition, crystalline compounds may have infinitely extended lattices of octahedral symmetry such as MnO and NiO crystallizing in NaCl lattice, or lattices of approximate octahedral symmetry such as the perovskites $KNiF_3$ and $CsNiBr_3$ and the anhydrous $NiCl_2$, MnF_2, and $CrCl_3$ which all have each transition group atom surrounded by a more or less regular octahedron of six halogen atoms. Traces of transition group elements substitutionally built in various lattices, such as Cr(III) in Al_2O_3 (ruby) and Ni(II) in MgO, frequently have absorption spectra appropriate to octahedral symmetry.

The *working hypothesis of MO theory* is to study the necessary properties of the solutions of HFSCF of the molecular symmetry, *though we cannot* at present produce these solutions in a numerical form. If we continue to neglect relativistic effects, the terms are characterized by the total spin S and a group-theoretical quantum number Γ_n rather than S and L as in spherical symmetry. The MO configurations put 0, 1, 2, . . . 2e electrons into each subshell, each set of e degenerate MO characterized by γ_n rather than l. We use file numbers n in the description of subsequent, orthogonal MO $1\gamma_2$, $2\gamma_2$, $3\gamma_2$, . . . and the final theory of energy levels belonging to partly filled subshells is very closely related to that of Chapter 2. The state of a completely occupied subshell, "a closed-shell molecule", is $^1\Gamma_1$, again writing $2S+1$ as a left-hand superscript.

The various symmetry groups can be placed in a hierarchy such that some of the lower symmetries are subgroups of higher symmetries, from which they can be produced by removing some of the symmetry elements. All symmetries of molecules are subgroups of the three-dimensional rotational group with centre of inversion, R_3, i.e. the spherical symmetry discussed in the two previous chapters. The lowest possible symmetry C_1 has no symmetry elements at all except identity and is represented by nearly any fairly irregular disposition of four or more atoms in space. Between these two extreme limits, the hierarchy is not one well-ordered ladder, but contains many independent bifurcations. For instance, the *linear symmetries with centre of inversion* $D_{\infty h}$ (represented by homonuclear, diatomic molecules X_2 and by linear molecules such as OCO and OUO^{++}) and *without centre of inversion* $C_{\infty v}$ (represented by heteronuclear, diatomic molecules XY and by NCS$^-$) are not in a clear-cut way higher or lower than O_h, and these three symmetries are not subgroups of each other (except that $C_{\infty v}$ is a subgroup of $D_{\infty h}$).

From one point of view, the two linear symmetries are very exceptional in having an infinity of different γ_n. They are called λ in these two particular cases. λ is a non-negative integer and has trivial names closely related to the names of different l values:

$$\begin{array}{ccccccc} \lambda=0 & 1 & 2 & 3 & 4 & 5 & \ldots \\ \sigma & \pi & \delta & \varphi & \gamma & \eta & \ldots \end{array} \qquad (4.1)$$

The occurrence of an infinite number of γ_n values is closely related to the fact that, in linear symmetry, rotation by an arbitrarily small amount around the linear axis does not change the physical situation. The spherical symmetry has arbitrary rotational freedom around an infinity of lines.

On the other hand, the three Cartesian axes x, y, z are not equivalent in the two linear symmetries, while they are so in the octahedral symmetry. There occur only ten different γ_n in O_h, i.e. even or odd parity combined with one of the five values:

Bethe:	γ_1	γ_2	γ_3	γ_4	γ_5
Mulliken:	a_1	a_2	e	t_1	t_2
e:	1	1	2	3	3

$$(4.2)$$

to which Mulliken has proposed other names than Bethe (1929). Though there are only ten different γ_n in O_h, four of them have $e=3$, whereas the two linear symmetries at most have $e=2$ (that is for all positive λ, and $\lambda=0$ has $e=1$).

The *tetragonal symmetry with centre of inversion* D_{4h} is a subgroup of O_h which occurs by making, say, the z axis different from the x and y axis remaining equivalent. Consequently, e cannot be higher than 2. The ten possible γ_{tn} are even or odd parity combined with

Bethe:	γ_{t1}	γ_{t2}	γ_{t3}	γ_{t4}	γ_{t5}	
Mulliken:	a_1	a_2	b_1	b_2	e	(4.3)
e:	1	1	1	1	2	

D_{4h} is also a subgroup of $D_{\infty h}$. Figure 4.1 attempts to give an impression of a part of the hierarchy of possible, molecular symmetries.

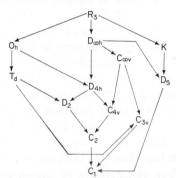

FIG. 4.1. Hierarchy of subgroups of three-dimensional, spherical symmetry R_3 down to the lowest symmetry C_1. The figure is simplified in the sense that many other symmetry groups exist between these two extremes. It is remarked how the hierarchy is not everywhere well ordered; there is no answer to the question whether $D_{\infty h}$ or O_h is the highest symmetry. K is the icosahedral symmetry.

Since O_h like all other molecular symmetries is a subgroup of spherical symmetry, each definite symmetry type l of spherical symmetry corresponds to one or more definite symmetry types γ_n. The contrary is not necessarily true: an orbital in a molecule *does not need to have a well-defined l.*

Bethe (1929) gave a list of γ_n corresponding to various values of l. This is a very simple question in the two linear symmetries, where the λ values $0, 1, 2, \ldots, l$ occur. In octahedral symmetry, the list is:

$$l=$$

0	s	γ_1
1	p	γ_4
2	d	$\gamma_3 + \gamma_5$
3	f	$\gamma_2 + \gamma_4 + \gamma_5$
4	g	$\gamma_1 + \gamma_3 + \gamma_4 + \gamma_5$
5	h	$\gamma_3 + 2\gamma_4 + \gamma_5$
6	i	$\gamma_1 + \gamma_2 + \gamma_3 + \gamma_4 + 2\gamma_5$
7	k	$\gamma_2 + \gamma_3 + 2\gamma_4 + 2\gamma_5$
8	l	$\gamma_1 + 2\gamma_3 + 2\gamma_4 + 2\gamma_5$
9	m	$\gamma_1 + \gamma_2 + \gamma_3 + 3\gamma_4 + 2\gamma_5$
10	n	$\gamma_1 + \gamma_2 + 2\gamma_3 + 2\gamma_4 + 3\gamma_5$
11	o	$\gamma_2 + 2\gamma_3 + 3\gamma_4 + 3\gamma_5$
12	q	$2\gamma_1 + \gamma_2 + 2\gamma_3 + 3\gamma_4 + 3\gamma_5.$

(4.4)

The list is periodic with the period 12 in l, the coefficient e appearing to γ_n q times for $l=12q+r$, added to the result for $l=r$. A sort of hole equivalency may be remarked, $l=11-m$ have the γ_n of $l=12$, minus one γ_1 and minus the γ_n of $l=m$.

It is not possible here to present the group-theoretical arguments for the γ_n occurring; many good texts such as Eyring, Walter, and Kimball (cited in Chapter 1) and particularly Griffith make a very thorough treatment. However, by comparison with the angular functions eqs. (2.4) to (2.6), many of the regularities at the beginning of eq. (4.4) can be illustrated. The three degenerate p orbitals with the angular functions (x/r), (y/r), and (z/r) obviously remain degenerate in octahedral symmetry and form the odd γ_4 set of MO. The three of the d orbitals, (xy/r^2), (xz/r^2), and (yz/r^2), evidently are also equivalent in a symmetry, where the names of the three Cartesian axes can be interchanged without physical consequences, and they form the set even γ_5. The two other d orbitals (x^2-y^2/r^2) and $(2z^2-x^2-y^2/r^2)$ form the set even γ_3. It is less evident that these two orbitals are equivalent, but a rotation of the regular octahedron can actually be shown to transform them into linear combinations of each other. Among the seven f orbitals (xyz/r^3) correspond to the odd γ_2 of eq. (4.4). The two sets of three orbitals in eq. (2.6) are the two sets odd γ_4 and odd γ_5 respectively.

Originally, *crystal field theory* was imagined as the electrostatic perturbation from a lattice with a definite symmetry on the energy levels of a transition group ion with a partly filled shell put into a given position in the lattice (Prather, 1961). Since a similar situation was found to occur in isolated molecules such as IrF_6 or isolated ions in solutions such as $RhCl_6^{---}$ or $Ni(H_2O)_6^{++}$, it became customary later to talk about the *ligand field*. We may define the ligand field as the difference between the *core field* $U(x, y, z)$ in the final molecule or complex ion and the central field $U(r)$ in the original, isolated transition group ion.

The electrostatic model of the ligand field V takes into account only the first-order electrostatic perturbation $<V>$ on the partly filled shell, but does not consider the second-order perturbation, changing the form of the orbitals ψ due to the presence of V. It may be remarked that V, being a potential invariant for rotations of the co-ordinate system, retaining the apices of the regular octahedron in the same directions, must itself necessarily have the group-theoretical quantum number even γ_1 and must therefore be a linear combination of the following expressions known from the angular functions A_l:

$$\text{s-type: } P_0(r)$$
$$\text{g-type: } (x^4+y^4+z^4-\tfrac{3}{5}r^4)P_4(r) \tag{4.5}$$
$$\text{i-type: } [x^6+y^6+z^6+\tfrac{15}{4}(x^4y^2+x^2y^4+x^2z^4+x^4z^2$$
$$+y^2z^4+y^4z^2)-\tfrac{15}{14}r^6]P_6(r).$$

(The i-type contribution has been reported by Low, 1960.) The genuine electrostatic model, considering the ligands as external sources of the field, at larger distances than the partly filled shell, assumes $P_0(r)$, $P_4(r)$, and $P_6(r)$ to be constant functions inside the sphere having as radius r_L the distance of the ligands, i.e. the sources of the ligand field. One of the results of the electrostatic model is that the energy difference Δ [also called 10 Dq or $(E_1 - E_2)$ by many authors] between the subshell even γ_3 and the subshell even γ_5 formed by the partly filled d shell of M in MX_6, surrounded by six point charges q at the distance r_L representing the six X, is approximately

$$\Delta \sim \frac{5}{3} \frac{<r^4>}{r_L^5} \text{ rydbergs} \tag{4.6}$$

the average value of r^4 being taken of the partly filled d shell. However, as the present writer has elaborated in several review papers and in a previous book, the *electrostatic model of the ligand field is entirely in disagreement with at least five types of experimental facts*. This does not hide the fact that it has been of some use, historically speaking, by making several results known and accepted that would not have been accepted on the more general assumptions in MO theory. Actually, it gives good results when the common group theoretical properties of MO theory are involved, and it invariably gives bad results when the distinct assumptions of the electrostatic model, as contrasted to the other cases of MO theory are specifically applied.

It left at least to MO theory a most useful physical idea of expansion of the core field in a series of *components of decreasing symmetry* and (usually) of strongly decreasing numerical size. This is an idea rather foreign to group theory itself and very illustrative of a certain antagonism that very frequently develops between the physicist or chemist applying mathematics and the mathematician. For a group theorist the core field dissected in eq. (4.5) simply has octahedral symmetry; and in general, the core field has the same symmetry as its component with the lowest symmetry. For a physicist, however, it is tempting to write the core field of MX_6 as the sum of a large component V_0 of spherical symmetry and a smaller component V_{oct} of *specific octahedral* symmetry

$$V = V_0(r) + V_{oct}(x, y, z) \tag{4.7}$$

and in a molecule of lower symmetry, say MX_4Y_2 or MX_5Y, it is possible to define a component V_{oct} which it is not possible to include in $V_0(r)$, but which is invariant for an exchange of the names of three Cartesian axes. Therefore, it does not include the components, say, of tetragonal symmetry V_{tet} invariant for an exchange of the names of x and y, but not of x and z, and lower components.

Written in this way, the *expanded radial function model* becomes plausible. Since $V_0(r)$ varies as a function of r, due to the overlap of the ligand atoms X with the central atom M, and since in general the effective charge of M may be expected to be smaller than of the corresponding gaseous ion $V_0(r)$ participates in the effective central field of M, producing smaller parameters of interelectronic repulsion, etc. On the other hand, the partly filled shell may to a certain approximation retain its well-defined value of l and still be written as a product of the appropriate angular function A_l and the new, expanded radial function $R*/r$.

The perturbation from the ligands, corresponding to the effects of covalent bonding cannot be predicted at present in a very satisfactory way, as we shall see in Chapter 7. However, the qualitative aspects can be studied by the hypothesis LCAO of *linear combination of atomic orbitals* and then controlled by comparison with experimental data, e.g. on the rather extensively investigated hexahalides MX_6^{+z-6} where M is a metal with the oxidation number $+z$ and X either F, Cl, Br, or I. The main idea of the LCAO model is that the symmetry types γ_n of the appropriate combinations of ligand orbitals are found by group theoretical methods, and that linear combinations then are formed with central atom orbitals having the *same symmetry type* as the appropriate combinations of ligand orbitals. If only two sets of orbitals cooperate significantly in a given symmetry type, the lower energy is said to correspond to the *bonding* LCAO while the LCAO of higher energy is *antibonding* and always have one more node between the M and X nuclei than the bonding combination has. The situation of three or more LCAO $1\gamma_n$, $2\gamma_n$, $3\gamma_n$, . . . corresponds also to an increasing number of nodes, but the notation with respect to antibonding becomes less clear. If orbitals from either M or X alone participate in a given γ_n (to the approximation in which LCAO is applied) it is called *nonbonding*.

The LCAO model is a marvellous instrument for obtaining qualitative ideas of the energy order and symmetry type of the MO of a given molecule, preferably of high symmetry, from knowledge of the atomic orbitals involved in the lower configurations of the isolated atoms. However, it must be used with much critical sense and is only of value when extrapolating by analogy with already known molecules. The formal difficulty is that the number already of stationary orbitals of each atom is infinite, and that the expansion in a series of MO for the whole molecule yields an over-complete set. The practical difficulty is that only the lowest, and fairly localized orbitals of each atom can be considered.

As an example, let us study the hexahalides MX_6^{+z-6}. We assume that the inner shells of M and X are very little affected by chemical bonding, and we consider only a small number of relatively loosely bound atomic orbitals in an intermediate range of energy close to the limit of actual occupation in the neutral atoms, again neglecting the very high, empty orbitals. If the atom M belongs to the first transition group, we choose the set (3d, 4s, 4p) of important shells. Of the second (4d, 5s, 5p) and third (5d, 6s, 6p) transition groups the principal quantum number is simply shifted one unit. In the same way, the shells $2p(F)$, $3p(Cl)$, $4p(Br)$, and $5p(I)$ are the only ones considered of the halogen. Equation (4.4) tells us the γ_n (and the parity of l) of the M orbitals. The presence of six X atoms at a given distance away from origin of the co-ordinate system gives a slightly more complicated picture. We shall further justify the idea of "local symmetry", microsymmetry, in Chapter 6 and only mention here that the core field in the bond region between each X and the M atom has approximately the linear symmetry $C_{\infty v}$ without centre of inversion (more exactly C_{4v}), and hence eq. (4.1) describes the X orbital symmetry types to be expected. The np shell of the halogen atom splits into a σ subshell and a π subshell consisting of two degenerate orbitals. The σ orbital is directed along the axis M–X, and the square of the two π functions is a cylindrical symmetric doughnut around the M–X axis. Mulliken (1932) and Van Vleck (1935) indicated the symmetry types of the appropriate linear combinations of the six σ orbitals:

$$
\begin{aligned}
\text{even } \gamma_1: \quad & (-x_1+x_2-y_3+y_4-z_5+z_6)/\sqrt{6} \\
\text{even } \gamma_3: \quad & (-2z_5+2z_6+x_1-x_2+y_3-y_4)/\sqrt{12} \\
& (-x_1+x_2+y_3-y_4)/2 \\
\text{odd } \gamma_4: \quad & (-x_1-x_2)/\sqrt{2} \\
& (-y_3-y_4)/\sqrt{2} \\
& (-z_5-z_6)/\sqrt{2}.
\end{aligned}
\tag{4.8}
$$

The combinations of the twelve π orbitals were given by Kimball (1940):

$$
\begin{aligned}
\text{even } \gamma_4: \quad & (z_3-z_4-y_5+y_6)/2 \\
& (z_1-z_2-x_5+x_6)/2 \\
& (y_1-y_2-x_3+x_4)/2 \\
\text{odd } \gamma_4: \quad & (x_3+x_4+x_5+x_6)/2 \\
& (y_1+y_2+y_5+y_6)/2 \\
& (z_1+z_2+z_3+z_4)/2 \\
\text{even } \gamma_5: \quad & (z_3-z_4+y_5-y_6)/2 \\
& (z_1-z_2+x_5-x_6)/2 \\
& (y_1-y_2+x_3-x_4)/2 \\
\text{odd } \gamma_5: \quad & (x_3+x_4-x_5-x_6)/2 \\
& (y_1+y_2-y_5-y_6)/2 \\
& (z_1+z_2-z_3-z_4)/2.
\end{aligned}
\tag{4.9}
$$

The ψ given in eqs. (4.8) and (4.9) refer to the co-ordinate system shown in Fig. 4.2, the orbitals x_3, y_3, and z_3 being the three p orbitals of ligand No. 3 having the angular functions (x/r), (y/r), and (z/r), respectively. Assuming each p orbital to be normalized, the ψ indicated are normalized neglecting a possible overlap integral between p orbitals on different X atoms.

According to the principle of chemical bonding by formation of LCAO of a definite symmetry type γ_n, we expect the order of energy to be:

$$2e=$$

3 odd γ_4	6	$(5pM)-(\sigma X)-(\pi X)$	
2 even γ_1	2	$(5sM)-(\sigma X)$	
2 even γ_3	4	$(4dM)-(\sigma X)$	
2 even γ_5	6	$(4dM)-$little (πX)	
even γ_4	6	πX	
odd γ_5	6	πX	(4.10)
1 even γ_5	6	$(\pi X)+$little $(4dM)$	
2 odd γ_4	6	$(\pi X)-$little $(\sigma X)+(5pM)$	
1 even γ_3	4	$(\sigma X)+(4dM)$	
1 odd γ_4	6	$(\sigma X)+(5pM)+$little (πX)	
1 even γ_1	2	$(\sigma X)+(4sM)$.	

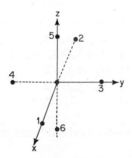

Fig. 4.2. Co-ordinate system in octahedral complex MX_6 with the nucleus of the central ion at origin.

The file numbers in eq. (4.10) neglect the presence of inner shells, having also their appropriate γ_n in M according to eq. (4.4) and in X according to eqs. (4.8) and (4.9). As a specific example, we have used M from the second transition group. If, in the corresponding gaseous ion M^{+z}, the 4d shell is empty, the seven lowest sets of MO in eq. (4.10) will be fully occupied by 36 electrons (cf. the column $2e$). In the process of filling the 4d shell, the two next subshells, 2 even γ_5 and 2 even γ_3, become occupied, at most with 10 electrons. In a hypothetical octahedral complex of tin (II) or antimony (III), the following orbital 2 even γ_1 is filled, and it will be possible to observe absorption bands caused by transitions from 2 even γ_1 to the highest MO of eq. (4.10), 3 odd γ_4.

One should not be too naïve in filling electrons in a set of MO such as eq. (4.10) exactly according to increasing orbital energy, if some of the MO has large J and K integrals with itself, i.e. is concentrated fairly closely to a definite nucleus. We saw an example of that in gaseous vanadium ions V^{+n}

eq. (2.21), and in complexes MX_6 some competition is frequently met between *high-spin* and *low-spin* behaviour for some intermediate values of q in a corresponding gaseous d^q configuration. The choice between the ground state with a high value of S or a low value of S depends on the relative size of Δ compared with parameters of interelectronic repulsion:

$$
\begin{aligned}
q=4 \ \gamma_5^4 \text{ below } \gamma_5^3\gamma_3 \text{ if } & \Delta>4D \text{ or } & \Delta>6B+5C \\
5 \ \gamma_5^5 \text{ below } \gamma_5^3\gamma_3^2 \text{ if } 2\Delta>8D & & \Delta>\tfrac{15}{2}B+5C \\
6 \ \gamma_5^6 \text{ below } \gamma_5^4\gamma_3^2 \text{ if } 2\Delta>6D & & \Delta>\tfrac{5}{2}B+4C \\
7 \ \gamma_5^6\gamma_3 \text{ below } \gamma_5^5\gamma_3^2 \text{ if } & \Delta>3D & \Delta>7B+4C.
\end{aligned}
\tag{4.11}
$$

The values given as multiples of D are calculated from eq. (2.59) considering the maximum value of S possible in a given configuration $\gamma_5^a\gamma_3^b$. Slightly more accurate values can be calculated for the diagonal elements of interelectronic repulsion of the individual terms, as elaborated below, and are given in the last column of eq. (4.11) as multiples of Racah parameters.

Incidentally, all octahedral 4d and 5d complexes known are actually low-spin γ_5^q, while in the 3d group the high-spin forms $\gamma_5^{q-2}\gamma_3^2$ (q=5, 6, 7) are somewhat more frequent than the low-spin forms.

As will be further discussed in Chapter 7, the so-called "electron transfer spectra" have clarified the variation of the energy differences between the MO of eq. (4.10) as a function of the central ion M^{+z} and the halogen X^-, transitions being observed from at least the MO's 1 odd γ_4, 2 odd γ_4, odd γ_5, and even γ_4 to the two partly filled subshells 2 even γ_5 and 2 even γ_3. The energy difference Δ as a function of M^{+z} and the ligands X form the *spectrochemical series*. It is seen from eq. (4.10) that Δ roughly can be considered as the sum of three contributions

$$
\Delta \cong \Delta<V_{oct}>_X + \sigma_X - \pi_X
\tag{4.12}
$$

where the electrostatic contribution $\Delta<V_{oct}>_X$ has been shown to be quite small; σ_X arises from the antibonding character of 2 even γ_3 and π_X from the (usually much weaker) antibonding character of 2 even γ_5.

In a homonuclear diatomic molecule it is fairly evident that the bonding ψ_b and antibonding ψ_a in the LCAO approximation have the forms

$$
\begin{aligned}
\psi_b &= (\psi_1 + \psi_2)/(2+2S_{12})^{1/2} \\
\psi_a &= (\psi_1 - \psi_2)/(2-2S_{12})^{1/2}
\end{aligned}
\tag{4.13}
$$

with the overlap integral S_{12} between ψ_1 and ψ_2. The two subshells 2 even γ_3 and 2 even γ_5 can be written in the same way

$$
\psi_{MO} = a\psi_M(nl, Z_*) - b\Sigma\psi_X
\tag{4.14}
$$

but it is very difficult to tell whether the coefficients a and b can be calculated in any reliable way. We shall return to this problem in the following chapters, but we may make some general comments on eq. (4.14). We believe that this expression only has some chance of conveying some physical understanding if at least two provisions are made:

(1) The normalization condition is $a^2+b^2-2abS_{12}=1$; there is something fundamentally absurd in a MO treatment neglecting overlap integrals between the atoms participating in the chemical bond; and

(2) the central atom orbital ψ_M is allowed to adapt to a new central field due to the presence of V_0. We may as a first approximation assume this adaptation to be a sort of scaling process, decreasing the effective charge Z_*. Similar remarks apply in principle to X, where one expects increased values of Z_*.

A much more fundamental question is, of course, to what extent MO *can be written* as LCAO such as eq. (4.14); we cannot expect the (unknown) HFSCF of the molecule to be very closely related to the atomic orbitals in the region between the nuclei.

The electron transfer spectra of hexahalide complexes show a considerable energy difference between the MO odd γ_5 and even γ_4 amounting to some 3 to 4 kK, though they are both nonbonding according to the approximation given in eq. (4.10). This may be explained according to the lines suggested by McClure (1959) as caused by halogen-halogen antibonding effects. The highest π subshell, even γ_4, has as many angular node planes as a g electron, i.e. four, as also seen in eq. (4.9) where ψ shifts sign going from one X to the next X in a plane containing MX_4, and also shifts sign at each X nucleus. The set of MO odd γ_5 has only three angular node planes like an f electron, while π odd γ_4 and π even γ_5 are halogen-halogen bonding. In general, the symmetry types γ_n can be classified according to the lowest l value they occur with in eq. (4.4),

$$
\begin{array}{lccccc}
 & \gamma_1 & \gamma_2 & \gamma_3 & \gamma_4 & \gamma_5 \\
\text{even parity:} & 0 & 6 & 2 & 4 & 2 \\
\text{odd parity:} & 9 & 3 & 5 & 1 & 3
\end{array}
\tag{4.15}
$$

indicating the lowest number of angular nodes possible in a given MO. It may be remarked that odd γ_1 and even γ_2 need particularly complicated ψ.

Whether LCAO is a good approximation or not to the actual MO, and whether one by accident neglects bonding phenomena, such as the halogen-halogen interactions discussed above, it has at least a very great advantage: *that the number of MO of each symmetry type γ_n is correctly given* though the method of finding them is only an approximation. This is closely comparable to the situation discussed in Chapter 3, where the number of L, S terms of a well-defined configuration in spherical symmetry is correctly given though the correlation effects distort the Ψ. It is therefore possible to recognize a part of the structure of atomic orbitals in the distribution of MO in the molecule, though the individual MO only in very special cases (such as the 4f shell of the lanthanides) is a good approximation to an atomic orbital. The covalent bonding is a perturbation which decreases the energy of the bonding combination (never to a very great extent, at most some 20 kK) and increases the energy of the antibonding combination to a *larger* extent, moving the baricentre of bonding and antibonding MO to higher energy. This corresponds to the well-known strong repulsion between closed shells at small internuclear distances, which is the main reason why molecules do not collapse.

Hence, the concept of the electron configuration p^6, d^0, d^q, $d^{10}s^2$, or f^q of "the corresponding gaseous ion" has a certain support from the validity of MO configurations as a *classification* of the energy levels observed. (The difference between p^6 and d^0 is the rather subtle one that in the former case, the lowest empty MO is related to a s orbital, while it involves a d subshell in the latter case. By the same token, UF_6 and UO_2^{++} can be said to be f^0 systems, because they have low-lying empty MO partly deriving from the 5f shell.)

Terms $^{2S+1}\Gamma_n$ have symmetry types Γ_n behaving in much the same way as one-electron quantum numbers γ_n. Thus, a given L, S term in spherical symmetry splits according to eq. (4.4) into the same Γ_n values as an l shell splits into γ_n subshells.

It is possible to find rules for the occurrence of $^{2S+1}\Gamma_n$ of a given MO configuration $\gamma_n{}^a\gamma_m{}^b$ . . . . Analogous to the vector coupling of S and L values of electrons in different shells $l_1 l_2 l_3$ . . . in spherical symmetry, the coupling of S_1 and S_2 gives here

$$S_1+S_2,\ S_1+S_2-1,\ S_1+S_2-2,\ .\ .\ .,\ |S_1-S_2| \qquad (4.16)$$

for two electrons with $S_1=S_2=1/2$; hence $S=1$ and 0.

In spherical symmetry, the coupling of L values also follows eq. (4.16), but the five Γ_n values have another coupling scheme in octahedral symmetry. Table 4.1 gives these combinations as a multiplication table which is seen to be associative and commutative. The rules for the parity are always:

$$\text{even}+\text{even}=\text{odd}+\text{odd}=\text{even};\ \text{even}+\text{odd}=\text{odd}. \qquad (4.17)$$

The restrictions caused by Pauli's principle for degenerate orbitals necessitates the knowledge of some particular term distributions, *viz.*:

$$\begin{aligned}
\gamma_3{}^2: \quad & ^3\Gamma_2,\ ^1\Gamma_3,\ ^1\Gamma_1 \\
\gamma_4{}^2=\gamma_5{}^2: \quad & ^3\Gamma_4,\ ^1\Gamma_3,\ ^1\Gamma_5,\ ^1\Gamma_1 \\
\text{even } \gamma_5{}^3: \quad & ^4\Gamma_2,\ ^2\Gamma_3,\ ^2\Gamma_4,\ ^2\Gamma_5 \\
\text{odd } \gamma_4{}^3: \quad & ^4\Gamma_1,\ ^2\Gamma_3,\ ^2\Gamma_5,\ ^2\Gamma_4.
\end{aligned} \qquad (4.18)$$

With help of eq. (4.18), Table 4.1, and Pauli's hole-equivalency principle that $\gamma_5{}^a\gamma_3{}^b$, $\gamma_5{}^{6-a}\gamma_3{}^b$, $\gamma_5{}^a\gamma_3{}^{4-b}$, and $\gamma_5{}^{6-a}\gamma_3{}^{4-b}$ produce exactly the same terms S, Γ_n, all terms of importance for the partly filled shell of octahedral complexes of the three transition groups (3d, 4d, 5d) can be calculated.

TABLE 4.1. Multiplication table for Γ_n and Γ_J in octahedral and tetrahedral symmetries

	Γ_1	Γ_2	Γ_3	Γ_4	Γ_5	Γ_6	Γ_7	Γ_8
Γ_1	Γ_1	Γ_2	Γ_3	Γ_4	Γ_5	Γ_6	Γ_7	Γ_8
Γ_2	Γ_2	Γ_1	Γ_3	Γ_5	Γ_4	Γ_7	Γ_6	Γ_8
Γ_3	Γ_3	Γ_3	$\Gamma_1+\Gamma_2+\Gamma_3$	$\Gamma_4+\Gamma_5$	$\Gamma_4+\Gamma_5$	Γ_8	Γ_8	$\Gamma_6+\Gamma_7+\Gamma_8$
Γ_4	Γ_4	Γ_5	$\Gamma_4+\Gamma_5$	$\Gamma_1+\Gamma_3+\Gamma_4+\Gamma_5$	$\Gamma_2+\Gamma_3+\Gamma_4+\Gamma_5$	$\Gamma_6+\Gamma_8$	$\Gamma_7+\Gamma_8$	$\Gamma_6+\Gamma_7+2\Gamma_8$
Γ_5	Γ_5	Γ_4	$\Gamma_4+\Gamma_5$	$\Gamma_2+\Gamma_3+\Gamma_4+\Gamma_5$	$\Gamma_1+\Gamma_3+\Gamma_4+\Gamma_5$	$\Gamma_7+\Gamma_8$	$\Gamma_6+\Gamma_8$	$\Gamma_6+\Gamma_7+2\Gamma_8$
Γ_6	Γ_6	Γ_7	Γ_8	$\Gamma_6+\Gamma_8$	$\Gamma_7+\Gamma_8$	$\Gamma_1+\Gamma_4$	$\Gamma_2+\Gamma_5$	$\Gamma_3+\Gamma_4+\Gamma_5$
Γ_7	Γ_7	Γ_6	Γ_8	$\Gamma_7+\Gamma_8$	$\Gamma_6+\Gamma_8$	$\Gamma_2+\Gamma_5$	$\Gamma_1+\Gamma_4$	$\Gamma_3+\Gamma_4+\Gamma_5$
Γ_8	Γ_8	Γ_8	$\Gamma_6+\Gamma_7+\Gamma_8$	$\Gamma_6+\Gamma_7+2\Gamma_8$	$\Gamma_6+\Gamma_7+2\Gamma_8$	$\Gamma_3+\Gamma_4+\Gamma_5$	$\Gamma_3+\Gamma_4+\Gamma_5$	$\Gamma_1+\Gamma_2+\Gamma_3+2\Gamma_4+2\Gamma_5$

The energies in terms of interelectronic repulsion parameters can be evaluated along the lines indicated in Chapter 1. In the general MO theory, nine different integrals can be shown to be involved in the diagonal elements, viz.:

$$
\begin{array}{ll}
J(1, 3) \sim A - 4B + C & K(1, 3) \sim 4B + C \\
J(1, 4) \sim A - 4B + C & K(1, 4) \sim 4B + C \\
J(3, 4) \sim A + 4B + C & K(3, 4) \sim C \\
J(4, 4) \sim A + 4B + 3C & K(4, 5) \sim 3B + C. \\
J(4, 5) \sim A - 2B + C &
\end{array}
\tag{4.19}
$$

The numbers 1, 3, 4, 5 refer to the tetragonal orbital classification γ_{tn} of eq. (4.3), the angular functions being for pure d orbitals with well-defined $l = 2$:

$$
\begin{array}{ll}
\gamma_{t1}(2z^2 - x^2 - y^2)/r^2 & \gamma_{t4}(xy)/r^2 \\
\gamma_{t3}(x^2 - y^2)/r^2 & \gamma_{t5}(xz)/r^2 \text{ or } (yz)/r^2
\end{array}
\tag{4.20}
$$

the tetragonal axis being taken to be the z axis. If nondiagonal elements of interelectronic repulsion are wanted between different terms of $\gamma_5^a \gamma_3^b$, the nine parameters of eq. (4.19) and one further integral,

$$
\iint \frac{1}{r_{12}} \psi_3 \psi_5 d\tau_1 \psi_4 \psi_5' d\tau_2 \sim 3B
\tag{4.21}
$$

are sufficient, as pointed out by Griffith (1961).

If the orbitals γ_5 and γ_3 *can* be separated in the product of angular functions corresponding to $l = 2$ and the *same* radial function, all the ten parameters in eqs. (4.19) and (4.21) can be expressed as multiples of Racah's A, B, and C. It is emphasized that the existence of the symmetry types γ_{tn} in eq. (4.20) has nothing to do with the polynomiae appropriate for $l = 2$.

As first calculated by Tanabe and Sugano (1954), and further discussed by the writer (1958) and Griffith (1961), the energies of γ_5^2 are

$$
\begin{array}{ll}
{}^3\Gamma_4 & J(4, 5) - K(4, 5) \sim A - 5B \\
{}^1\Gamma_5 & J(4, 5) + K(4, 5) \sim A + B + 2C \\
{}^1\Gamma_3 & J(4, 4) - K(4, 5) \sim A + B + 2C \\
{}^1\Gamma_1 & J(4, 4) + 2K(4, 5) \sim A + 10B + 5C
\end{array}
\tag{4.22}
$$

closely related to eq. (2.41) for p^2 in spherical symmetry. The two equations can actually be derived by exactly the same group theoretical arguments. The degeneracy between ${}^1\Gamma_3$ and ${}^1\Gamma_5$, participating in ${}^1D$ of p^2, occurs also for γ_5 orbitals with $l = 2$. In the same way, eq. (2.42) for p^3 applies, with a small modification [see eq. (4.18)],

$$
\begin{array}{ll}
{}^4\Gamma_2 & 3J(4, 5) - 3K(4, 5) \sim 3A - 15B \\
{}^2\Gamma_3 & 3J(4, 5) \sim 3A - 6B + 3C \\
{}^2\Gamma_4 & J(4, 4) + 2J(4, 5) - 2K(4, 5) \sim 3A - 6B + 3C \\
{}^2\Gamma_5 & J(4, 4) + 2J(4, 5) \sim 3A + 5C.
\end{array}
\tag{4.23}
$$

Tanabe and Sugano pointed out that $^2\Gamma_3$ and $^2\Gamma_4$ are degenerate for $l=2$. These degeneracies can be proved for $l=2$ from eqs. (2.38) and (2.39), but are not generally valid for all possible γ_5 orbitals.

In the configuration $\gamma_3{}^2$, the energies are:

$$
\begin{aligned}
&^3\Gamma_2 \; J(1,\,3)-K(1,\,3)\sim A-8B \\
&^1\Gamma_3 \; J(1,\,3)+K(1,\,3)\sim A+2C \\
&^1\Gamma_1 \; J(1,\,3)+3K(1,\,3)\sim A+8B+4C
\end{aligned}
\tag{4.24}
$$

as can easily be demonstrated by considerations of $M_S=1$ with the spin-orbital configuration 1^+3^+, giving the energy of $^3\Gamma_2$; and of the Heisenberg determinants with $M_S=0$, one having the symmetry type 1 and consisting of (1^+1^-) and (3^+3^-) giving the energy of $^1\Gamma_1$ and one of the states $^1\Gamma_3$, and the other having the symmetry type 3 and consisting of (1^+3^-) and (1^-3^+) giving the energy of $^3\Gamma_2$ again and the other state of $^1\Gamma_3$. In this particular case, eq. (2.38) follows from first principles as we saw, regardless of the condition $l=2$.

Since the closed subshells such as $\gamma_5{}^6$ and $\gamma_3{}^4$ do not change the relative energy differences in a partly filled subshell, eq. (4.24) applies also to the term distances between $^3\Gamma_2$, $^1\Gamma_3$, and $^1\Gamma_1$ of $\gamma_5{}^6\gamma_3{}^2$, which are of importance for octahedral nickel (II) complexes, $^3\Gamma_2$ being the ground state and $^1\Gamma_3$ being the excited state of a spin-forbidden band.

It follows from simple arguments that of $\gamma_5\gamma_3$

$$
\begin{aligned}
&^3\Gamma_4 \; J(3,\,4)-K(3,\,4)\sim A+4B \\
&^3\Gamma_5 \; J(1,\,4)-K(1,\,4)\sim A-8B \\
&^1\Gamma_4 \; J(3,\,4)+K(3,\,4)\sim A+4B+2C \\
&^1\Gamma_5 \; J(1,\,4)+K(1,\,4)\sim A+2C.
\end{aligned}
\tag{4.25}
$$

Tanabe and Sugano calculated all the secular determinants of interelectronic repulsion energy for $\gamma_5{}^a\gamma_3{}^b$ subshell configurations, assuming $l=2$ and identical radial functions. We shall give only as a simple example the energies of $^6\Gamma_1$ and $^4\Gamma_1$ of $\gamma_5{}^3\gamma_3{}^2$ where no configuration interaction between $\gamma_5{}^a\gamma_3{}^b$ occurs,

$$
\begin{aligned}
^6\Gamma_1 \; &J(1,\,3)-K(1,\,3)+3J(1,\,4)-3K(1,\,4)+3J(3,\,4)-3K(3,\,4) \\
&+3J(4,\,5)-3K(4,\,5)\sim 15A-35B \\
^4\Gamma_1 \; &J(1,\,3)-K(1,\,3)+3J(1,\,4)-1/2K(1,\,4)+3J(3,\,4)-1/2K(3,\,4) \\
&+3J(4,\,5)-3K(4,\,5)\sim 15A-25B+5C
\end{aligned}
\tag{4.26}
$$

which incidentally therefore reproduces the term energies ^6S and ^4G of d^5 in spherical symmetry mentioned in eq. (2.52). With $\Delta=0$, i.e. no energy difference between γ_5 and γ_3, the eigenvalues of Tanabe and Sugano's determinants correspond to the expressions valid for spherical symmetry.

In practice, there is one case of interaction of subshell configurations which is particularly important. Among d^2 terms in octahedral symmetry, the only two $^3\Gamma_4$ belong to $\gamma_5{}^2$ and $\gamma_5\gamma_3$ and have the diagonal elements given in eqs. (4.22) and (4.25). Their nondiagonal element [say between the spin-orbital configurations $(5^+, 5_*{}^+)$ and $(4^+3^+)]$ can be found from eq. (2.27) to be equivalent to twice the expression eq. (4.21), i.e. $6B$ in the special case of $l=2$.

The same nondiagonal element occurs between the two ${}^4\Gamma_4$ of d^3, and by Pauli's hole-equivalence theorem, between the two ${}^4\Gamma_4$ of d^7 and the two ${}^3\Gamma_4$ of d^8. Since this is the only case of interaction of subshell configurations which attacks terms with a maximum value of S, this nondiagonal element is of great influence on the position of spin-allowed bands of octahedral, and as we shall see at the end of this chapter, tetrahedral high-spin complexes.

In the Tanabe-Sugano diagrams, the variable is Δ/B assuming a fixed ratio C/B, for instance equal to 4. According to second-order perturbation theory, the effects of interaction of subshell configurations can be approximated by a constant k, writing the energy of the lowest term of a given symmetry type S, Γ_n

$$bB+cC-kB^2/\Delta \qquad (4.27)$$

where k is the sum of the squares of all nondiagonal elements of $1/r_{12}$, divided by Δ (or 2Δ in the case of two-electron substituted subshell configurations $\gamma_5{}^{a-2}\gamma_3{}^{b+2}$).

No studies of the correlation effects in octahedral symmetry have yet been made. Seniority numbers v can be defined in the same manner as in Chapter 3. Thus, the only terms of eq. (4.22) to (4.24) not having the maximum value of v are ${}^1\Gamma_1$ of $\gamma_5{}^2$ and $\gamma_3{}^2$ $(v=0)$ and ${}^2\Gamma_5$ of $\gamma_5{}^3$ $(v=1)$. It is possible to define spin-pairing energy parameters D as for spherical symmetry, and the ratio $(2l+2)/(2l+3)$ of eq. (2.62) becomes $3/4$ in the case of $\gamma_3{}^2$ allowing an interpretation as $(e+1)/(e+2)$.

Figure 4.3 gives the Tanabe-Sugano diagrams for d^2, d^3, d^5, d^6, and d^8 as functions of Δ/B. It is seen that, whereas d^2 invariantly has the ground state ${}^3\Gamma_4$ in octahedral symmetry, d^3 has ${}^4\Gamma_2$ and d^8 has ${}^3\Gamma_2$ (the two latter terms have the well-defined subshell configurations $\gamma_5{}^3$ and $\gamma_5{}^6\gamma_3{}^2$ if we neglect interaction with configurations containing orbitals other than γ_5 and γ_3 of the partly filled shell). The d^5 systems may change from high-spin behaviour having the ground state ${}^6\Gamma_1$ (well-defined $\gamma_5{}^3\gamma_3{}^2$) to low-spin behaviour with the ground state ${}^2\Gamma_5$ (nearly well-defined $\gamma_5{}^5$; other ${}^2\Gamma_5$ interact) as suggested by eq. (4.11). The d^6 systems may change from high-spin behaviour in the ground state ${}^5\Gamma_5(\gamma_5{}^4\gamma_3{}^2)$ to low-spin behaviour ${}^1\Gamma_1$ (nearly well-defined $\gamma_5{}^6$) as function of increasing Δ/B. The *Orgel diagram* is the d^q terms as functions of Δ, assuming fixed values of the interelectronic repulsion parameters B and C, e.g. the semiempirical values appropriate for the gaseous ion.

Orgel (1952, 1955), Tanabe and Sugano (1954), and Owen (1955) all suggested that the semiempirical parameters of interelectronic repulsion in octahedral complexes are smaller than in the corresponding gaseous ion M^{+z}, considering as examples hexaaquo $M(H_2O)_6{}^{+z}$ and hexaammine complexes $M(NH_3)_6{}^{+z}$. Schäffer emphasized that, in chromium (III) and cobalt

(III) complexes, anion ligands such as Cl⁻, CN⁻, and oxalate frequently produce a much stronger decrease of the interelectronic repulsion parameters than the neutral ligands (F^-, however, is more royalistic than the king, having a smaller effect than H_2O). Based on a material of energy levels in Mn(II), Ni(II), Cr(III), Fe(III), Ir(III), Rh(III), and Co(III) complexes, Schäffer and Jørgensen (1958) proposed the *nephelauxetic series* of central atoms (having a definite oxidation number) and of ligands. The Greek word constructed by Professor Kaj Barr means "cloud-expanding" suggesting that partly covalent bonding expands the electron cloud of the partly filled shell, decreasing $<r^{-1}>$, and hence also decreasing quantities proportional to $<r_{12}^{-1}>$. Undoubtedly, there is a close relation between the extent of covalent bonding and the nephelauxetic effect which becomes the more pronounced, the more reducing the ligands and the more oxidizing the central ion.

Jørgensen (1958) investigated the transition $^6\Gamma_1 \rightarrow {}^4\Gamma_1$ (and the first $^4\Gamma_3$ which is degenerate with $^4\Gamma_1$ for $l=2$) of high-spin $3d^5$ complexes of manganese (II) and iron (III). As seen in eq. (4.26), this transition is particularly undisturbed by variations in Δ. Originally, it was assumed as a first approximation that, for a given complex, a *nephelauxetic ratio* β exists, such that

$$B = \beta B_0 \text{ and } C = \beta C_0. \tag{4.28}$$

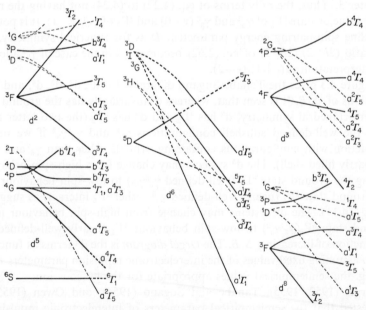

FIG. 4.3. Tanabe-Sugano diagrams for octahedral d^2, d^3, d^5 (also tetrahedral), d^6 and d^8 complexes. The variable is Δ/B, assuming $C=4B$. Excited terms of another value of S than the ground state are punctuated (except in the $^6\Gamma_1$ part of d^5, where excited quartet terms are given as full lines).

The values B_0 and C_0 are for the corresponding gaseous ion. The nephelauxetic effect can be explained by a mixture of two different phenomena which are illustrated by eq. (4.14).

1. *Central-field covalency* where the radial function is expanded because the effective charge Z_* is decreased by the electrons from the ligands invading the central ion forming bonding MO and changing the central field. Orgel (1955) made the first allusion to this effect by comparing the effect of the six water molecules on the 3d shell in $Mn(H_2O)_6^{++}$ with the effect of the two 4s electrons in neutral, gaseous Mn atoms (having the distance $^6S - {}^4G$ of the configuration $3d^5 4s^2$ equal to 25.28 kK) compared to gaseous Mn^{++} (where the similar term distance is 26.85 kK). For illustration of the Z_* dependence, it may be mentioned that gaseous Cr^+ has $^6S - {}^4G$ at the distance 20.52 kK.

2. *Symmetry-restricted covalency* where the coefficient b in the antibonding MO representing the partly filled shell in eq. (4.14) is positive. Whereas the central-field covalency is a spherically symmetric effect and acts even if b vanishes, this effect depends on the symmetry type γ_n of the MO considered. Among other authors, Stevens (1953) predicted that term distances would be proportional to a^4 because only the part of the MO localized in the central atom contribute significantly to the interelectronic repulsion parameters, and because both J and K integrals then involve the square of the electron density a^2.

In a recent review (1962), the writer has enumerated the reasons for believing that, if the nephelauxetic effect is comparatively weak [as in the lanthanides and in manganese (II)], then the central-field covalency presumably gives the strongest contribution; i.e. a direct comparison is possible between Z_* of complexes and of gaseous ions. If the radial functions are different for the two subshells γ_3 and γ_5, but the angular separation still remains with a well-defined $l=2$, we have the situation described by Koide and Pryce (1958) where a parameter ε can be introduced such that the values of B and C for interaction between electrons in the (only π-antibonding) γ_5 subshell are multiplied by:

$$J(1, 4),\ J(3, 4),\ K(1, 4) \text{ and } K(3, 4) \text{ the factor } (1 - \varepsilon)$$
$$J(1, 3) \text{ and } K(1, 3) \text{ the factor } (1 - \varepsilon)^2 \qquad (4.29)$$

representing a larger radial expansion of the σ-antibonding γ_3 subshell. If π-antibonding is neglected $(1 - \varepsilon)$ can be more or less identified with a^2 of the γ_3 subshell. There is no doubt, however, that, if symmetry-restricted covalency is of considerable importance, the introduction of three parameters ε, B, and C is not sufficient, and that all nine parameters of the general MO description of $\gamma_5{}^a \gamma_3{}^b$ must be used.

A general expression for the nephelauxetic ratio β for parameters from the same subshell can be written with the coefficients from eq. (4.14)

$$\beta \sim a^4 (Z_* \text{ complex})/(Z_* \text{ gaseous}) \qquad (4.30)$$

while for parameters involving two subshells [such as $J(1, 4)$] with a_1 and a_2:

$$\beta \sim a_1^2 a_2^2 (Z_* \text{ complex})/(Z_* \text{ gaseous}). \tag{4.31}$$

The nephelauxetic ratio in eq. (4.31) is frequently denoted by β_{35}, while the ratios in eq. (4.30) are called β_{33} and β_{55} according to the subshell considered.

The experimental distinction between the central-field and symmetry-restricted covalency effects in eqs. (4.30) and (4.31) is not easy. One way is to study d^3 complexes where both β_{35} and β_{55} can be determined and assume that Z_* complex has the same value in both cases. The values thus found are remarkably large of the effective charge:

	β_{35}	$\beta_{55} =$	$a^4(\gamma_5)\dfrac{Z_{*\text{complex}}}{Z_{*\text{gaseous}}}$	$a^2(\gamma_3)/a^2(\gamma_5)$
$Cr(H_2O)_6^{+++}$	0.79	0.91	0.91	0.87
$Cr(NH_3)_6^{+++}$	0.71	0.90	0.90	0.79
$Cr(S_2P(OC_2H_5)_2)_3$	0.45	0.80	0.80	0.56
MnF_6^{--}	0.56	0.84	0.84	0.67
$MoCl_6^{---}$	0.73	0.81	0.81	0.90.

$$\tag{4.32}$$

If it is assumed that $a^4(\gamma_5)$ has its extreme value 1, the values of Z_* complex are 5.2, 5.1, 4.6, 5.6, and 4.6, respectively, if the values for the gaseous ions are (V^{++} 4.7, Cr^{+3} 5.7, Mn^{+4} 6.7, and Mo^{+3} 5.7) as can be implied from the variation of the semiempirical value of B in an isoelectronic series. On the other hand, if Z_* has at most the same value in the complex and in the gaseous ion, $a^2(\gamma_5)$ cannot be lower than 0.955, 0.95, 0.895, 0.92, and 0.90 in the five examples.

Of course, the value of Z_* in the partly filled shell does not give any immediate information of the atomic charge in the molecule, if such a concept can be defined at all. We shall see in Chapters 11 and 12 that internal shells have a much smaller variation of Z_*, at a given degree of partly covalent bonding, than fairly external shells with a larger $<r>$.

Another way to estimate the relative importance of the delocalization parameter a^4 and the ratio of effective charges will be explained in Chapter 10 on the electrodynamic (relativistic) effects, where another, measurable quantity involves these two parameters in another proportion. Finally, as already pointed out by Stevens and Owen, certain small effects of hyperfine structure caused by nuclear magnetic moments and various other features of electron paramagnetic spin resonance experiments can be used to estimate a^2 and b^2 of the partly filled subshell.

Tetrahedral symmetry has the same five γ_n or Γ_n as octahedral symmetry, given in eq. (4.3), but due to the lack of a centre of inversion, the parity is not well defined. The values of γ_n corresponding to a definite value of l are the same as in eq. (4.4), except that for odd parity γ_1 and γ_2 are mutually interchanged, and also γ_4 and γ_5. This has the consequence that among easily available central atom orbitals both p and one of the two d subshells has the same γ_5, which is not the case in octahedral symmetry.

The linear combinations of ligand orbitals have the following symmetries:

$$\text{four } \sigma: \ \gamma_1 \text{ and } \gamma_5$$
$$\text{eight } \pi: \ \gamma_3, \ \gamma_4, \text{ and } \gamma_5 \tag{4.33}$$

and the order of MO energies in tetroxo complexes MO_4^{+z-8} (and presumably also in tetrahalides MX_4^{+z-4}) has been found by Carrington, Schonland, Symons, and the present writer to be, in analogy with eq. (4.10), again taking an example from the second transition group:

$$
\begin{array}{lll}
2e= & & \\
4\gamma_5 & 6 & (5pM)-(\sigma X)-(\pi X)-(4dM) \\
2\gamma_1 & 2 & (5sM)-(\sigma X) \\
3\gamma_5 & 6 & (4dM)+\text{little } (5pM)-(\sigma X)-(\pi X) \\
2\gamma_3 & 4 & (4dM)-\text{little } (\pi X) \\
\gamma_4 & 6 & \pi X \\
2\gamma_5 & 6 & (\pi X)+\text{little } (4dM)-\text{little } (\sigma X)+(5pM) \\
1\gamma_3 & 4 & (\pi X)+\text{little } (4dM) \\
1\gamma_5 & 6 & (\sigma X)+\text{little } (\pi X)+(4dM)+(5pM) \\
1\gamma_1 & 2 & (\sigma X)+(5sM).
\end{array}
\tag{4.34}
$$

The lowest five sets of MO are filled in the ground state with 24 electrons. The partly filled shell is constituted by $2\gamma_3$ and $3\gamma_5$. The energy difference between these two subshells is called $-\Delta$ because the order of γ_3 and γ_5 is reversed relative to octahedral symmetry.

For the subshell configurations $\gamma_3^a\gamma_5^b$, exactly the same expressions of interelectronic repulsion energy apply for tetrahedral and octahedral symmetry for the terms $^{2S+1}\Gamma_n$, and hence, the Tanabe-Sugano diagrams can be consulted, using negative values of Δ/B. As emphasized originally by Van Vleck, very interesting analogies occur between the distribution of energy levels in the two symmetries. Actually, the Tanabe-Sugano diagram is the same for d^q in octahedral and d^{10-q} (with reversed sign of Δ) in tetrahedral symmetry. Hence, the tetrahedral d^7 complexes represented by cobalt (II) have the ground state $^4\Gamma_2$ and the same distribution of excited levels as octahedral d^3 complexes, though the detailed energy differences, of course, depend on the numerical value of Δ/B. In the special case of d^5 systems, the Tanabe-Sugano diagrams are identical for octahedral and tetrahedral symmetry, regardless of the sign of Δ.

Eight-co-ordinated cubic complexes MX_8 have the symmetry O_h which also therefore is often called the cubic-octahedral symmetry. They are comparatively little known, though solid compounds such as CaF_2, BaF_2, CdF_2, anhydrous $SrCl_2$ and ThO_2, may be expected substitutionally to include transition group ions. Stahl-Brada and Low (1959) studied cobalt (II) in

CaF_2 and found the smallest nephelauxetic effect known in any transition group complex ($\beta = 0.96$) and a negative value (-3.4 kK) of Δ. This can be understood in terms of the symmetry types of the σ orbitals given by Eisenstein (1956):

$$\text{eight } \sigma: \quad \text{even } \gamma_1 + \text{odd} \gamma_2 + \text{odd } \gamma_4 + \text{even } \gamma_5$$
$$\text{sixteen } \pi: \text{odd and even } (\gamma_3 + \gamma_4 + \gamma_5) \tag{4.35}$$

and also from electrostatic considerations, the angular functions of the combined subshell γ_5 (page 46) represent an electron density concentrated in the eight directions of the ligands X. Equation (4.4) and all results pertaining to interelectronic repulsion are the same for cubic complexes MX_8 and regularly octahedral MX_6.

REFERENCES

Bethe, H. (1929), *Ann. Physik*, [5]3, 133.
Carrington, A., and Symons, M. C. R. (1960), *J. Chem. Soc.*, 889.
Carrington, A., and Jørgensen, C. K. (1961), *Mol. Phys.*, **4**, 395.
Eisenstein, J. C. (1956), *J. Chem. Phys.*, **25**, 142.
Griffith, J. S. (1961), "The Theory of Transition-Metal Ions", Cambridge University Press.
Jørgensen, C. K. (1958), *Discuss. Faraday Soc.*, **26**, 110.
Jørgensen, C. K. (1958), *Acta Chem. Scand.*, **12**, 903.
Jørgensen, C. K. (1962), "Absorption Spectra and Chemical Bonding in Complexes" Pergamon Press, Oxford.
Jørgensen, C. K., *Adv. Chem. Phys.*, **5**.
Jørgensen, C. K. (1962), "Solid State Phys.", **13**, 375.
Jørgensen, C. K. (1962), *Progress Inorg. Chem.*, **4**.
Kimball, G. E. (1940), *J. Chem. Phys.*, **8**, 188.
Koide, S., and Pryce, M. H. L. (1958), *Phil. Mag.*, **3**, 607.
Low, W., "Survey of Paramagnetic Resonance in Solids", Supplement to Solid State Physics, Academic Press, New York, 1960.
McClure, D. S. (1959), "Solid State Physics", **9**, 399.
Mulliken, R. S. (1932), *Rev. Mod. Phys.*, **4**, 1.
Mulliken, R. S. (1935), *J. Chem. Phys.*, **3**, 375; 586.
Orgel, L. E. (1952), *J. Chem. Soc.*, 4756.
Orgel, L. E. (1955), *J. Chem. Phys.*, **23**, 1004; 1824.
Orgel, L. E. (1960), "An Introduction to Transition-Metal Chemistry", Methuen, London.
Owen, J. (1955), *Proc. Roy. Soc. (London)*, **A227**, 183.
Prather, J. L. (1961), "Atomic Energy Levels in Crystals", Nat. Bur. Standards Monograph 19, Washington, D.C.
Schäffer, C. E., and Jørgensen, C. K. (1958), *J. Inorg. Nucl. Chem.*, **8**, 143.
Stahl-Brada, R., and Low, W. (1959), *Phys. Rev.*, **113**, 775.
Stevens, K. W. H. (1953), *Proc. Roy. Soc. (London)*, **A219**, 542.
Tanabe, Y., and Sugano, S. (1954), *J. Phys. Soc. Japan*, **9**, 735; 766.
Van Vleck, J. H. (1935), *J. Chem. Phys.*, **3**, 803 and 807.

5. Systems with Large Internuclear Distances

A criticism frequently raised against MO theory is that the assumption of well-defined configurations break down completely at large internuclear distances, and that, e.g., the ground configuration of a hydrogen molecule is predicted by MO theory to have equal probability of dissociating to two neutral hydrogen atoms and to the (system of much higher energy) H^+ and H^-. It is indeed illustrative to consider this, simplest, case which discloses that the fundamental difficulty for MO configurations at large internuclear distances is caused by nondiagonal elements of interelectronic repulsion.

For our purpose, it is useful to consider MO constructed from the $(1s)_1$ and $(1s)_2$ orbitals of the two hydrogen atoms, and hence write for very great distances:

$$\text{even } \sigma: \psi_b = [(1s)_1 + (1s)_2]/\sqrt{2}$$
$$\text{odd } \sigma: \psi_a = [(1s)_1 - (1s)_2]/\sqrt{2} \qquad (5.1)$$

the symmetry types in linear symmetry with centre of inversion being mentioned in eq. (4.1). The two orbitals obviously have the same nuclear attraction energy and kinetic energy, $-t_a = -t_b$ for large distances. They form six states from the three configurations, having as diagonal elements the energies:

$$
\begin{aligned}
(\text{even } \sigma)^2: \text{even } {}^1\Sigma: &\quad -2t_b + J(b, b) \\
(\text{even } \sigma)(\text{odd } \sigma): \text{odd } {}^1\Sigma: &\quad -t_b - t_a + J(b, b) + K(a, b) \\
\text{odd } {}^3\Sigma: &\quad -t_b - t_a + J(b, b) - K(a, b) \\
(\text{odd } \sigma)^2: \text{even } {}^1\Sigma: &\quad -2t_a + J(a, a)
\end{aligned}
\qquad (5.2)
$$

as can be derived with the methods of Chapters 1 and 2. However, the two terms of the symmetry type even ${}^1\Sigma$ have a nondiagonal element $K(a, b)$. This is a quite serious affair at large internuclear distances, where the two diagonal elements given in eq. (5.2) are identical [since $J(a, a) = J(b, b) = \frac{1}{2}J(1s, 1s)$]. Hence, the Heisenberg determinant has in this case the eigenvalues

$$
\begin{aligned}
B: &-(t_a + t_b) \\
A: &-(t_a + t_b) + J(1s, 1s)
\end{aligned}
\qquad (5.3)
$$

the nondiagonal element being $K(a, b) = \frac{1}{2}J(1s, 1s)$ of eq. (5.1). Summarizing the case of large internuclear distance r_L: the six states of eq. (5.2) are distributed in two energy levels, B of eq. (5.3) and the odd ${}^3\Sigma$ forming a degenerate set of four states, and A of eq. (5.3) and the odd ${}^1\Sigma$ at an energy $J(1s, 1s)$ higher, i.e. the energy characterizing H^+ and H^- relative to two isolated H atoms.

Incidentally, at decreasing r_L where t_a and t_b begin to be sensibly different, the energy difference between the B term of symmetry type even $^1\Sigma$ and the odd $^3\Sigma$ is not as large as a multiple of $(t_b - t_a)$ but only, according to second-order perturbation formulae,

$$(t_b - t_a)^2/2K(a, b). \qquad (5.4)$$

At internuclear distances close to $r_L = 0.76$ Å, the MO configuration (even $\sigma)^2$ is a good approximation to the ground state of H_2, and $(t_b - t_a)$ is now so large, $\sim$40 kK, that the nondiagonal element between the two even $^1\Sigma$ of eq. (5.2) is of minor practical importance. ψ_b cannot any longer be written as in eq. (5.1), for two reasons: the overlap integral between $(1s)_1$ and $(1s)_2$ modify the normalization factor $1/\sqrt{2}$, and the deformation of the atomic orbitals, participating in the actual MO, no longer completely permit the LCAO approximation.

From a group-theoretical point of view, a hydrogen molecule constitutes a system of linear symmetry with centre of inversion, even when r_L is very large. That it (even $\sigma)^2$ is a fairly good approximation to Ψ of the ground state near the minimum of the "potential curve" as function of r_L, and that it is a bad approximation to the state B of eq. (5.3) where another configuration, (odd $\sigma)^2$, participates with equal weight, is of little concern to the pure group theorist. The idea of configurations of MO having well-defined symmetry type γ_n has no approbation as soon as the Hamiltonian contains the inter-electronic repulsion $1/r_{12}$ which can mix together different configurations. On the other hand, so long as electrodynamic effects are not included in the Hamiltonian, the total symmetry type Γ_n is well defined.

However, from a physical point of view, there is some reason to say that the hydrogen molecule being stretched beyond a definite limit, some 2Å, is better described as two hydrogen atoms in spherical symmetry than as one hydrogen molecule in linear symmetry. The fundamental argument for this rather surprising division is the nondiagonal elements such as $K(a, b)$ between the two even $^1\Sigma$ of eq. (5.2) which may be larger than the MO energy differences such as $(t_b - t_a)$ at large r_L. The condition for fairly well-defined configurations $\gamma_n{}^a\gamma_m{}^b\gamma_k{}^c$ . . . is that the orbital energy differences $(t_n - t_m)$, $(t_m - t_k)$, etc., are considerably larger than the nondiagonal elements of inter-electronic repulsion energy between the configurations.

The Tanabe-Sugano diagrams in Chapter 4 illustrate this effect on the subshell configurations $\gamma_5{}^a\gamma_3{}^b$ as functions of Δ/B. If we imagine an octahedral complex MX_6 increasing all distances $M-X$ to the same large value r_L, Δ would become very small, and the term distances of the isolated central ion M^{+z} would appear as a good approximation to the energy levels observed. Thus, the nondiagonal element between the two Γ_4 given on page 56 would be important for restoring the energies of the F and the P terms in spherical symmetry rather than the diagonal elements corresponding to well-defined configurations $\gamma_5{}^a\gamma_3{}^b$ in octahedral complexes. The elaborate discussion of weak-field diagonal determinants (diagonal elements corresponding to well-defined L, S terms) and strong-field diagonal determinants given in the literature is nothing but a discussion of whether the energy levels of MX_6 can best be classified according to *spherical microsymmetry* or according to *octahedral microsymmetry*. In Chapter 4 we have adhered to the "strong-field" consideration of octahedral microsymmetry, firstly because experience shows that the actual terms $S.\Gamma_n$ have energies much closer to the strong-field diagonal elements, with a few exceptions, and secondly because this is the only treatment which can be extended naturally to the MO description of symmetry-restricted covalency. If we do not deviate more from the electro-static ligand field model than expressed in the expanded radial function model (identical radial functions for the two subshells), the final eigenvalues of the weak-field and strong-field determinants, taking all the nondiagonal elements into account, are invariably identical.

One of the main practical difficulties leading to the *principle of micro-symmetry*, i.e. that the orbitals ψ should be chosen in an appropriate symmetry which may be higher than the group-theoretical symmetry of the many-electron system, is the enormous degeneracy numbers occurring of molecules where more than one atom has a partly occupied shell in spherical symmetry. This is already the case in diatomic molecules such as O_2 and N_2, and Moffitt (1951) described the transition from linear to spherical microsymmetry as a transition from "valence coupling" to "L, S coupling of the individual atoms" as functions of increasing r_L. Recently, Nesbet (1961) calculated how the ground state even $^1\Sigma$ belonging approximately to the MO configuration (1 even σ)^2(1 odd σ)^2(2 even σ)^2(2 odd σ)^2(3 even σ)^2(1 odd π)^4 is only the ground state of the nitrogen molecule at such r_L where the MO energy differences [particularly between (3 even σ) and (3 odd σ), and between (1 odd π) and (1 even π), essentially formed from the 2p shells of the two nitrogen atoms] are large, indicating strong chemical bonding. At larger r_L, states with higher S approach and cross the $^1\Sigma$ ground state, as in a Tanabe-Sugano diagram for decreasing Δ. At very large r_L, the two nitrogen atoms are left in the ground term ^4S of the configuration $1s^22s^22p^3$. Such two nitrogen atoms each have four states, and the total number of independent states of $(^4S)_1(^4S)_2$ is hence sixteen. However, if the 2p shell is considered to be the raw material for formation of available MO by LCAO, the number of the states, $q=20$ according to eq. (2.22), of p^3 of each of the two nitrogen atoms produce 400 independent states. This is not all; the ionized states [such as H^+ and H^- in eq. (5.3)] produce $2 \times 15 \times 15 = 450$ more states of $(p^2N^+)(p^4N^-)$ and $(p^4N^-)(p^2N^+)$, $2 \times 6 \times 6 = 72$ states of $(pN^{++})(p^5N^{--})$ and $(p^5N^{--})(pN^{++})$, and finally two states of the p^6, p^0 combinations, making a total of 924 states out of the two 2p shells. Whereas these 924 states are represented in a majority of closely adjacent energy levels of N_2 at large r_L, the actual minimum energy at $r_L =$

1.094 A corresponds to a very isolated ground state $^1\Sigma$, the first excited levels being at some 60 kK. Incidentally, the first excited levels of a molecule, e.g. Cl_2 or F_2, frequently are situated at a higher energy, at the equilibrium value of r_L of the ground state, than necessary for the dissociation of the molecule, r_L increasing toward infinity. *Franck-Condon's principle* says that optical transitions do not change r_L to any great extent, and, therefore, vertical projections on the potential curves, similar to those made on the Tanabe-Sugano diagrams, indicate the positions of the absorption bands. On the other hand, if the excited state of the molecule lives long enough (i.e. all the energy is not immediately transformed into heat and far-infrared radiation) it may drop down in the minimum of *its* potential curve at another r_L and radiate from this position. Consequently, *fluorescence* may occur with emission maxima at much lower wavenumber than the absorption bands.

The situation encountered in the case of N_2 becomes much more extreme in systems containing more than one transition group ion with a partly filled shell. Since a chromium (III) atom with the spherical symmetry configuration [Ar]$3d^3$ has 120 states according to eq. (2.22), two Cr(III) have $120^2 = 14,400$ independent states and q chromium (III) 120^q states. Here, we have ignored the "charge transfer" states where, e.g., Cr(II) and Cr(IV) are formed, and which are much more numerous. In the case of 1000 Cr(III), the number of pure $(3d^3)$ states is about 10^{2079}, but the number of "charge transfer" states essentially a question of putting 3000 electrons in 10,000 available spin orbitals. The number of ways can be calculated according to eq. (2.22) and is larger than 10^{2651}. Hence, only one out of every 10^{573} states is not of the charge-transfer type.

Actually, the absorption spectra of most *binuclear* or *polynuclear complexes*, i.e. containing two or more metal atoms, are rather simple and closely analogous, in most cases, to the mononuclear species. Thus, Schäffer (1958) reports that the binuclear chromium (III) complex $(NH_3)_5Cr(OH)Cr(NH_3)_5{}^{+5}$ has a spectrum very much like $Cr(NH_3)_5OH^{++}$, suggesting two atoms with approximately octahedral microsymmetry. In other cases, like $(NH_3)_5 CrOCr(NH_3)_5{}^{+4}$, a more anomalous spectrum is observed, no longer having the paramagnetism corresponding to $<S(S+1)> = 15/4$ of each chromium atom (ground state $^4\Gamma_2$), but rather much lower $<S(S+1)>$ at low absolute temperatures T.

The latter phenomenon is called *antiferromagnetism*; at low T, many compounds exhibit such interactions between adjacent transition group atoms that ground states with $S=0$ or very low values of the total system. As discussed by Slater (1960) and Nesbet (1960), the S-dependent energies of such systems often can be approximated by

$$+J_s S(S+1) \tag{5.5}$$

which is, though formally similar, entirely different from the spin-pairing energy in a definite configuration, eq. (2.59). The antiferromagnetic coupling is essentially a second-order perturbation expression for the weak effects of intermixing of well-defined microsymmetry orbital configurations, of which a simple but instructive example was given in eq. (5.4). It was seen that the MO energy differences in the new symmetry appropriate at smaller internuclear distances may very well be considerably larger than the parameter J_S in eq. (5.5). From the point of view of absorption spectra, J_S is usually a very small quantity, some 0.001 to 0.1 kK, showing indeed very large r_L measured by our criterion of comparison with nondiagonal elements of interelectronic repulsion which do not vanish at large r_L because they involve parts of the MOs coexisting on the same atom (e.g. M in the MX_6 case) or on the same atoms (the diatomic molecules discussed above).

Experience shows that a measurable J_S occurs when two transition atoms are co-adjacent in the compound with a distance not larger than some 3Å; *or* if they are connected with a bridging atom X, the total distance MXM not exceeding some 5Å. In substances such as K_2IrCl_6, Owen (1958) points out the occurrence of antiferromagnetic effects between two iridium atoms separated by two pairs of chlorine atoms MX_2X_2M. Usually, the antiferromagnetism can be quenched by dilution in an isomorphous, diamagnetic material, such as K_2PtCl_6, where the average distance between two ions with positive S becomes large.

Exceptions to the rule of octahedral microsymmetry in binuclear and polynuclear complexes occur in the case of mixed oxidation numbers where MO must be formed delocalized on the various metal atoms, not leaving (a+b) as an integer in each subshell configuration $\gamma_5{}^a\gamma_3{}^b$. Some of the best studied cases, such as $(NH_3)_5CoO_2Co(NH_3)_5{}^{+5}$, are slightly complicated by the fact that not only can the cobalt atoms choose between the oxidation numbers +3 and +4 (i.e. $\gamma_5{}^6$ or $\gamma_5{}^5$), but the bridging ligand has also a partly filled shell, being able to have four electrons in the MO set (1 even π) (i.e. being $O_2{}^{--}$) or three electrons ($O_2{}^-$), whereas the oxygen molecule has two such electrons.

In slightly more complicated cases such as Delépine's $N(Ir(SO_4)_2(H_2O))_3{}^{-4}$ with Ir in the average oxidation number $+3\frac{2}{3}$, or ruthenium red shown by Fletcher *et al.* to be $(NH_3)_5RuORu(NH_3)_4ORu(NH_3)_5{}^{+6}$ with Ru having the average oxidation number $+ 3\frac{1}{3}$, Jørgensen and Orgel (1961) rationalized the behaviour by pointing out the influence of π bonding of nitrogen and oxygen on the three γ_5 subshells of the three metal atoms.

A series is known of dark-coloured chloride complexes of transition group ions with mixed oxidation number in hydrochloric acid solution, but unfortunately their constitution is not known. Among dinuclear halogen complexes, one may distinguish the three types X_5MXMX_5 with one corner shared between the two octahedra, $X_4MX_2MX_4$ with a common side (as realized in Nb_2Cl_{10}) and $X_3MX_3MX_3$ with a common face and relatively strong interaction between the two M (as in $W_2Cl_9^{-3}$). Polynuclear halides can have rather complicated structures; thus, Peacock *et al.* have demonstrated that molybdenum (V) forms a tetramer Mo_4F_{20} with four Mo in a square with four F bridges, or Sheldon has showed that $Mo_6Cl_8^{+4}$ has the six Mo in a regular octahedron, circumscribed by a cube formed of the eight chlorine atoms.

From a quantum-mechanical point of view, it is indeed surprising that crystals containing some 10^{18} atoms frequently have the same absorption spectra, i.e. the same distribution of excited energy levels, as the corresponding entities, e.g. $Cr(H_2O)_6^{+++}$, $Co(NH_3)_6^{+++}$, or $IrBr_6^{--}$, in dilute aqueous solution. We shall return to this question in Chapter 9 and only retain for the moment the fact that optical excitations frequently seem localized to a cluster of a few atoms.

REFERENCES

Herzberg, G. (1950), "Molecular Spectra and Molecular Structure", Vol. I; "Spectra of Diatomic Molecules" (2 ed.), Van Nostrand, New York.
Jørgensen, C. K., and Orgel, L. E. (1961), *Molecular Phys.*, **4**, 215.
Moffitt, W. (1951), *Proc. Roy. Soc. (London)*, **A210**, 224; 245.
Nesbet, R. K. (1960), *Phys. Rev.*, **119**, 658.
Nesbet, R. K. (1961), *Phys. Rev.*, **122**, 1497.
Owen, J. (1958), *Discus. Faraday Soc.*, **26**, 53.
Peacock, R. D. (1960), *Progr. Inorg. Chem.*, **2**, 193.
Schäffer, C. E. (1958), *J. Inorg. Nucl. Chem.*, **8**, 149.
Sheldon, J. C. (1960), *J. Chem. Soc.*, 1007.
Slater, J. C. (1960), *Quart. Progr. Rep.*, October, p. 4, Solid-State and Molecular Theory Group, M.I.T.

6. Equivalent Orbitals and Microsymmetry

During more than a century the theory of valency has oscillated between two extreme positions, which we may call the idea of *oxidation number with positive or negative sign* and the idea of *positive bond number* being characteristic for each atom in a definite compound. The first idea has always been of most appeal to inorganic chemists starting with the assumption of Berzelius that the compounds such as CaO and SO_3 which are capable under heat evolution of uniting themselves to $CaSO_4$ in some way are carriers of residual electric charges, while Wöhler initiated the usual idea of substitution (and constant bond number 4 of carbon) for organic chemists, pointing out that CH_3COOH, $CH_2ClCOOH$, $CHCl_2COOH$, and CCl_3COOH have essentially the same properties. This could only be explained by oxidation numbers if Cl and H in these compounds have the same oxidation number, *viz.* -1.

Around 1915 these two ideas were more clearly formulated under the strong impression gained of the exceptional stability of inert-gas electron configurations in spherical symmetry, eq. (2.19). W. Kossel pointed out that atoms with atomic numbers Z just before or just after the inert-gas numbers 2, 10, 18, 36, 54, 86, . . . have a strong tendency to form anions and cations, respectively, such as the series O^{--}, F^-, Ne, Na^+, Mg^{++}, Al^{+++}, . . . all containing ten electrons. The interpretation of oxidation number as really expressing the electric charge of ions in the unit of the protonic charge was soon very successful in some compounds such as NaCl. With the knowledge of crystals obtained from X-ray crystallography and the calculation of electrostatic (Madelung) energy of such crystals, it became clear that the heat of formation of NaCl from gaseous Na^+ and Cl^- (which, of course, cost a lot of energy to produce from crystalline Na metal and gaseous Cl_2) was some 90 per cent of the electrostatic energy of the crystal thus formed, assuming that the ions did not overlap each other. This was an extremely satisfactory result, because the potential of the steeply increasing repulsion at small internuclear distances, and the introduction of partly penetrating ions must necessarily give a small, positive contribution to the total energy. On the other hand, it was clear that these arguments, first applied by Born and Haber, do not work in all compounds; the molecules CO_2 and CCl_4 or the solid SiO_2 cannot be maintained to consist of the ions C^{+4}, O^{--}, Cl^-, and Si^{+4}, though the oxidation numbers are indeed $+4$, -2, -1, and $+4$ with the usual definitions. K. Fajans attempted to make a continuous range of descriptions between ionic and covalent bonding, invoking strong polarizations of the ions, when small cations have large positive charges and when large anions are very polarizable.

The same year as Kossel, G. N. Lewis published the theory that classical valence strokes are to be considered as electron pairs, shared between the two atoms bonded and completing their electron configuration in such a way as to achieve an inert-gas number. This interpretation seems very satisfactory for a large part of the molecules occurring in organic and inorganic chemistry. Again, as Fajans pointed out, some molecules with fractional *bond orders*, such as the $1\frac{1}{2}$ bond between two adjacent carbon atoms in benzene C_6H_6 or between carbon and oxygen in carboxylates such as CH_3COO^-, need consideration of delocalized electrons, called more-atom *quanticules* by Fajans.

Lewis's idea got a quantum-mechanical picture by Heitler and London's *valency-bond treatment* of H_2 considered as two interacting, neutral hydrogen atoms. Many chemists made the extrapolation that Lewis is correct in ascribing one electron pair to each chemical bond. In the writer's opinion, this is an *exceedingly doubtful procedure which disagrees with the distribution of energy levels in a majority of molecules*.

Recently, in the theory of transition group complexes, the electrostatic ligand field model represented the extreme ionic description and Pauling's hybridization theory being an extension of the valency-bond theory corresponded to the idea of covalent electron-pair bonds. The conspicuous disagreement of these two models with the distribution of energy levels observed shows clearly that the truth must be somewhere between these two extremes.

Actually, the time may have come now where the acceptance of *Mulliken's MO theory* in a satisfactory way may end the oscillation between assumptions of ionic and of covalent bonding. Already in the rough approximation of LCAO, this theory shows one of its great virtues: by a continuous variation of the delocalization parameters a and b [such as in eq. (4.14)], fractional charges can be obtained of the individual atoms, going from the extreme case ($a=1$, $b=0$) where they equal the oxidation number, to a case of electroneutrality. This is very appealing to the chemist, because most molecules give an impression of having intermediate values of the atomic charges, though numerical estimates are difficult to obtain. Some cases, such as crystalline NaCl (but not the gaseous, diatomic molecule) approach closely the electrostatic extreme, whereas homonuclear molecules such as N_2 and P_4 or solid diamant or tellurium are obvious candidates for the covalent extreme. However, in most cases, relatively electrovalent compounds such as MgO, NiO, or PbS (all crystallizing in NaCl lattice) have some covalent features, and the series of tetrahedrally co-ordinated compounds CuBr, ZnSe, GaAs have some ionic features though their logical limit is the isomorphous germanium.

We must make a distinction between *closed-shell molecules with $S=0$ and no low-lying excited energy levels* (with $S=0$) and other, we may loosely call them degenerate, molecules. The organic chemist may feel that the closed-shell molecules are the normal entities, whereas molecules with positive S, particularly those with one unpaired electron, i.e. $S=1/2$, are termed "free radicals" and are expected to be very unstable, to dimerize to an ordinary molecule with $S=0$. The inorganic chemist can by no means participate in this feeling. Actually, very stable entities with up to seven unpaired electrons occur in nature. We are giving a few examples of each spin value:

$$S=1/2: \text{NO}, \text{ClO}_2, \text{VCl}_4, \text{Cu(NH}_3)_4^{++}, \text{Fe(CN)}_6^{-3}, \text{IrCl}_6^{--}, \text{NpO}_2^{++}$$
$$S=1:\quad \text{O}_2, \text{RuO}_4^{--}, \text{Ni(H}_2\text{O)}_6^{++}, \text{VCl}_4^{-}, \text{OsCl}_6^{--}, \text{OsF}_6$$
$$S=3/2: \text{Cr(NH}_3)_6^{+++}, \text{MoCl}_6^{---}, \text{ReBr}_6^{--}, \text{IrF}_6, \text{CoCl}_4^{--}, \text{Co(H}_2\text{O)}_6^{++}$$
$$S=2:\quad \text{Fe(H}_2\text{O)}_6^{++}, \text{CoF}_6^{---}, \text{Cr(NH}_3)_4^{++} \tag{6.1}$$
$$S=5/2: \text{Mn(H}_2\text{O)}_6^{++}, \text{FeF}_6^{---}, \text{FeCl}_4^{-}, \text{MnBr}_4^{--}, \text{Sm(H}_2\text{O)}_9^{+++}$$
$$S=3:\quad \text{Eu(H}_2\text{O)}_9^{+++}, \text{Tb(H}_2\text{O)}_9^{+++}$$
$$S=7/2: \text{Gd(H}_2\text{O)}_9^{+++}, \text{Cm(H}_2\text{O)}_9^{+++}.$$

Of these examples, the four first cited for $S=1$ have a half-filled subshell, i.e. two electrons in a set of two degenerate MO. In the same way, the five first examples of $S=3/2$ have three electrons in three degenerate MO (the subshell γ_5 which could contain six electrons). The four first examples of $S=5/2$ and the two examples given of $S=7/2$ have also half-filled shells. A close connection is seen to occur between the existence of molecules and complex ions with $S \geq 1$ and the presence of degenerate orbitals in high microsymmetries. As seen in eq. (2.59), the ground state has the *maximum* value of S in the case of degenerate sets of orbitals.

If Ψ of a closed-shell molecule, as defined above, is approximated by a Slater antisymmetrized determinant, the individual orbitals ψ_n can be combined to new linear combinations $\psi = \Sigma a_n \psi_n$ giving the same electronic density and indeed exactly the same Ψ as before. *This is not* the case in degenerate molecules, neither with positive S nor in the case of low-lying excited states and $S=0$ (where the interaction of configurations necessarily destroy the validity of the assumption of one Slater determinant).

Hence, in closed-shell molecules, we have a certain freedom in rearranging the shape of the orbitals, if we are only interested in the *ground state*. Excited states generally will be very badly approximated by such rearranged orbitals. The reason is the existence of an approximate central field (in spherical symmetry) or core field which has vanishing nondiagonal elements (of one-electron operator quantities) between the self-consistent orbitals. Our rearranged orbitals have such nondiagonal elements between them, and hence, ionization and excitation processes are not expected to occur at only one such rearranged orbital at the time, but rather at a linear combination of them which undoes the recombination and isolates the HFSCF atomic or molecular orbitals.

Then, what interest can we possibly have in constructing such rearranged orbitals? In most cases indeed none at all, but we can find some advantages in two, somewhat related, occasions. The first is the possibility of higher microsymmetry than the total symmetry, as discussed in the previous chapter. If the nondiagonal elements of one-electron operator quantities between the new orbitals are rather small, and if we avoid the occurrence of nondiagonal elements of the two-electron operator quantity of the same or large size, it is useful to define the new orbitals. Secondly, we may want to give as much support as possible to the concept of electron-pair bonds.

Lennard-Jones (1950) and Hall (1950) introduced *equivalent orbitals* which do not have well-defined symmetry type γ_n. They are usually defined in a molecule MX_q such that q equivalent orbitals exist, each concentrated in the bond region between M and a definite X atom, and the total electronic density $\psi_1{}^2 + \psi_2{}^2 + \ldots + \psi_q{}^2$ having the symmetry type Γ_1. Lennard-Jones indicated as an advantage of these equivalent orbitals that the total energy has a more physically significant set of contributions from the interelectronic repulsion energy, because the sum of J' integrals of equivalent orbitals is smaller than the J integrals of the original, self-consistent orbitals, and the sum of K' integrals is equally smaller than the sum of K integrals, and nearly vanishing, because two different equivalent orbitals have a very small squared overlap. Hence, the interelectronic repulsion energy in a system of equivalent orbitals is reduced nearly exclusively to classical Coulomb energy. As a specific example, Lennard-Jones mentioned the term ^3P of the electron configuration 2s2p (say of a beryllium atom) where equivalent orbitals can be defined:

$$\psi_1 = (\psi_s/\sqrt{2}) + (\psi_x/\sqrt{2})$$
$$\psi_2 = (\psi_s/\sqrt{2}) - (\psi_x/\sqrt{2}) \qquad (6.2)$$

where ψ_s is the 2s and ψ_x is one of the three 2p orbitals of the atom. Hence, ψ_1 and ψ_2 have neither well-defined l nor parity. In the special case of ^3P, Ψ of the configuration $(2s^+2p^+)$ is exactly the same as $(\psi_1{}^+\psi_2{}^+)$, with $J(1, 2) - K(1, 2) = J(s, p) - K(s, p)$ and $K(1, 2) < K(s, p)$. However, the example also illustrates the large inherent difficulties in the concept of equivalent orbitals. The term ^1P of 2s2p no longer has a well-defined expression in equivalent orbital configurations, but is one of four eigenvalues (the three other representing ^1S of $2s^2$ and ^1S of $2p^2$ and the $M_s = O$ state of ^3P) of a secular determinant involving as diagonal elements the configurations $(\psi_1{}^+\psi_1{}^-)$, $(\psi_1{}^+\psi_2{}^-)$, $(\psi_1{}^-\psi_2{}^+)$, and $(\psi_2{}^+\psi_2{}^-)$.

We may divide the class of closed-shell molecules into a class of σ-bonded molecules and a class of molecules with bond orders different from one. In the class of σ-bonded molecules containing q bond regions between q pairs of closely adjacent atoms, an approximate MO configuration can be written in such a way that 2q electrons occupy orbitals which are bonding linear combinations of σ-electrons, classified according to the linear microsymmetry of each bond region, and low-lying orbitals of the atoms involved. It is a well-known experimental fact that, excepting molecules with very weak σ bonds such as Cl_2 and I_2, the first excited levels occur at much higher energy in σ-bonded molecules than in the other class; i.e. the necessary and sufficient condition for colour is in nearly all cases that the molecule considered is not purely σ-bonded, is not "aliphatic" in the organic sense. As examples of σ-bonded molecules may be mentioned:

H_2, CH_4, CCl_4, HCl, NH_3, H_2O, SO_4^{--}, ClO_4^-, $ClBr$, $ZnCl_4^{--}$, $HgCl_2$, $Be(H_2O)_4^{++}$, BeF_4^{--}, Al_2Cl_6, and crystalline Si, Ge, GaAs, ZnS, BeO, and CdTe   (6.3)

also including rather weak associates with high co-ordination number such as $La(H_2O)_9^{+++}$, $Zn(H_2O)_6^{++}$, $Cd(NH_3)_6^{++}$, $Mg(H_2O)_6^{++}$, crystalline NaCl, CsBr, and CaF_2, and as members of the other class:

O_2, CO_2, CS_2, CO_3^{--}, NO_3^-, SO_3^{--}, C_2H_4, C_2H_2, C_6H_6, $Cr(H_2O)_6^{+++}$, $Pb(OH)_3^-$, $BiCl_3$, IrF_6, Fe_2Cl_6, UO_2^{++}, CrO_4^{--} (6.4)

and in general, all transition group complexes. It is evident from the remarks made above that the concept of equivalent orbitals has its field of possible application in the σ-bonded class and not in the examples given in eq. (6.4). However, the core field acting on those mobile electrons which are not σ electrons is sometimes described in the latter class as partly caused by a set of equivalent σ orbitals, one per chemical bond. One warning may be given: excepting linear molecules such as N_2 and C_2H_2, the words σ and π orbitals are used in the theory of aromatic molecules in another sense than in eq. (4.1), but considering the plane of the molecule (say benzene C_6H_6 or naphthalene $C_{10}H_8$). The so-called π orbitals then have a different sign of ψ above and below the plane, whereas the σ orbitals have the same sign.

In the class of σ-bonded molecules, as exemplified in eq. (6.3) (obviously this list is not exhaustive, not even with respect to the types occurring), there is a further subclass of those molecules where the atoms have nearly the same electronegativity (a concept to be discussed further in Chapter 7). This particular subclass of *homeopolar σ-bonded molecules* is the last hope of a consistent application of the valency-bond theory. Among the examples in eq. (6.3), H_2, CH_4, $ClBr$, and crystalline Si, Ge, and GaAs are included in this subclass. The major difficulty for the valency-bond theory in molecules where the bonds are not approximately homeopolar is that the number of "resonance structures between ionic and covalent bonding" is much greater than qualitative valence-stroke formulae may suggest. For instance, SO_4^{--} has five cores (S^{+6} and four O^{+6}) each having places available for eight electrons. Since 32 electrons are going to be placed on the 40 available positions, the number of independent states is according to eq. (2.22) 76,904,685. It must be admitted, however, that only 5,799,465 of the states have $S=0$. If, for chemical reasons, we restrict the variation of the charge of oxygen to assume the values 0, -1, or -2, our problem is to place 8 electrons on 16 available positions, producing 12,870 states among which only 1,764 have $S=0$. By similar arguments as given in Chapter 5 for assuming spherical rather than linear microsymmetry in diatomic molecules stretched to large r_L, it is unreasonable to make such a number of states participate in Ψ of the ground state of SO_4^{--}, since MO theory opens the possibility of having *one* MO configuration as a classification (i.e. neglecting the correlation effects which, anyhow, would disturb the valency-bond description, too) of the $^1\Gamma_1$ ground term.

In the very interesting discussion between Mulliken, Van Vleck, and Pauling published in a series of papers in the three first volumes of the *Journal of Chemical Physics* (1933–1935), the conclusion seemed more or less to be that both MO theory and valency-bond theory represent fair approximations to the actual Ψ of somewhat comparable quality, MO theory being slightly better at small r_L and valency-bond theory distinctly better at large r_L. The present writer does not agree at all on this point; with the amplification concerning large r_L exposed in the last chapter, MO theory is assumed to be intrinsically superior as a classification of the energy levels occurring, in the same way as the n,l-shell configurations classify (i.e. give the correct number of low-lying terms of each symmetry type and in most cases the correct order of increasing energy) the energy levels known in atomic spectroscopy. It may be remarked that even the somewhat dubious assumption of equivalent orbitals work better in the case of ground states of the heteropolar σ-bonded molecules of eq. (6.3), such as SO_4^{--}, because the σ bond is permitted to be asymmetrically disposed with respect to the two atoms, the greater part of the electron density being found closest to the atom with highest electronegativity. Usually, the increased electron density in the bond region is described by the cross product $2ab\psi_A\psi_B$ in the square of the LCAO $\psi=a\psi_A+b\psi_B$, but from a group-theoretical point of view, there is nothing wrong in considering the (square root of) the electron density as consisting of *three* contributions having the *same* γ_n, *viz.* atomic orbitals from the atom A and B, *and* the σ orbitals such as given for MX_6 and MX_8 of cubic-octahedral symmetry in eqs. (4.8) and (4.35) and for MX_4 in tetrahedral symmetry in eq. (4.33). Thus, one might consider the two last subshells in the MO configuration of CH_4 $(1\gamma_1)^2(2\gamma_1)^2(1\gamma_5)^6$ as contributed predominantly by the four σ-bond regions more than by the carbon or the hydrogen atoms. This opens the way for the description in terms of equivalent orbitals $(1sC)^2(q)^8$, since the distinction between $(2\gamma_1)$ and $(1\gamma_5)$ with respect to energy does not occur in the bond region as much as in the 2s and 2p contributions close to the carbon nucleus.

What are the reasons why many chemists prefer $(q)^8$ rather than $(2\gamma_1)^2(1\gamma_5)^6$ as the bonding orbitals of methane? There is at least one point where we cannot give these chemists satisfaction. As emphasized by Mulliken (1935), there is no doubt that *methane has two different ionization energies*— $(1\gamma_5)$ at 116 kK and $(2\gamma_1)$ at some 178 kK. However much the four bonds are ever equivalent in methane, there is *no* reason for all eight bonding electrons to have the same ionization energy (as predicted by a theory neglecting the nondiagonal elements between the four equivalent orbitals); group theory demands only the same ionization energy for six of the electrons $(1\gamma_5)$ and the same, other value for two of them $(2\gamma_1)$.

However, there is a particular reason why the errors in the estimate of the naïve application of equivalent orbitals are particularly small in carbon and nitrogen compounds (some 50 per cent in CH_4 mentioned above). This is the same reason why 2s–2p "near orbital-degeneracy" was particularly important for explaining the correlation effects in the beryllium atom in Chapter 3. The 2p series of atoms have only a very insignificant atomic core, consisting of only two electrons very close to the nucleus, and hence the central field $U(r)$ in eq. (2.11) is rather similar to the central field in a hydrogen atom, where 2s and 2p are degenerate. In heavier atoms, the atomic core consisting of 10, 18, or 36 electrons modify the central field to a much greater extent, and consequently, ns and np are more separated in radial behaviour.

The similar errors can be much larger in other molecules. Thus, many chemists have felt that q orbitals necessarily should participate in the bonding of MX_q. From the point of view of MO theory, this is a quite superfluous assumption. In cases such as SiF_6^{--}, PF_6^-, and SF_6, it has been argued that the six σ orbitals of eq. (4.8) only might participate in the so-called sp^3d^2 hybridization of the complex, if the radial functions of 3s, 3p, and 3d of the central atom are roughly identical. Quite independently of the question whether 3d participates to any great extent in the even γ_3 set of MO or not, MO theory predicts that the six fluoride ligands may as well be bound by the four σ-bonding MO even γ_1 and odd γ_4, combined with some proportion of electrostatic attraction. The recent development of the knowledge of transition group complexes has shown that it is also impossible there to maintain such assumptions on the 3d, 4s, 4p radial functions of the central atom belonging to the 3d group. Actually, any theory of equivalent orbitals or "worse" variants such as the valency-bond theory have generally met great difficulties when dealing with octahedral molecules.

There remains actually a very perplexing problem: why many molecules become hemihedric, i.e. lose their centre of inversion, or more generally, exhibit a lower symmetry than is potentially available to the constituent atoms. The best-known cases are H_2O, H_2S, and a variety of compounds R_2O and R_2S, which could have been expected to be linear but actually are bent, with an angle around or slightly above 90 deg. Similarly, NH_3, PH_3, and a series of R_3N and R_3P, are pyramidal rather than trigonal planar. The first comment one may make is that the directive, angular part of the covalent bonding is rather weak compared to the much stronger part of spherical symmetry. Usually, the energies necessary for linearization of R_2O and planarization of R_3N are only a few per cent of the bonding energy with respect to isolated atoms.

The valency-bond theory seems to offer a ready explanation of approximately right-angled bonding by the three different p orbitals having as angular functions (x/r), (y/r), and (z/r). A closer analysis shows that this argument is rather weak. To the *first* approximation, the overlap integral between the same p orbital with the two ligands in a linear MX_2 molecule is the same as the sum of the overlap integrals between two different p orbitals and each a ligand X in a right-angled MX_2; hence the covalent bonding would be expected to be equally effective. Electrostatic repulsions between the two X would then be predicted to favour the linear structure. Actually, there exists a second-order effect stabilizing the angled molecule. The electronic density of an atomic orbital, i.e. ψ^2, always has even parity. This is also the case of the orbitals in the linear MX_2 because the perturbations caused by the presence of the X atoms occur on both sides of M. In the angled MX_2 the square of a given p orbital may become unsymmetrical and be concentrated in the region of low potential energy between M and X, whereas less than half of its electron density is spread out in a more diffuse ψ^2 on the rear side of M. Actually, Ellison and Shull (1953, 1955) (cf. also Pople's remarks on equivalent orbitals, 1953) calculated a very weakly pronounced energy minimum of H_2O near the experimental value of the angle 107 deg. Walsh (1953) indicated general principles for the behaviour of the MO predicting bent structures in some, but not all (e.g. not in CO_2, NO_2^+, NCO^-, NCS^-, etc.) cases. Schmidtke (1962) discussed these rules further.

Gillespie and Nyholm (1957) elaborated Sidgwick's idea that lone pairs take about as much angular space on the surface of a given central atom M as the ligands X do. This gives a very satisfactory classification of the low symmetries occurring; e.g. CR_4, NR_3, and OR_2 are all essentially tetrahedral, having zero, one, and two lone pairs occupying four of the co-ordination positions. Actually, a very long series of rather anomalous stereochemical features can be explained, such as ClF_3 with two lone pairs having the three fluorine atoms on three (the two axial and one equatorial) positions of a trigonal bi-pyramid. There is only one weak point in Gillespie and Nyholm's explanation: there exists no internal attraction between the two electrons in a lone pair, and hence it is difficult to understand why the lone pair concentrates in a hemihedric position in NH_3 rather than be equally distributed above and below the plane of a planar molecule. The solution of this problem may be found in the fact hinted above that the lone pairs, being the loosest bound electrons in the molecule, are expected to have the bulkiest ψ of lowest density, and hence that lone pairs need somewhat *more* angular space than the ligands.

Spontaneous deviations from high symmetries have attracted much attention recently in the transition group complexes. We may have *first-order Jahn-Teller effect*, influencing ground states with the orbital degeneracy number e above 1, and *second-order Jahn-Teller effects* where excited states perturb the ground state (even though not degenerate). Both effects occur in a *static* and a *dynamic* form. In the former case, the identical ligands perform their vibrations around equilibria positions at different distances from the same central atom. This may be observed in crystals where all central atoms have chosen the same direction of the local distortion, but occurs undoubtedly also in solutions. In the case of the dynamic Jahn-Teller effect, the potential barrier preventing jumps from one direction to another, equivalent direction of the distortion is not large compared to the Boltzmann energy kT at a given absolute temperature T. Then, a sample containing a large number of a given complex species shows a statistical distribution on the various distortional possibilities (and hence, a crystal may have a high macroscopic symmetry). Though the variation of each complex molecule is very rapid in this case, it is slower than the mechanism of the optical excitation, and therefore, the absorption spectrum indicates the instantaneous low symmetry. This case is presumably realized in $Cu(H_2O)_6{}^{++}$ at room temperature.

The only octahedral and tetrahedral complexes of the d transition groups fulfilling the conditions for having no first-order Jahn-Teller effect are

octahedral	tetrahedral	
$d^0\ {}^1\Gamma_1$	$d^0\ {}^1\Gamma_1$	
$d^3\ {}^4\Gamma_2\ \gamma_5{}^3$	$d^2\ {}^3\Gamma_2$	
$d^5\ {}^6\Gamma_1\ \gamma_5{}^3\gamma_3{}^2$ (high-spin)	$d^4\ {}^1\Gamma_1\ \gamma_3{}^4$ (low-spin)	(6.5)
$d^6\ {}^1\Gamma_1\ \gamma_5{}^6$ (low-spin)	$d^5\ {}^6\Gamma_1\ \gamma_3{}^2\gamma_5{}^3$ (high-spin)	
$d^8\ {}^3\Gamma_2\ \gamma_5{}^6\gamma_3{}^2$	$d^7\ {}^4\Gamma_2\ \gamma_3{}^4\gamma_5{}^3$	
$d^{10}\ {}^1\Gamma_1\ \gamma_5{}^6\gamma_3{}^4$	$d^{10}\ {}^1\Gamma_1\ \gamma_3{}^4\gamma_5{}^6$	

showing the conspicuous analogy between d^q in octahedral and d^{10-q} in tetrahedral symmetry. However, experience shows that the first-order Jahn-Teller effect is only pronounced in octahedral high-spin d^4 complexes ($^5\Gamma_3\ \gamma_5{}^3\gamma_3$) and d^9 ($^2\Gamma_3\ \gamma_5{}^6\gamma_3{}^3$), where tetragonal symmetry with formation of square-planar MX_4 is common. The explanation is that, in these two particular cases, the σ-antibonding γ_3 are involved in the first-order Jahn-Teller effect (only subshells which are not half filled or filled are thus responsible). In other cases, such as the $3d^1$ $Ti(H_2O)_6{}^{+++}$ or the high-spin $3d^6$ ($^5\Gamma_5\ \gamma_5{}^4\gamma_3{}^2$) $Fe(H_2O)_6{}^{++}$ and $CoF_6{}^{---}$ (studied by Cotton and Meyers, 1960), smaller effects are observed in the absorption spectrum, probably corresponding to a dynamic Jahn-Teller effect. Here, the only π-antibonding subshell γ_5 is active. A somewhat more subtle question is whether the vibrational structure observed in many absorption bands in solids at low temperature might be interpreted in terms of Jahn-Teller effects in excited degenerate states in such complexes where the ground state is nondegenerate.

Second-order Jahn-Teller effects may or may not occur in any given molecule, because there are always excited states of different symmetry types. Their influence is dependent on a numerical question, whether the squares of the nondiagonal elements of vibrational interaction with excited electronic states ("vibronic interaction") along a given normal mode of distortion are larger or smaller than the potential of the "restoring forces" from closed-shell repulsions, etc. Orgel (1958, 1959) invoked such second-order effects for explaining the particular linear stereochemistry of d^{10} systems with low oxidation number [i.e. where the empty $(n+1)$s shell has relatively low energy] such as Cu(I), Ag(I), Au(I), and Hg(II) and the tendency of $d^{10}s^2$ systems to lose their centre of inversion and assume very distorted microsymmetries as known of Sn(II), Sb(III), Pb(II), and Bi(III). Orgel explained the latter tendency by the presence of relatively (30–50 kK) low-lying d^{10}sp levels of opposite parity to that of the ground state.

There is no sharp distinction possible between this case and the Sidgwick-Gillespie-Nyholm effects of lone pairs in N(III), P(III), S(IV), Cl(V), Te(IV), and I(V) which also might be described formally as second-order Jahn-Teller effect from excited states of opposite parity. These are frequently only dynamic, e.g. NH_3 at high temperature would move rapidly between the two pyramidal forms, separated by the flat potential maximum of the planar form; and though PbS and TlI crystallize in NaCl and CsCl lattice, respectively, their polarizability and other properties make one suspect a tendency to statistically disordered distortion.

Unfortunately, it is at present very difficult to predict when the second-order Jahn-Teller effects actually are effective, this being an example of the general difficulty for MO theory for predicting the most stable geometrical arrangement of nuclei, whereas MO theory is much more successful in classifying the excited levels once the symmetry is prescribed. The only sensible thing to do is to try to find some empirical correlations in the material of evidence for and against second-order Jahn-Teller effect in various classes of compounds.

A very intriguing case is low-spin d^8 [Ni(II), Pd(II), Pt(II), Au(III)] and d^9 [Cu(II)] where the four ligands are coplanar in a square arrangement, but where the metal atom might be expected to be slightly out of the plane in average. This suspicion is partly built on Nyholm's demonstration that $Ni(CN)_4^{--}$ takes up a fifth cyanide forming $Ni(CN)_5^{---}$ but not a sixth one [J. Bjerrum presented similar evidence in 1934 for $Cu(NH_3)_5^{++}$] and partly on the square-pyramidal configuration of a nickel (II) compound with the environment $NiAs_3Br_2$. In the Gillespie-Nyholm language this corresponds to the hemihedric concentration of the $(2z^2 - x^2 - y^2)$ lone pair on one side of the x, y plane. At lower oxidation numbers, such as Mn(−I), Fe(0), Co(I), predominantly represented by carbon monoxide and isonitrile complexes, Nyholm (1961) reports mainly trigonal bi-pyramidal configuration.

The internal transitions in the partly-filled shells always correspond to comparatively weak absorption bands in octahedral symmetry because the electric dipole moment vanishes between a ground state Ψ_1 and an excited state Ψ_2 having the same parity. The vibronic mechanism of providing a weak intensity to these *Laporte-forbidden* bands is essentially a dynamic second-order Jahn-Teller effect, mixing with excited states of opposite parity (in particular the electron transfer states $\pi^{-1}d^{q+1}$ and $\sigma^{-1}d^{q+1}$). The other possible mechanism, hemihedric distortions, known to be of importance in ruby and in tris (oxalates), (Piper and Carlin, 1960) where the octahedra MO_6 are trigonally distorted, may be described as a static second-order Jahn-Teller effect. In MX_6 with monodentate X, no signs have yet been found of static hemihedric effects; i.e. the lone pairs in the partly filled shell are not sufficiently free from the d-shell conditions to initiate Gillespie-Nyholm behaviour.

REFERENCES

Cotton, F. A., and Meyers, M. D. (1960), *J. Am. Chem. Soc.*, **82**, 5023.
Ellison, F. O., and Shull, H. (1953), *J. Chem. Phys.*, **21**, 1420, and (1955), **23**, 2348.
Gillespie, R. J., and Nyholm, R. S. (1957), *Quart. Rev.*, **11**, 339.
Hall, G. G. (1950), *Proc. Roy. Soc.*, **A202**, 323.
Hall, G. G. (1959), *Rep. Progress Phys.*, **22**, 1.
Lennard-Jones, J., and Pople, J. A. (1950), *Proc. Roy. Soc.*, **A202**, 166.
Mulliken, R. S. (1935), *J. Chem. Phys.*, **3**, 517.
Nyholm, R. S. (1961), *Proc. Chem. Soc.*, 273.
Orgel, L. E. (1958), *J. Chem. Soc.*, 4186; (1959), 3815.
Piper, T. S., and Carlin, R. L. (1960), *J. Chem. Phys.*, **33**, 608.
Pople, J. A. (1953), *J. Chem. Phys.*, **21**, 2234.
Schmidtke, H. H. (1962), *Z. Naturforsch*, **17a**, 121.
Walsh, A. D. (1953), *J. Chem. Soc.*, 2260; 2266; 2296; 2301.

7. Electronegativity and Chemical Bonding

Chemistry is characterized by the very great variety of compounds (and elements which are not monatomic) formed by the different atoms. This is not only a matter of composition, by permutation of the 102 known atoms in binary, ternary, . . . compounds, but also, and very predominantly so, a matter of the type of chemical bonding. *Electronegativity* is a fundamental, but not very sharply defined, concept in chemistry. Compounds with large differences in the electronegativity x of the elements occurring tend to be *electrovalent* and to a good approximation the salts can be described as consisting of negative and positive ions of elements having high and low x respectively. If the electronegativities of the constituent atoms are nearly the same, and fairly high, we have homopolar *covalent* bonds, and finally, if the values of x are nearly identical and fairly low, we have *metallic* bonding in alloys and metallic modifications of elements.

It is worth emphasizing that the electronegativity of a given element increases as a function of *increasing oxidation number* and also to some extent may be a function of the detailed nature of the chemical bonds formed (say by carbon in C_2H_6, C_2H_4, and C_2H_2). The former amplification is of minor concern to organic chemistry, but is exceedingly important in the transition group compounds. For instance, there is no doubt that Mn(II) has a very low x, comparable to magnesium, and Mn(VII) a rather high x, comparable to gold, and there does not exist a quantity such as the x of manganese in general.

Pauling defined a thermochemical scale of electronegativities built on the assumption that the bond energy E_{AB} of the heteropolar bond between the two atoms A and B are related to the homopolar bond energies E_{AA} and E_{BB} and the square of the difference in electronegativity between the two atoms

$$E_{AB} = \tfrac{1}{2}(E_{AA} + E_{BB}) + \varkappa(x_A - x_B)^2 \qquad (7.1)$$

where the proportionality constant $\varkappa$ is 8.1 kK, accidentally very close to 1eV. However, it has become evident that the thermochemical scale eq. (7.1) induces many difficulties and to some extent must be a secondary effect of something more fundamental.

This fundamental idea is related to the LCAO approximation in MO theory as the *diagonal elements* of energy of the constituent atom orbitals, high x corresponding to the most negative energy. Said in a less restrictive way, one imagines the MO energies corrected for the effects of chemical bonding (i.e. the effects of the nondiagonal elements in LCAO language between different atoms, forming bonding or antibonding MO) and measuring the effective bonding of the electrons to the individual atoms.

Mulliken (1934) suggested the consideration of the arithmetic average $(I+A)/2$ of the first ionization energy I and the electron affinity A of a given atom X (i.e. A is the ionization energy of X^-) as a measure of the electronegativity. In addition, he suggested the use of *valence states* in particular cases where the atom X in its ground state could not form the number of covalent bonds observed. Thus, the energy is obviously increased in beryllium (2s2p), boron (2s2p^2), carbon (2s2p^3), and N^+ (2s2p^3) forming compounds with two, three, four, and four ligands. It was argued that the normal ground states, Be(2s^2), B(2s^{2}2p), C, and N^+ (2s^{2}2p^2) would only be able to form 0, 1, and 2 covalent bonds, respectively.

Actually, a great number of physical and chemical properties can be related to the electronegativity scale thus defined. A good example is the shift of nuclear quadrupole resonance frequencies discussed by Gordy (1955). However, at least one general misunderstanding subsisted: that an unequivocal relation exists between the ionicity of a chemical bond [say, (a^2-b^2) in LCAO expressions such as eq. (4.14)] and $(x_A - x_B)$. Such a relation would be more or less equivalent to the assumption of nearly constant nondiagonal elements of one-electron operator energy between the atomic orbitals interacting. This assumption is highly incredible, because it is well known that the homopolar bond energies vary in a wide degree (H_2 36 kK, Li_2 9, Cl_2 20, K_2 4 kK). These are slightly less than twice as large as the nondiagonal elements between the equivalent atomic orbitals.

It is quite evident that some compounds are so ionic, say NaCl and KBr, that the discussion of the electronegativities of the elements in slightly less ionic compounds such as MgO, BaS, PbS, CdO hardly can be expected to be aided by Mulliken's definition $(I+A)/2$. The behaviour at some more positive charge of the metal, say $+1$, and at some more negative charge of the chalkogen, say -1, must be of greater importance than the behaviour of the neutral atoms which is more pertinent in nearly homopolar bonds. The main reason why this argument has slightly smaller practical importance than might logically be expected is that the consecutive ionization energies $I_1, I_2, I_3, \ldots$ of a given element (and $A=I_0$) keeping inside a given shell has a roughly constant increase for each unit of positive charge z. We saw in eq. (2.20) that $\dfrac{dI}{dz}$ is roughly identical with the Coulomb integral J and is some 80–120 kK in the 2p shell, some 50–80 kK in the 3p, 4p, and 5p shells, and some 100 kK in the 3d shell. The large difference between J(2p, 2p) and J(3p, 3p) for a given z explains why A of fluorine is even smaller than of chlorine, but I_1 of fluorine is 36 kK larger than of chlorine. It is seen, however, that the value of I at a definite z is fairly characteristic of the element and may be used for more general comparisons, where the slopes dI/dz cancel.

Sanderson (1952) proposed the idea that the mechanism of the partly electrovalent, partly covalent heteropolar bond is that the more electronegative atoms attract electrons and hence decrease their value of the electronegativity to such an extent that the less electronegative atoms, now being positively charged and hence having their x increased, finally have the same, intermediate value of x. The principle of *electronegativity equilibrization* is an intuitively very appealing one, Fig. 7.1 giving a qualitative representation. In the special case of MX, it is seen how the equilibrium condition produces a charge separation on the components, $M^{+z}X^{-z}$ which geometrically is found as the horizontal line cutting equal distances from the X slope to the vertical axis at $z=0$ and from this axis to the M slope. It is seen how NaF is expected to be very ionic, NaCl slightly less, and AgCl to be more nearly covalent.

Sanderson has written a book, "Chemical Periodicity", which the present writer finds one of the most fascinating books he has ever seen on chemistry, though by no means does he agree with all the opinions expressed in it. Sanderson exposes here the equilibrization principle in connection with a definition of electronegativity based on stability ratios, i.e. on relative atomic sizes compared to isoelectronic, realized or fictive, inert gas atoms. Increase in x means contraction; the electronic density per A^3 becomes larger and larger. There is no doubt that atomic or ionic size has something to do with electronegativity, but as we shall see below, it is rather believed to be a

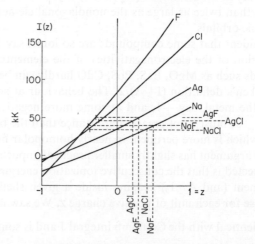

FIG. 7.1. Illustration of equilibrated electronegativity in compounds. The lines indicate the functions I(z) in the interval $-1<z<1$. If no correction for Madelung energy is made, the effective charges of the atoms in a definite compound such as AgF would correspond to the crossing points of the I-functions of Ag and F with the horizontal line expressing the electronegativity of the compound and having the same length before and after $z=0$ (i.e. expressing the electroneutrality of the binary compound).

secondary effect, the electronegativity itself essentially being a question of ionization energy per unit of charge.

The problem of ionic and atomic size is by itself a very interesting one. As recently reviewed by Dunitz and Orgel (1960), there exists a large class of approximately ionic compounds where ionic radii r_M and r_X can be defined in such a way that the crystals can be described as a tight packing of hard spheres. For simplification, we shall only consider the compounds with the global composition MX. If r_M and r_X are nearly identical (this usually happens only to metallic alloys), 12-co-ordinated lattices (cubic face-centred and hexagonal close-packed structures) and the 14-co-ordinated (8 near neighbours in a cube, 6 slightly more distant neighbours in a regular octahedron) cubic body-centred lattices occur. If r_M is somewhat smaller than r_X, but larger than 0.73 r_X, this 8-co-ordinated CsCl lattice is stable, and r_M in the range between 0.41 r_X and 0.73 r_X should produce the 6-co-ordinated NaCl lattice. Finally, for $r_M < 0.41$ r_X, the two 4-co-ordinated lattices, cubic zincblende and hexagonal wurtzite (having their names from two modifications of ZnS), should be stable. This agrees surprisingly well with the ionic radii as usually defined.

It is well known that a certain indeterminacy attaches to the separation of a given distance between the two nuclei M and X in the sum $r_M + r_X$. The consequences would not be changed significantly (except in cases like LiI, where the anions are supposed to touch each other) if all r_M were increased by a certain amount and all r_X decreased by the same amount. This is more or less what happened in the "covalent radii", originally derived from homonuclear bonds, where all r_M are some 0.7A larger than the established ionic radii and all r_X some 0.7A smaller. There is no doubt that the ionic radii is a successful concept even in the domain where the chemical bonding is predominantly covalent. This has a quite paradoxical consequence in the isoelectronic series which are extrapolated to neutral elements, say CuBr, ZnSe, GaAs, and Ge. The ionic radius of Zn^{++} is so small (0.83A) and of S^{--} so large (1.74A) that the 4-co-ordinated structure is well explained. The same is *a fortiori* true for Ga^{+++} and As^{---}, but there are many reasons to believe that this is a rather bad approximation to the compound GaAs which looks rather covalent. The argument of ionic radius ratios can be reduced *ad absurdum* in the case of germanium, which has to be considered as consisting of very small Ge^{+4} and very bulky Ge^{-4}, obviously leading to pure nonsense.

Hence, there are other reasons which "mimicrize" the ionic radii, producing the same variation of crystal structures. Mooser and Pearson (1959) suggested that the 4-co-ordinated structures (such as diamond, Si, Ge, and grey Sn) are caused by very strong directional valency forces (which are more pronounced in the 2p than in the following p groups), whereas, outside the transition groups, octahedral 6-co-ordination is a sign of the absence of strong directional forces. However, d group compounds such as Cr_2O_3, NiO, and $IrAs_3$

most evidently have a positive tendency to octahedral microsymmetry. Finally, 8- and 12-co-ordination indicates nondirectional, electrostatic or metallic bonding. Mooser and Pearson demonstrated that in a plot with two variables, the average principal quantum number $(n_M + n_X)/2$ (considering only np group atoms) and the electronegativity difference $(x_X - x_M)$, the transition from 4- to 6- to 8-co-ordination occurred in very sharply defined borderlines. If one goes along a diagonal from the origin, one meets the zinc-blende structure at low values of the two parameters, then the wurtzite structure in a very narrow region, then NaCl lattice, and finally, at very large values of both $(n_M + n_X)/2$ and $(x_X - x_M)$, the CsCl lattice occurs.

Mooser and Pearson undoubtedly express another, and a new, part of the truth. It must be realized, however, that their two parameters to a great extent express the one parameter r_M/r_X of the ionic model. When $(n_M + n_X)/2$ is large, the heavy atoms M and X tend to have roughly the same size, i.e. high co-ordination number, and on the other hand, when $(x_X - x_M)$ is small, r_M/r_X tends to very small values, i.e. low co-ordination number. In Mooser and Pearson's model, the paradox of extrapolation to the elements remains that, for vanishing $(x_X - x_M)$, the crystal assumes *either* 4-co-ordination (such as germanium) *or* a very high co-ordination number (such as the usual metals). Mooser and Pearson avoided this difficulty by restricting themselves to "normal valence compounds", excluding metallic bonding and "unsaturated valencies"; and also by excluding certain transition group hydrides, borides, carbides, and nitrides, frequently crystallizing in the NaCl lattice, which were deemed to be "interstitial compounds" (like lithium iodide mentioned above).

The present writer has learned very much from Palmer's book "Valency", but there is one point where he disagrees: the tacit assumption that one can conclude from the crystal structure whether the chemical bonding is predominantly electrovalent or covalent. Thus, AgCl and AgBr crystallizing in NaCl lattice were expected to be mainly ionic, whereas the 4-co-ordinated AgI was described as covalent. This argumentation is patently uncertain. Not only does solid argon and krypton crystallize in the same 12-co-ordinated lattice as copper and calcium metal, but the CsCl lattice is represented by all possible intermediate cases between ionic salts and Daltonian alloys: TlCl, TlBr, TlBi, AgMg, AgZn, CuBe, CuPd, MgAu, MgHg, NiAl, NiBe, and CuZn besides the 14-co-ordinated metals such as sodium, tantalum, tungsten, and the iron modification magnified in the Brussels World Exhibition Area. The compounds crystallizing in NaCl lattice cannot either all be called *bona fide* ionic salts: BaS, CaSe, MnS, NbC, NbN, NiO, PbTe, ScN, SnAs, SnTe, TaC, TiC, TiN, TiO, VN, ZrC, and ZrN.

It is true that the M−X distances are some 0.2A shorter in the 4-co-ordinated structures than calculated from the ionic radii appropriate to 6-co-ordination. However, it is well known in the lanthanides with varying co-ordination numbers, 12, 9, 8, 7, 6, that the ionic radii decrease about a tenth of an Angström going to the lower number of neighbours. This may as well be explained by an increasing strength of covalent bonding as by the model of purely electrostatic bonding superposed very steep closed-shell repulsions. The distinction between a covalent and an electrovalent description of the same compound is usually rather difficult to make, and, for instance, it is not completely clear that the words "effective charge z of the individual atoms in a compound" have an even approximately well-defined meaning. However, many properties such as the nephelauxetic effect seem to be related to z, though not directly proportional to this quantity. One difficulty in defining z is immediately obvious: if the covalent radius of a metal atom M is indeed some 0.7Å larger than the ionic radius r_M, we might very well have the situation that the total number of electrons inside the sphere with the smaller radius r_M was the expected value for the ion M^{+z} with z as large as the oxidation number, and at the same time, the number of electrons in the larger sphere was equal to the atomic number of M. In such a rather extreme case, which may be realized in crystalline lithium hydride, the compound would simultaneously fulfil some of the conditions for covalent *and* ionic bonding. However, there seems to be good evidence for what Pauling calls the *principle of electroneutrality* that the effective charge z (even taken in the ionic sense, small r_M) of the least electronegative elements rarely is above $+1$ and similarly of the most electronegative elements rarely below some -0.8. Anyhow, a great practical interest is attached to the possibility of comparing different compounds by assigning effective charges to the constituent atoms, though the absolute values of z may rather limit physical significance.

The present writer attempted (1962) to define a function I(z) of each element, the *differential ionization energy*, as the differential quotient of the energy of the isolated atom with respect to z. If the total energy of the atom is $-T$, I(z) is defined as an interpolated, smooth function which can be expanded in a Taylor series with few terms:

$$I(z) = \frac{dT}{dz} = a_0 + a_1 z + a_2 z^2 + \ldots \tag{7.2}$$

which are connected with experimental facts by the consecutive values I_n of the ionization energies for the process $M^{+n-1} \to M^{+n}$

$$I_n = \int_{n-1}^{n} I(z)dz = \left(a_0 - \frac{a_1}{2} + \frac{a_2}{3}\right) + (a_1 - a_2)n + a_2 n^2 + \ldots \tag{7.3}$$

It may be noted that if the coefficient a_2 in eq. (7.2) is neglected I_n of eq. (7.3) becomes simply $I(n-1/2)$. In this case, which is a rather good approximation (the curves in Fig. 7.1 are nearly straight lines), the Mulliken electronegativity is $I(0)$.

The physical significance of eq. (7.2) is quite different from the isoelectronic series discussed in eq. (3.24), though formally very similar. Since we are now dealing with a definite element, $I(z)$ is only an analytical function inside each n, l shell and makes discontinuous jumps when a new shell is becoming ionized. Thus, for chlorine, the 3p behaviour obtains in the region $z = -1$ to $z = +5$, then comes a jump to the 3s region $z = +5$ to $z = +7$, and then a very large jump to the 2p region, and so on. We have chosen to correct the observed ionization energies for spin-pairing phenomena, assuming the validity of eq. (2.58). Said in other words, the ionization energy of nitrogen ($2p^3\ {}^4S \rightarrow 2p^2\ {}^3P$) is larger than of oxygen ($2p^4\ {}^3P \rightarrow 2p^3\ {}^4S$) due to the large value of $S(S+1)$ of the half-filled shell, but when the baricentres $N(2p^3 \rightarrow 2p^2)$ and $O(2p^4 \rightarrow 2p^3)$ are considered, a smooth development is observed in the 2p group, the corrected ionization energy monotonically increasing in the series B, C, N, O, F. Tables 7.1 to 7.3 give the coefficients from eq. (7.2) for

TABLE 7.1. Taylor series coefficients for the differential ionization energy function $I(z)$ of eq. (7.2) for p^q elements in kK

	a_0	a_1	a_2		a_0	a_1	a_2
B	27	(70)	(14)	Ga	21	(50)	(6)
C	40	(83)	(14)	Ge	30	56	(6)
N	55	96	(14)	As	41	(62)	(6)
O	69	110	14	Se	52	66	6
F	83	127	14	Br	60	73	6
Al	21	(50)	(6)	In	26	(46)	(6)
Si	32	(57)	(6)	Sn	35	49	(6)
P	(45)	64	6	Sb	45	51	6
S	55	74	6	Te	52	55	(6)
Cl	67	82	6	I	59	61	(6)

TABLE 7.2. Taylor series coefficients for the differential ionization energy function $I(z)$ of eq. (7.2) for s^q elements in kK

	a_0	a_1	a_2		a_0	a_1	a_2
Li	(14) / (21)	(53) / (35)	(6) / (12)	Cu	(35)	(51)	(6)
Be	(43) / (48)	(59) / (47)	(6) / (12)	Zn	45	57	(6)
Na	(19)	(41)	(6)	Ag	(35)	(46)	(6)
Mg	36	47	(6)	Cd	44	52	(6)
K	(19)	(28)	(6)	Au	(49)	(49)	(6)
Ca	30	34	(6)	Hg	54	55	(6)
Rb	(19)	(25)	(6)				
Sr	28	31	(6)				
Cs	(19)	(20)	(6)				
Ba	27	26	(6)				

TABLE 7.3. Taylor series coefficients for the differential ionization energy function $I(z)$ of eq. (7.2) for d^q elements in kK

	a_0	a_1	a_2
V	-74	97	7.5
Cr	-58	99	8
Mn	-53	101	8.5
Fe	-46	102	9
Co	-36	103	10
Ni	-28	103	11

these corrected ionization energy values which otherwise are directly obtained from atomic spectroscopy. The Mulliken electronegativity is $a_0 + \frac{1}{3}a_2$. Various warnings may be given: the coefficients given in parentheses are estimated from the behaviour of neighbour elements in the periodic table. This is particularly true for the s^1 elements, the alkali metals and the coinage metals, where only one experimental datum is available, that is I_1. In the s^2 elements, I_1 and I_2 are known and permit the determination of a_0 and a_1 with some confidence, if it is assumed that a_2 has a value similar to those found in the p^q elements. The uncertainty is demonstrated in the case of Li and Be, which are exhibited with two different estimates, $a_2 = 6$ kK and 12 kK. The truth is probably somewhere between. Finally it may be remarked that the baricentres of $3d^q$ alone, and not $3d^{q-2}\,4s^2$, have been considered in the transition groups. Hence, the values of I decreases very strongly for small z and becomes more negative than the alkali metals for z below $+1$.

The most primitive assumption one can make on the charge separation in a compound MX is that the atoms assume such charges, M^{+z} and X^{-z}, that the total energy $-T_M - T_X$ is as negative as possible. Hence, the differential quotient of this expression has a zero point:

$$I_M(z) - I_X(-z) = O. \tag{7.4}$$

This corresponds to a very simple classical picture: small amounts of charge are transported from the atom M to the atom X until an equilibrium is reached, where the differential ionization energy is the same at both atoms, and charge conservation then demands that X has the opposite charge, $-z$, of that of M.

In a binary compound MX_q it is convenient to define a parameter of ionicity ξ such that the charge of M is $+q\xi$ and of X is $-\xi$. Assuming that the q atoms X are at equivalent positions, eq. (7.4) then becomes

$$I_M(q\xi) - qI_X(-\xi). \tag{7.5}$$

In the same way as in Sanderson's "Chemical Periodicity", the charge separations suggested by eqs. (7.4) and (7.5) are usually very small, exaggerating the obedience to the electroneutrality principle. With the aid of Tables 7.1 and 7.2, we may calculate two simple examples. In sodium chloride

$$\begin{aligned} I_{Na}(z) = &\quad 19+41z+6z^2 \\ -I_{Cl}(-z) = &-67+82z-6z^2 \\ \hline &-48+123z \end{aligned} \qquad (7.6)$$

having the zero point at $z=48/123=0.39$, whereas for zinc sulphide

$$\begin{aligned} I_{Zn}(z) = &\quad 45+57z+6z^2 \\ -I_S(-z) = &-55+74z-6z^2 \\ \hline &-10+131z \end{aligned} \qquad (7.7)$$

having the zero point at $z=10/131=0.076$, i.e. at nearly neutral atoms.

There is a very simple physical reason why these results are not realistic. In an actual compound, the separated charges are relatively close to each other and have a mutual attraction which is the larger the smaller the internuclear distances. The seemingly divergent problem of calculation of the electrostatic potential energy of an infinitely extended crystal MX_q can be made convergent and a Madelung constant α characteristic for a given crystal lattice occupied by point charges can be defined:

$$E_{Mad} = -\alpha z^2/(r_M+r_X). \qquad (7.8)$$

It is customary to ascribe to z the lowest integer occurring in the lattice. In other words, NaCl and CaF_2 have both $z=1$ in eq. (7.8), but ThO_2 crystallizing in CaF_2 lattice would have $z=2$ if it were completely ionic. The assumptions of eq. (7.8) are valid if the ions though extended are spherically symmetric (i.e. suffering no angular polarization) and not overlapping. The latter condition is not fulfilled in practice and is usually cited as one of the reasons why eq. (7.8) overestimates the heat of formation of typically electrovalent salts from gaseous ions by some 10 per cent, taken together with the (numerically less important) potential energy of the steeply increasing repulsion between the closed shells of the ions at their equilibrium positions.

We shall also talk about Madelung energy in isolated molecules MX_q. They were previously much discussed in Magnus and van Arkel's electrostatic model of the geometrical shape of simple molecules (cf. Rabinowitch and Thilo, 1930). Values of α are:

Gaseous molecules		Crystal lattices		
MX	1.000	NaCl	1.748	
linear MX_2	3.500	CsCl	1.763	
trigonal MX_3	7.26	wurtzite	1.641	(7.9)
tetrahedral MX_4	12.32	zincblende	1.638	
octahedral MX_6	25.99	CaF_2	5.039.	

The way of remedying eqs. (7.4) and (7.5) is to introduce

$$E_{Mad} = -(\alpha \xi^2/(r_M + r_X))(115 \text{ kK/A}) \qquad (7.10)$$

and to differentiate this expression with respect to ξ and add it to the differential quotient of the total energy of the atoms:

$$I_M(q\xi) - qI_X(-\xi) - 2\alpha\xi/(r_M + r_X). \qquad (7.11)$$

In sodium chloride, $r_{Na} + r_{Cl}$ is 2.81A and the new expression hence

$$
\begin{array}{ll}
I_{Na}(z) = & 19 + 41z + 6z^2 \\
-I_{Cl}(-z) = & -67 + 82z - 6z^2 \\
-2\alpha z/(r_{Na} + r_{Cl}) = & \underline{-142z} \\
& -48 - 19z
\end{array} \qquad (7.12)
$$

Hence, the expression no longer has any zero point, that is the minimum energy is represented by perfect electrovalent bonding where Na is at the upper limit of the 3s region, i.e. $z = +1$, and Cl at the lower limit of the 3p region, i.e. $z = -1$. If we perform the same calculation for the isostructural magnesium sulphide having $r_{Mg} + r_s = 2.60A$, the result is

$$
\begin{array}{ll}
I_{Mg}(z) = & 36 + 47z + 6z^2 \\
-I_s(-z) = & -55 + 74z - 6z^2 \\
-2\alpha z/(r_{Mg} + r_s) = & \underline{-155z} \\
& -19 - 34z
\end{array} \qquad (7.13)
$$

again suggesting completely electrovalent bonding. However, if we assume that the Madelung energy is only 70 per cent effective (due to the overlap of ions, etc.), eq. (7.13) would become $-19 + 13z$ having the root $z = 19/13 = 1.46$. It is worth remarking that a calculation not interfering with the size of the Madelung energy shows that crystalline $MgCl_2$ should be entirely ionic, but a gaseous, linear molecule has $z = +1.3$ and -0.65 on Mg and Cl. Though the distances are smaller in the gaseous molecule, the Madelung constant α, on the other hand, is always much smaller in eq. (7.9) than in the solid compound of the same composition.

Obviously, E_{Mad} is not the only correction to make to the total energy of the combined system (crystal or molecule). The influence of the chemical bonding can be described, in a rather tautological way, by a quantity E_{cov} such that the energy of the polynuclear system is $\Sigma(-T_n) + E_{Mad} + E_{cov}$. However, the chemical bonds are relatively weak, of the order of magnitude 40 kK or smaller. In the major part of simple molecules, the minimum value of E_{cov} occurs at electroneutrality $z = 0$. Hence, dE_{cov}/dz is positive. On the other hand, if the compound considered is really ionic with a large z, E_{cov} has presumably already a rather small numerical value, and dE_{cov}/dz may be expected to be some 10 kK. It is seen that the influence of dE_{cov}/dz in

O.A.M.–D

this case is to decrease the charge separation, since the z-independent coefficient becomes more positive in eq. (7.11), etc. However, this influence is only a tenth or so of the influence of the Madelung energy and may conveniently be included in a corrected version of E_{Mad}.

The situation is entirely different in the cases where E_{cov} has a minimum value at some value of z different from zero. This is the case in the CO molecule where the strong triple bond (isoelectronic with the N_2 molecule) can only be formed if the initial charge distribution is C^-O^+. Since the electronegativity differences otherwise would accumulate negative charge on the oxygen atom and positive charge on the carbon atom, the final result is a certain cancellation of the two effects. Actually, Rosenblum, Nethercot, and Townes (1958) demonstrated that the very low dipole moment of CO has the negative end on the carbon atom. A similar situation occurs in crystals like ZnSe and GaAs. If these compounds developed a set of covalent bonds comparable to Ge, their structures would be $Zn^{--}Se^{++}$ and Ga^-As^+, whereas the electronegativity differences obviously draw in the opposite direction toward $Zn^{+\xi}Se^{-\xi}$. Goodman (1960) and Mooser and Pearson (1961) discussed the inherent difference between "formal ionicity" and "real ionicity" in such cases, being 50 per cent and 0 per cent, respectively, if Zn and Se actually were neutral.

Recently, Iczkowski and Margrave (1961) developed independently a concept closely analogous to I(z), and they emphasized the discontinuities when a new shell is embarked. However, they did not consider the influence of the Madelung energy.

There are two formal difficulties in this treatment, and another, practically much more important, difficulty. The two formal difficulties are connected with the fact that a semiclassical charge transfer as implied in eq. (7.4) exaggerates the interelectronic repulsion effects as discussed on page 6; and that at large internuclear distances, the fractional atomic charges cannot be realized. Equation (7.6), considering such isolated atoms, would suggest that the sodium atom would carry a charge $+0.39$ and the chlorine atom a charge -0.39. Actually, the most stable system is represented by neutral sodium and chlorine atoms, whereas isolated Na^+ and Cl^- have 11 kK higher energy; and a closer analysis of the MO treatment shows that fractional charges cannot be realized. The relatively much more important question consists of knowing which orbitals are so strongly involved in the covalent bonding that their electronegativity is equilibrated. Using a metaphorical language, one may ask whether the molecule is conducting with respect to a given set of orbitals in the sense that, in a conductor, the electrostatic potential is everywhere constant. It is quite obvious that the 4f shell of a rare earth compound is so weakly engaged in the covalent bonding that it has its individually determined ionization energy [increasing from $4f^1$ Ce(III) to $4f^{14}$ Lu(III)] without much regard to the function I(z) of the other atoms constituting the compound. The same is true for the inner shells of ordinary atoms, such as 2p in sodium and chlorine. The partly filled d shell of transition group complexes may more or less represent an intermediate case, as we shall discuss in the interpretation of the electron transfer spectra.

There is no doubt, however, that the qualitative idea of equilibrated electroneutrality in fairly covalent molecules, represented by functions such as $I(z)$ corrected for E_{Mad} and E_{cov}, is a very useful one which might be developed along several lines in a more quantitative way. Thus, as Sanderson points out, the so-called "inductive effects" can be accounted for, at least qualitatively, by equilibrated electronegativity. In a series of compounds such as CF_4, $CClF_3$, CCl_2F_2, CCl_3F, and CCl_4, it is quite evident that the carbon charge is more positive in CF_4 than in CCl_4. We may calculate* the z taking the full Madelung energy into account in the two cases:

$$
\begin{array}{ll}
4I_C(4\xi) & 160+1328\xi+896\xi^2 \\
-4I_F(-\xi) & -332+508\xi-56\xi^2 \\
-2\alpha\xi/(r_C+r_F) & \underline{\qquad\qquad -1885\xi} \\
& -172-49\xi+840\xi^2
\end{array}
\tag{7.14}
$$

having the root $\xi=0.483$, i.e. $z_C=1.97$ and $z_F=-0.48$, whereas

$$
\begin{array}{ll}
4I_C(4\xi) & 160+1328\xi+896\xi^2 \\
-4I_{Cl}(-\xi) & -268+328\xi-24\xi^2 \\
-2\alpha\xi/(r_C+r_{Cl}) & \underline{\qquad\qquad -1375\xi} \\
& -108+281\xi+872\xi^2
\end{array}
\tag{7.15}
$$

having the root $\xi=0.226$, i.e. $z_C=0.90$ and $z_{Cl}=-0.23$. As we saw above, this is presumably an upper limit for the charge separation in the two molecules, more probable values being z_C roughly 1 and 0.5 respectively. However, the interesting result is that the three fluorine atoms in $CClF_3$ induce a value of the equilibrated electronegativity interpolated between the values of CF_4 and CCl_4. Consequently, the carbon charge is much higher than usual for a C–Cl bond, and hence the charge of chlorine is smaller in $CClF_3$ than in CCl_4. One may either say that the more electronegative fluorine atoms have an "inductive effect" on the C–Cl bond, drawing electrons away not only from the carbon but also from the chlorine atom; or one may say that the common electronegativity for the whole molecule has increased relative to CCl_4, making C more positive and Cl less negative. By the same token, the C–F bond in CCl_3F is unusual in the sense that the equilibrated electronegativity is lower than in CF_4 and therefore, the carbon atom is less positive and the fluorine more negative in CCl_3F. Lindqvist (1960) has made a comparative study of bond-length variations in mixed halides and other series of related molecules which is a rather good indicator for inductive effects.

*The factor 4 to the entry $I_C(4\xi)$ is caused by the fact that Table 7.1 lists $I(z)$ as a differential quotient with respect to z; and the quotient with respect to ξ needed in eqs. (7.14) and (7.15) is four times larger.

The tables of ionization energies of gaseous molecules given by Field and Franklin (1957) show clearly similar effects of substitutions. The presence of fluorine atoms in aliphatic hydrocarbons increases the ionization energies strongly, whereas the three heavier halogens tend to decrease the ionization energies. Dr. G. Klopman here at CERI has made a study of ionization energies of the hydrocarbons themselves (CH_4, C_2H_6, C_3H_8, . . .) mainly based on a valency-bond treatment. Actually, in agreement with the hypothesis of equilibrated electronegativity, the ionization energies decrease to a good approximation as a linear function of decreasing H/C ratio, indicating that the valence state of carbon (contrary to the assumption by Mulliken, but in agreement with atomic spectroscopy with regard to the usual ground states of hydrogen and carbon) has a slightly lower ionization energy than that of hydrogen. Dr. Klopman pointed out to me that the treatment in terms of differential ionization energies only is well defined in the cases where all the atoms of a given element are equivalent (such as in CH_4, C_2H_6, and C_6H_6, but not in C_3H_8 nor CH_3OH). Practically, this is a rather minor problem, compared to other more serious difficulties, because in a case like C_3F_8 one may distinguish the central carbon atom (with an environment C_2F_2) and the two external carbons (CF_3) and make a sort of iteration, constructing the appropriate charge distribution in the CF_3 groups from analogy to the CF_3 groups in C_2F_6 and hence get an idea of the residual CF_2 group.

Wolfsberg and Helmholz (1952) discussed the energy levels of tetroxo complexes such as CrO_4^{--} and MnO_4^- in a special model of LCAO theory. Actually, their specific results for these ions are incorrect (cf. Carrington's work mentioned on page 61), but the model is very interesting for giving some qualitative insight in the nature of the heteropolar bond. They assume determinants for a given symmetry type γ_n (and parity, if defined) of orbitals, where the diagonal elements H_{ii} correspond to atomic orbital energies [and they must be closely related to the function $I(z)$ discussed here, or possibly to the appropriate one-electron ionization energy, which rather is represented by $I(z+1/2)$]; the nondiagonal elements $H_{ij} - S_{ij}E$ are assumed to have the form (cf. Mulliken, 1952; 1955):

$$kS_{ij}(H_{ii}+H_{jj})/2 - S_{ij}E \qquad (7.16)$$

in the case of the nondiagonal element between two atomic orbitals having the overlap integral S_{ij} and the diagonal elements H_{ii} and H_{jj}. The constant k is assumed empirically to have values such as 1.67 or 2.

We may simplify the discussion by considering the interaction between two such orbitals only. The diagonal sum rule is no longer obeyed if S_{ij} is different from zero and if k is different from one. The sum of the two eigenvalues is actually

$$E_1+E_2=(H_{11}+H_{22})(1-kS_{12}^2)/(1-S_{12}^2). \qquad (7.17)$$

Since $(H_{11}+H_{22})$ ordinarily is negative, and k above one, the diagonal sum is less negative than $(H_{11}+H_{22})$. This illustrates the well-known fact that anti-bonding MO have their energies increased more than the bonding MO have their energies decreased. In the case where both the antibonding and bonding combinations are fully occupied, it exemplifies the repulsion between closed shells.

In the case of heteropolar bonds, it may be practical to orthogonalize the two original orbitals ψ_{11} and ψ_{22} in such a way that one of them is not changed:

$$\psi_{10}=\psi_{11}; \quad \psi_{20}=(\psi_{22}-S_{12}\psi_{11})/(1-S_{12}^2)^{1/2} \tag{7.18}$$

making ordinary second-order perturbation arguments valid. In this case, the orthogonalized, second diagonal element is

$$E_{20}=(H_{22}(1-kS_{12}^2)+H_{11}(1-k)S_{12}^2)/(1-S_{12}^2) \tag{7.19}$$

and the new nondiagonal element

$$E_{120}=\left(\left(\frac{k}{2}-1\right)H_{11}+\frac{k}{2}H_{22}\right)S_{12}/(1-S_{12}^2)^{1/2}. \tag{7.20}$$

It is useful to note that, to the first approximation, the square of this non-diagonal element behaves as $(kH_{22}S_{12})^2/4$ for small values of S_{12}. We must realize that in any case the treatment loses much of its physical significance for large S_{12}, since LCAO of only two atomic orbitals became a very bad approximation to the eigenvalues of the Schrödinger one-electron equation.

In the original Wolfsberg-Helmholz treatment, it was discussed whether the diagonal elements H_{ii} assumed are consistent with the distribution of atomic charges finally obtained in the molecule. This is a much more intri-cate problem than usual under perturbation treatments where the diagonal elements can be assumed to be constant. In our case, the diagonal elements vary strongly as functions of the charge distribution assumed, and frequently, H_{11} and H_{22} cross as functions of the charge separation, the ionicity para-meter ξ. As a secondary effect it may be mentioned that S_{12} also varies rather conspicuously with the effective charges acting on the atomic radial functions.

This rather anomalous situation is caused by the fact that our diagonal elements H_{ii} are not pure one-electron operator quantities but contain large contributions of two-electron repulsion. Hence, the variation principle cannot be applied in the same simple form as in the case of two interacting Ψ, because the total energy of the system *cannot* be expressed as the sum of the orbital energies. We do not need to worry too much if the total energy of the system has a minimum for such partitions of the individual LCAO which would not have been found by a direct application of the Wolfsberg-Helmholz method. In the special case of equilibrization of the diagonal elements $H_{11}=E_{20}$, the original perturbation still has some merit, because arbitrary linear combinations $a\psi_{10}+b\psi_{20}$ $(a^2+b^2=1)$ now can be formed. The eigenvalues are then, according to eqs. (7.19) and (7.20), approximately

$$H_{11}\pm((k-1)H_{11}S_{12}/(1-S_{12}{}^2)^{1/2}) \tag{7.21}$$

representing a stabilization of the bonding orbital roughly $1+(k-1)S_{12}$ times the original energy H_{11}. In the hydrogen molecule, this quantity is 1.17, which is roughly the upper limit expected in any molecule. This illustrates our previous remark that all chemical bonds are relatively weak, because H_{11} may very well vary by a factor of 3 or 5 as functions of the atomic charges. The idea of differential ionization energies must therefore express a part of the truth regarding charge separation in actual, heteropolar bonds.

Ballhausen and Gray (1962) treated $VO(H_2O)_5{}^{++}$ by the Wolfsberg-Helmholz method and obtained agreement with experiment and the previously suggested strong π-bonding of oxygen (Jørgensen, 1957).

Seeking for experimental data to estimate electronegativities, it is natural to look at the electron transfer spectra, e.g. of the octahedral hexahalide complexes MX_6 mentioned in eq. (4.10). It is quite surprising to observe that in a variety of complexes of different central atoms M (with a definite oxidation number), the absorption bands shift to lower wavenumbers as a function of the halide X in a very regular way, the shift from F to Cl being 28 kK, from Cl to Br 6 kK, and from Br to I 10 kK. These shifts are proportional to differences between electronegativity values x on the Pauling scale

$$F\ 3.9 \quad Cl\ 3.0 \quad Br\ 2.8 \quad I\ 2.5 \tag{7.22}$$

if one unit of this scale is made equivalent to 30 kK. It may be remarked that the value of the function $I(z)$ for $z=0.3$ in Table 7.1 shows similar differences, *viz.*:

$$F\ 122 \quad Cl\ 92 \quad Br\ 82 \quad I\ 77. \tag{7.23}$$

It is now possible to make a very hardy assumption that the wavenumber of electron transfer spectra is directly proportional to the electronegativity difference between the ligand and the central atom. We shall later expose why this assumption would be *a priori* unprobable, and try to explain why it actually works. We make one correction, however: we assume that the change of spin-pairing energy in a $d^q \rightarrow d^{q+1}$ transition can be described by eq. (2.58) with the parameter D estimated from internal d^q transitions. The corrected values of *optical electronegativities* are given in Table 7.4. The lowest subshell which is not σ-antibonding (γ_5 in octahedral, γ_3 in tetrahedral, one of the low orbitals in square-planar complexes) is indicated, the π orbitals of the ligands considered according to eq. (7.22). However, in d^{10} systems, the empty γ_1 is estimated. Obviously, the optical electronegativities of central ions have the character of MO electron affinities, whereas the ligand electronegativities have something to do with ionization energies. Already for this

TABLE 7.4. Optical electronegativity values estimated from electron transfer spectra

$3d^0$	Ti(IV)	1.8		Pd(IV) low-spin	2.7
$3d^2$	V(III)	1.9	$4d^8$	Pd(II) square	2.2–2.4
$3d^3$	Cr(III)	1.8–1.9	$4d^{10}$	Sn(IV) γ_1	1.5
$3d^4$	Mn(III) low-spin	2.0		Sb(V) γ_1	1.8
$3d^5$	Fe(III) high-spin	2.5	$5d^0$	W(VI)	2.0
	low-spin	2.1	$5d^2$	Os(VI)	2.6
$3d^6$	Co(III) low-spin	2.3	$5d^3$	Re(IV)	2.0_5
$3d^7$	Co(II)	1.9		Ir(VI)	2.9
$3d^8$	Ni(II) high-spin	2.1	$5d^4$	Os(IV) low-spin	2.2
	low-spin	~2.2		Pt(VI) low-spin	3.2
$3d^9$	Cu(II)	2.3	$5d^5$	Os(III) low-spin	1.95
$3d^{10}$	Ge(IV) γ_1	1.3		Ir(IV) low-spin	2.35
$4d^0$	Mo(VI)	2.1	$5d^6$	Ir(III) low-spin	2.25
$4d^3$	Mo(III)	1.7		Pt(IV) low-spin	2.7
	Tc(IV)	2.2	$5d^8$	Pt(II) square	2.3
$4d^4$	Ru(IV) low-spin	2.4		Au(III) square	~2.9
$4d^5$	Ru(III) low-spin	2.05	$5d^{10}$	Hg(II) γ_1	1.5
	Rh(IV) low-spin	2.6		Pb(IV) γ_1	1.9
$4d^6$	Rh(III) low-spin	2.3			

reason, we would not expect the existence of complexes with nearly identical optical electronegativity of the ligands and the central ion.

It is possible then to define the optical electronegativities of other ligands, though they are necessarily of secondary certainty compared to the four halogens of eq. (7.22). The Pauling electronegativities are also indicated:

	optical x	Pauling x	
H_2O	3.5	3.5	
CN^-	2.8	(2.6)	(7.24)
$dtp^- = (C_2H_5O)_2PS_2^-$	2.7	2.5	
$dsep^- = (C_2H_5O)_2PSe_2^-$	2.6	2.3.	

However, the same treatment is not successful in the case of the oxide complexes such as MO_4^{+z-8} or MO_2^{++}. The effect of chlorine substitution forming MO_3Cl (a red shift some 3–6 kK) suggests a value of the optical x of O^{--} close to 3.2, and then the values of x for the central atoms are found some 0.2 to 0.7 units lower than in the hexahalides. These results are compiled in Table 7.5. One explanation possible is the strong π-antibonding effects on the lowest subshell of the central ion, which is considered in Table 7.5. Thus $RuO_2Cl_4^{--}$ and $OsO_2Cl_4^{--}$ have their electron transfer spectra at some 20 kK higher wavenumber than the (extrapolated) values of $RuCl_6$ and $OsCl_6$, showing an oxide shift of the lowest subshell amounting to some 0.7 unit. Orgel and Jørgensen (1961) demonstrated that π-antibonding effects of a similar magnitude occur in polynuclear complexes of ruthenium and iridium containing oxide and nitride bridges. The bond distances in $OsO_2Cl_4^{--}$ are quite remarkable (Kruse, 1961). The distance Os–Cl 2.38Å combined with

TABLE 7.5. Optical electronegativities from oxo complexes compared with the values extrapolated from the behaviour of hexahalides

		oxides	extrapolated
$3d^0$	V(V)	2.0	2.2
	Cr(VI)	2.3	2.6
	Mn(VII)	2.6	3.0
$3d^2$	Mn(V)	2.3	2.6
	Fe(VI)	2.7	3.0
$4d^0$	Mo(VI)	1.7	2.1
	Tc(VII)	2.05	2.6
	Ru(VIII)	2.35	3.0
$5d^0$	W(VI)	1.5	2.0
	Re(VII)	1.8	2.4
	Os(VIII)	2.1	2.8
$5f^0$	U(VI)	2.4	2.5–3.0

the usual $r_{Cl}=1.81$Å indicates the ionic radius of Os(VI) 0.57Å. Then, r_0 is only 1.18Å (because Os–O in the complex is 1.75Å) and not 1.32Å as usually assumed for O^{--}. Similar short bond distances occur in the uranyl ion where U–O is some 1.7Å. The optical behaviour of U(VI) is not completely clarified; the absorption bands at 27 kK of UF_6 seem to indicate $x=3.0$, whereas UCl_6 is reported to have the first bands at 16 kK corresponding to $x=2.5$, close to the UO_2^{++} value.

When relating electron transfer spectra to MO energies, and hence, following Mulliken, to electronegativities (here with the unit 30 kK for the x values), it becomes highly pertinent to ask whether one seriously means one-electron ionization energies, or what else the word "MO energy difference" may denote. If we pursue the assumption of well-defined MO configurations, eq. (1.12) tells us that neglecting K integrals, the energy of the transition Ca→Cb, where C denotes the unchanged part of the configuration, can be written

$$I(a)-I(b)+J(b, b)-J(a, b)\equiv I(a)-A(b)-J(a, b) \qquad (7.25)$$

in terms of the ionization energies $I(a)$ and $I(b)$ of the two orbitals, the electron affinity $A(b)$ of the excited orbital, and the Coulomb integrals J. The *charge separation effect* in electron transfer spectra is caused by the presence of these two J integrals in eq. (7.25). In general, the hole created by the optical transition in the orbital a attracts the electron in b the more the smaller their spatial separation. We may distinguish between two extreme cases: the nearly coincident orbitals a and b, where $J(b, b)$ and $J(a, b)$ are roughly of the same size and hence $I(a)-I(b)$ is a good approximation to eq. (7.25); and the widely separated orbitals a and b, where $J(a, b)$ is a very small quantity, and whence $I(a)-A(b)$ is a good approximation. The latter case is realized in electron transfer between largely separated molecules or other isolated entities in a solid or in solution, and usually A(b) is considerably smaller than I(b), the difference J(b, b) being proportional to $<r^{-1}>$ of the orbital b. Though I(a) might be the same as I(b), as would be the case in electron transfer between two identical atoms with a partly filled shell, the electron transfer may need a very large energy, in this case determined by J(b, b). In the case of a compound containing the same atom in different oxidation numbers, one might argue with Dunn that a transition such as Fe(II), Fe(III)→Fe(III), Fe(II) would cost no energy. Actually, when optical transitions are possible, the interaction between the atoms is usually so strong that bonding and antibonding MO are formed, and the transitions have therefore a small, but not vanishing, wavenumber. In addition, the ligand internuclear distances may be appreciably different in the two atoms if they have distinctly different oxidation numbers, and the corresponding potential curves must be taken into account, giving a contribution of a few kK to the wavenumber. A very interesting case of the iron (II, III) cyanides was studied by Robin (1961), where the ion $Fe(CN)_6Fe^-$ contain a low-spin Fe(II) surrounded by six carbon atoms in the crystalline state, and a high-spin Fe(III) surrounded by six nitrogen atoms.

In the hexahalides MX_6, the $J(b,b)=J(nd, nd)$ of eq. (7.25) is expected to be somewhat larger than the $J(a, b)=J(\pi, nd)$, in particular in the 3d group. Consequently, the difference in ionization energy $I(\pi)-I(nd)$ is smaller than the wavenumber differences observed, and it might even be negative in cases such as $CuBr_4^{--}$ or OsI_6^{--} if $J(nd, nd)-J(\pi, nd)$ is larger than 20 kK.

The differences between consecutive ionization energies I_n of a gaseous ion has the order of magnitude of the J integral of the shell to be depopulated. It is seen in Table 7.4 that the energy difference between isoelectronic ions with the oxidation number $+q$ and $+q+1$ is some 0.5 to 0.6 electronegativity units, i.e. 15–18 kK, except in the first transition group, where the difference between $+2$ and $+3$ probably is somewhat larger. The similar values for the *same element* as functions of increasing oxidation number is 0.3–0.4 units, i.e. 9–12 kK.

In the gaseous ions J(3d, 3d) can be estimated to some 100 kK, whereas J(4d, 4d) and J(5d, 5d) are about 60 kK. The nephelauxetic effect in the halide complexes decrease these values, perhaps to 60 and 40 kK. There seems still to be a large difference between these numbers and the 9–12 kK cited above. However, since $J(\pi, nd)$ is expected to be some 30 kK, the difference $J(nd, nd)$ $-J(\pi, nd)$ may already have the correct order of magnitude. It is possible from thermodynamic data to get some idea of the relative ionization energies in complexes. As explained in "Absorption Spectra and Chemical Bonding in Complexes", the ionization energy of a species having the same oxidation potential as the standard hydrogen electrode is roughly 40 kK. This is the order of magnitude of oxidation potentials of M(II)→M(III) hexaaquo ions in the 3d group and M(III)→M(IV) hexachloro complexes in the 4d and 5d group. However, these processes are not optical transitions obeying the

Franck-Condon principle, but allow an establishment of new equilibrium values of internuclear distances. There is no doubt that in such compounds, the higher oxidation number is relatively more stabilized, to an extent of more than 100 kK for the oxidation number $+4$.

Until new experimental devices furnish data about MO ionization energies in complexes, one may take the empirical attitude to orbital energies well known among atomic spectroscopists: that since most optical transitions to a rather good approximation are one-electron jumps, and since the baricentre of a given configuration can be defined as *the* energy of the configuration, one may concentrate the interest on energy differences $Ca^q b^p \rightarrow Ca^{q-1} b^{p+1}$. We know that the orbital energy differences $(a \rightarrow b)$ thus defined are not necessarily consistent with the values of $(a \rightarrow c)$ and $(c \rightarrow b)$ found by other configurations.

Another aspect one may study is the question whether configuration energy differences $a^q b^{n-q} \rightarrow a^{q-1} b^{n-q+1}$ indicate the same value of $(a \rightarrow b)$ independent of q. If we assume that the three groups of J integrals $J(a, a)$, $J(a, b)$, and $J(b, b)$ have unique values in each group, and if we neglect K integrals, we see that the contribution of these Coulomb integrals to the transition energy is

$$-(q-1)J(a, a)+(2q-n-1)J(a, b)+(n-q)J(b, b). \qquad (7.26)$$

It is seen that this expression is independent of q if

$$2J(a, b)=J(a, a)+J(b, b). \qquad (7.27)$$

If the two orbitals a and b are nearly coincident with respect to average radius (which is the case with the two subshells γ_5 and γ_3 in octahedral transition group complexes), eq. (7.27) is approximately valid, and the energy difference $(a \rightarrow b)$ (in the example, Δ) is roughly independent of the choice of q for a definite number of electrons n in the partly filled shell.

On the other hand, if the orbital a has a much larger average radius than b (we are now thinking of $\pi \rightarrow \gamma_5$ electron transfer), it is roughly true

$$J(b, b) \gg J(a, b) \sim J(a, a). \qquad (7.28)$$

It may be remarked that eq. (7.25) degenerates to

$$I(a)-I(b)+(J(b, b)-J(a, a))/2 \qquad (7.29)$$

when combined with eq. (7.27), whereas eq. (7.28) leads to

$$I(a)-I(b)+J(b, b)-J(a, a). \qquad (7.30)$$

If the appropriate atomic charges are z_a and z_b, there is a close analogy between eq. (7.29) and the difference of differential ionization energy

$$I_a(z_a)-I_b(z_b) \qquad (7.31)$$

and between eq. (7.30) and

$$I_a(z_a - 1/2) - I_b(z_b - 1/2) \qquad (7.32)$$

which is essentially a difference between electron affinities.

If the principle of equilibrated electronegativity were applied to electron transfer spectra of MX_6, we would more or less expect that the wavenumber would express twice a nondiagonal element of the type of eq. (7.20) and be independent of the actual value of $I(z)$. The fact that a strong and constant dependence on the halogen is observed, eq. (7.22), suggests a mechanism of the type in eq. (7.32) where $I_X(z_X - 1/2)$ and $I_M(z_M - 1/2)$ actually have different values. The physical reason may be that the Stevens' delocalization coefficients a and b in eq. (4.14) are relatively close to 1 and 0, respectively, and that only in the case $a \sim b$ does the equilibration of electronegativities actually occur.

It is tempting to divide the correction for Madelung energy in eq. (7.11) in equal portions on the atoms M and X and assume that corrected functions $I_M^*(z)$ of the less electronegative and $I_X^*(z)$ of the more electronegative atom can be defined:

$$\begin{aligned} I_M^*(z) &= I_M(z) - \alpha\xi/(r_M + r_X) \\ I_X^*(-z) &= I_X(-z) + \alpha\xi/(r_M + r_X) \end{aligned} \qquad (7.33)$$

which may be one of the possible explanations why halogens in more or less covalent compounds obey the same spreading law eq. (7.22) and even seem to have roughly the same ionization energies for a definite halogen. The series in eq. (7.23) made by interpolation between the electron affinities and the ionization energies of the halogen atoms, and closest to the latter value since $I(0.3)$ was considered, may give a qualitative picture of the constancy of $I_X^*(-z)$ in eq. (7.33). In the more electrovalent compounds $I_X(-z)$ is not very positive, but $\alpha\xi/(r_M + r_X)$ is large. On the other hand, in the more covalent compounds where the Madelung contribution is negligible $I_X(-z)$ is large and may very well be comparable to $I_X^*(-z)$ in the ionic salts.

If a relation between a MO energy I_{MO} and the delocalization coefficients a and b in eq. (4.14) can be established, it would have the form

$$I_{MO} = a^2 I_M(z_M) + b^2 I_X(z_X) - a^2 I_{Mad} + b^2 I_{Mad} + 2ab I_{cov} \qquad (7.34)$$

involving corrections for Madelung and covalent energy. Equation (7.34) has a fairly realistic interpretation in terms of an approximate one-electron Hamiltonian and expresses the fact that complete equilibration of electronegativities may not be expected to occur as a general rule when either a or b is small.

REFERENCES

Ballhausen, C. J., and Gray, H. B. (1962), *Inorg. Chem.*, **1**, 111.

Dunitz, J. D., and Orgel, L. E. (1960), *Adv. Inorg. Chem. Radiochem.*, **2**, 1.

Field, F. H., and Franklin, J. L. (1957), "Electron Impact Phenomena", Academic Press, New York.

Goodman, C. H. L. (1960), *Nature*, **187**, 590.

Gordy, W. (1955), *Discuss. Faraday Soc.*, **19**, 14.

100   ORBITALS IN ATOMS AND MOLECULES

Iczkowski, R. P., and Margrave, J. L. (1961), *J. Am. Chem. Soc.*, **83**, 3547.
Jørgensen, C. K. (1957), *Acta Chem. Scand.*, **11**, 73.
Jørgensen, C. K., and Orgel, L. E. (1961), *Mol. Phys.*, **4**, 215.
Jørgensen, C. K. (1962), *Adv. Chem. Phys.*, **5**.
Kruse, F. H. (1961), *Acta Cryst.*, **14**, 1035.
Lindqvist, I., (1960), *Nova Acta Reg. Soc. Scient. Upsal.*, IV, **17**, No. 11.
Mooser, E., and Pearson, W. B. (1959), *Acta Cryst.*, **12**, 1015.
Mooser, E., and Pearson, W. B. (1961), *Nature*, **190**, 406.
Mulliken, R. S. (1934), *J. Chem. Phys.*, **2**, 782; (1935), **3**, 586.
Mulliken, R. S. (1952), *J. Phys. Chem.*, **56**, 295.
Mulliken, R. S. (1955), *J. Chem. Phys.*, **23**, 1841.
Palmer, W. G. (1948), "Valency", Cambridge University Press.
Pauling, L. (1944), "The Nature of the Chemical Bond", Cornell University Press, Ithaca.
Rabinowitch, E., and Thilo, E. (1930), "Periodisches System, Geschichte und Theorie", Ferdinand Enke, Stuttgart.
Robin, M. B. (1961), *Spectrochimica Acta*, **17**, 1095.
Robin, M. B. (1962), *Inorg. Chem.*, **1**, 337.
Rosenblum, B., Nethercot, A. H., and Townes, C. H. (1958), *Phys. Rev.*, **109**, 400.
Sanderson, R. T. (1952), *J. Am. Chem. Soc.*, **74**, 272.
Sanderson, R. T. (1960), "Chemical Periodicity", Reinhold, New York.
Wolfsberg, M., and Helmholz, L. (1952), *J. Chem. Phys.*, **20**, 837.

8. How to Identify Absorption Spectra

Literally thousands of complexes have had their excited levels described and classified by means of the MO method. There is not much use in attempting a survey of the individual cases here. In the references to Chapter 4, books and reviews by Orgel, McClure, and the present writer are listed which may be of some use for the reader seeking information about a definite transition group compound. Dr. T. M. Dunn wrote a very valuable chapter in Lewis and Wilkins's "Modern Coordination Chemistry", Interscience, New York,

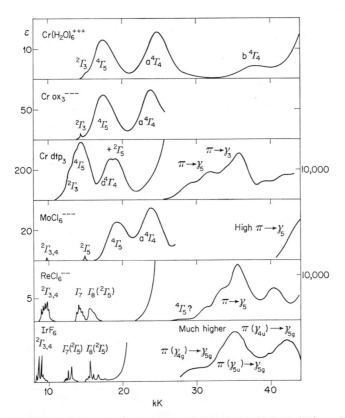

FIG. 8.1. Absorption spectra of d^3 complexes of Cr(III), Mo(III), Re(IV), and Ir(VI). The gaseous IrF_6 was measured by Moffitt, Goodman, Fred, and Weinstock (1959) and further discussed by Jørgensen (1960).

1960, and is going to give an introductory lecture at the Seventh International Conference on Co-ordination Chemistry in Stockholm, June, 1962, where more material will be presented. Dr. Charles S. Naiman, Department of Physics, Massachusetts Institute of Technology, Cambridge, Massachusetts, is going to publish a compilation of thousands of references to ligand field theory and its applications.

On the other hand, it may possibly be of some use to give a short description of how assignments of excited levels were made in a few key cases, which then can be extrapolated to the majority of complexes so far studied. We arrange these selected examples according to the number of d electrons in the corresponding gaseous ion. Their spectra are given in Figs. 8.1–8.7.

d^3 *complexes.* $Cr(H_2O)_6^{+++}$ is historically a very important example together with the ruby Cr(III) substitutionally situated in corundum Al_2O_3. Finkelstein and Van Vleck (1940) identified the weak and very narrow line

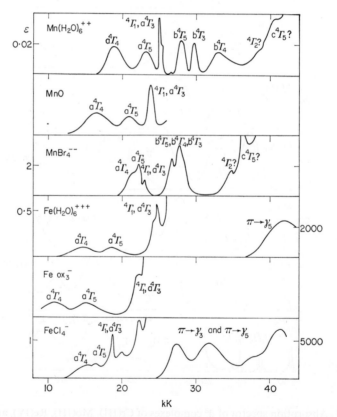

FIG. 8.2. Absorption spectra of high-spin $3d^5$ complexes of Mn(II) and Fe(III). The spectrum of MnO was measured by Pratt and Coelho (1959).

group at 15 kK with the transition from the ground state $\gamma_5^3\ {}^4\Gamma_2$ to the two approximately degenerate levels ${}^2\Gamma_3$ and ${}^2\Gamma_4$ of the same subshell configuration. As expected from eq. (4.23), ${}^2\Gamma_5$ can be observed at low temperatures as the excited level of a very weak band group at 21 kK. The two broad bands in the visible were not identified by Finkelstein and Van Vleck, who regretted that broad bands belonging to other configurations mask the two spin-allowed transitions expected to ${}^4\Gamma_5$ and $a^4\Gamma_4$ of $\gamma_5^2\gamma_3$. Actually, it is now clear that the broad bands are indeed the spin-allowed bands sought for, and that the large bandwidth is caused by the co-excitation of many vibrations when the subshell configuration changes from γ_5^3 to $\gamma_5^2\gamma_3$. The minimum of the latter potential curve occurs at a larger Cr–O distance than in the ground state. The third spin-allowed transition to $b^4\Gamma_4$ of $\gamma_5\gamma_3^2$ is observed as a weak, broad band at 38 kK. It would be forbidden as a two-electron jump if it were not for the nondiagonal element between the two ${}^4\Gamma_4$ mentioned on page 56. Hence, the distance between the two first spin-allowed bands are $12B-x$, x being the small quantity implicitly given by

$$x = 36B^2/(\Delta - 9B + x) \qquad (8.1)$$

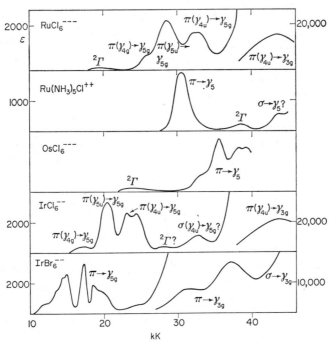

FIG. 8.3. Absorption spectra of low-spin d^5 complexes of Ru(III), Os(III), and Ir(IV). The spectrum of $Ru(NH_3)_5Cl^{++}$ was measured by Hartmann and Busch-beck (1957).

where the wavenumber of the first spin-allowed absorption band directly gives Δ in the expanded radial function model.

Cr ox$_3$$^{---}$ though not perfectly octahedral (the small trigonal distortion produces interesting dichroitic effects studied by Piper and Carlin, see page 79) has nearly the spectrum expected of octahedral microsymmetry of CrO$_6$ (each ox^{--}, oxalate ion C$_2$O$_4$$^{--}$ supplying two oxygen atoms). Δ has the same value as in the hexaaquo ion, since the transitions to $^4\Gamma_5$ have the maxima in the two complexes at the same place, 17.5 kK. On the other hand, as originally pointed out by Schäffer, B must be smaller [620 K in Cr ox$_3$$^{---}$, 725 K in Cr(H$_2$O)$_6$$^{+++}$, whereas gaseous Cr^{+++} has 920 K], as can be implied

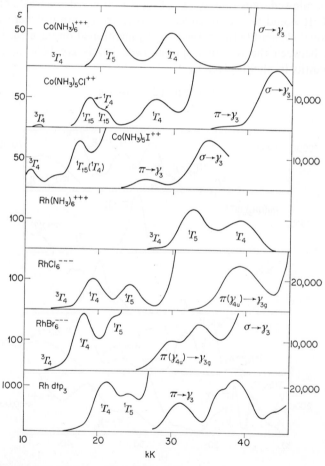

FIG. 8.4. Absorption spectra of low-spin 3d^6 and 4d^6 complexes of Co(III) and Rh(III). The spectra of Co(NH$_3$)$_5$Cl^{++} and Co(NH$_3$)$_5$I^{++} were measured by Linhard and Weigel (1957).

from the position of the second spin-allowed transition to $a^4\Gamma_4$ and eq. (8.1). The larger nephelauxetic effect in the tris-oxalate can also be observed in the position of $^2\Gamma_3$ of γ_5^3 at 14.35 kK, hence having K(4, 5) of eq. (4.23) slightly decreased. The strong, Laporte-allowed transitions in the ultraviolet are not well known at present.

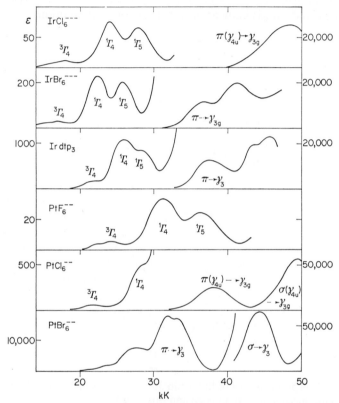

FIG. 8.5. Absorption spectra of low-spin $5d^6$ complexes of Ir(III) and Pt(IV). The spectrum of PtF_6^{--} was kindly communicated by Dr. Perros.

Cr dtp$_3$ has $\Delta=14.4$ kK, showing an earlier position of the dtp$^-$, diethyldi-thiophosphate $(C_2H_5O)_2PS_2^-$ in the spectrochemical series. The octahedron CrS_6 is slightly distorted and produces dichroitic effects as in the tris-oxalate. The very small distance between $^4\Gamma_5$ and $a^4\Gamma_4$ shows an unusually pronounced nephelauxetic effect, $B=410$ K. The spin-forbidden transitions to $^2\Gamma_3$ and $^2\Gamma_4$ can be perceived as weak shoulders at 13.1 and 13.6 kK. Hence, the nephelauxetic effect is comparatively less pronounced in the γ_5^3 configuration, which may be related to eqs. (4.28) and (4.32) or to a complete breakdown of the expanded radial function model. The Laporte-allowed bands at 31.8 and

35.7 kK are presumably caused by electron transfer from the strongly reducing dtp$^-$ to the γ_5 and γ_3 subshells.

MnF$_6$$^{--}$ has $\Delta=21.75$ kK. $^4\Gamma_5$ and a$^4\Gamma_4$ indicate $B=600$ K, whereas gaseous Mn^{+4} has $B=1065$ K. The similar CrF$_6$$^{---}$ has a much smaller nephelauxetic effect ($B=820$ K). The weak, spin-forbidden transitions to $^2\Gamma_3$ and $^2\Gamma_4$ occur around 16.3 kK (15.7 and 16.4 kK in CrF$_6$$^{---}$). Only a reflection spectrum of K$_2$MnF$_6$ is known; the ion decomposes in solution.

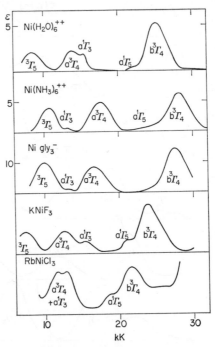

FIG. 8.6. Absorption spectra of high-spin 3d^8 complexes of Ni(II). The spectrum of RbNiCl$_3$ was measured by Asmussen and Bostrup (1957).

MoCl$_6$$^{---}$ occurs in very strong HCl solutions of Mo(III) and was first discussed by Hartmann and Schmidt (1957). $^2\Gamma_3$ and $^2\Gamma_4$ now occur at 9.7 kK and $^2\Gamma_5$ of $\gamma_5{}^3$ at 14.8 kK, showing much smaller parameters of interelectronic repulsion parameters in the 4d group compared to the analogous 3d complexes. $\Delta=19.2$ kK (larger than in CrCl$_3$, 13.8 kK) and the distance between $^4\Gamma_5$ and a$^4\Gamma_4$ indicating $B=440$ K (extrapolated value in gaseous Mo^{+3} 610 K). A Laporte-allowed electron transfer band $\pi^{24}\gamma_5{}^3\rightarrow\pi^{23}\gamma_5{}^4$ occurs at 45.3 kK.

ReCl$_6$$^{--}$ has $^2\Gamma_3$ and $^2\Gamma_4$ at 9.4 kK and $^2\Gamma_5$ as two components (the reason for this anomaly will be discussed in Chapter 10 on relativistic effects) with a highly unusual vibrational structure at 14.0 and 15.4 kK. Hence, K(4, 5) is slightly smaller than in MoCl$_6$$^{---}$. Δ is at least 27 kK and is possibly represented by a weak shoulder on the steeply increasing Laporte-allowed electron transfer bands. In the section on low-spin d^5 complexes, we shall closer inspect the nature of the $\pi \rightarrow \gamma_5$ transitions observed at 33.3, 35.6, and 39.1 kK.

IrF$_6$ have transitions to $^2\Gamma_3$ and $^2\Gamma_4$ at 6.4 and 9.0 kK and to $^2\Gamma_5$ (again separated for relativistic reasons) at 12.6 and 15.8 kK, which were identified by Moffitt, Goodman, Fred, and Weinstock (1959). Jørgensen (1960) identified the stronger bands at 30, 35.4, and 42.0 kK as $\pi^{24}\gamma_5^3 \rightarrow \pi^{23}\gamma_5^4$ electron transfer bands in close analogy to the three groups of RuCl$_6^{---}$ discussed below. This gaseous molecule shows vibrational structure of most of the absorption bands observed.

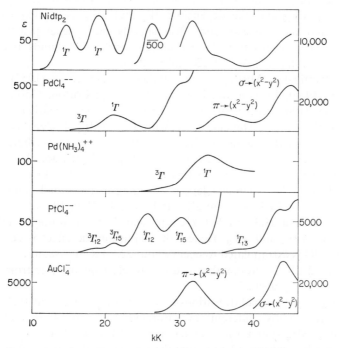

FIG. 8.7. Absorption spectra of low-spin d^8 complexes of Ni(II), Pd(II), Pt(II), and Au(III).

High-spin d^5 complexes. Mn(H$_2$O)$_6^{++}$ is also historically very important, because the close analogy between the absorption spectra of this ion in aqueous solution and of solid MnF$_2$ and KMnF$_3$ measured by Stout (1959, 1960) led Orgel (1955) to conclusions about the correlation of bandwidth and variation of subshell configurations; and to a general belief that the energy levels of the localized entities MnO$_6$ and MnF$_6$ are essentially identical. The transition from $^6\Gamma_1$ to $^4\Gamma_1$ of eq. (4.26) and to a$^4\Gamma_3$ at the same energy, all levels belonging sharply to $\gamma_5^3\gamma_3^2$, occurs as two very narrow and very weak (spin-forbidden) bands at 24.97 and 25.3 kK. The corresponding term difference $^6S - {}^4G$ of $3d^5$ in gaseous Mn^{++} is 26.85 kK. The two broader, but weak, bands at 18.9 and 23.1 kK have $a^4\Gamma_4$ and $a^4\Gamma_5$, predominantly of $\gamma_5{}^4\gamma_3$, as excited levels. The narrow bands at 28.0 and 29.7 kK have $b^4\Gamma_5$ and $b^4\Gamma_3$ as excited levels, and the band at 32.9 kK $b^4\Gamma_4$, all approximately of $\gamma_5{}^3\gamma_3{}^2$, the same subshell configuration of the ground state. As discussed by Jørgensen (1958) and Heidt, Koster, and Johnson (1958), Δ is calculated from the first broad bands to be 8.3 kK, a rather small value.

Solid MnO was studied by Pratt and Coelho (1959). The two broad bands at 16.4 and 20.8 kK and the narrow band at 23.8 kK is a perfect analogy to the hexaaquo ion (the NaCl type of lattice has the environment MnO_6) and must have $a^4\Gamma_4$, $a^4\Gamma_5$, and the degenerate $^4\Gamma_1$ and $a^4\Gamma_3$ as excited levels. Δ is 9.4 kK and the nephelauxetic effect slightly more developed than in the aquo ion. The isostructural MnS is closely similar with bands at 16.7, 19.8, and 22.2 kK, showing $\Delta = 7.1$ kK and $\beta = 0.83$.

The tetrahedral $MnBr_4{}^{--}$ were studied by Jørgensen (1957), Gill and Nyholm (1959), Furlani and Furlani (1961), and Cotton, Goodgame, and Goodgame (1962). Δ is very small, -3.1 kK, and consequently the two levels $a^4\Gamma_4$ and $a^4\Gamma_5$ of $\gamma_3{}^3\gamma_5{}^2$ coincide nearly with $^4\Gamma_1$ and $a^4\Gamma_3$ of $\gamma_3{}^2\gamma_5{}^3$. The shoulder at 21.4 kK and the bands at 22.2 and 23.0 kK must be distributed between these four levels. The three levels $b^4\Gamma_5$, $b^4\Gamma_3$, and $b^4\Gamma_4$ are also difficult to assign individually to the three bands at 25.9, 26.7, and 27.7 kK.

$Fe(H_2O)_6{}^{+++}$ has a much larger spreading of the broad bands, Δ being estimated to be 14.2 kK from $a^4\Gamma_4$ at 12.6 and $a^4\Gamma_5$ at 18.5 kK, whereas the narrow bands at 24.3 and 24.6 kK represent the intra-subshell configuration transition to $^4\Gamma_1$ and $a^4\Gamma_3$. Hence, the nephelauxetic effect is conspicuous, since $^6S - {}^4G$ is extrapolated to occur about 32.8 kK in gaseous Fe^{+3}. A strong band at 42 kK is presumably caused by electron transfer from the H_2O ligands to the γ_5 subshell.

Fe $ox_3{}^{---}$ with broad transitions to $a^4\Gamma_4$ at 10.7 and $a^4\Gamma_5$ at 15.2 kK (these bands are slightly different in saturated, aqueous K_2ox and in solid $K_3[Fe\ ox_3]$, $3H_2O$) and a narrow band at 22.1 kK closely corresponds to the hexa-aquo ion, Δ being 13.6 kK and the nephelauxetic ratio $\beta = 0.68$ (whereas it is 0.78 in $FeF_6{}^{---}$).

$FeCl_4{}^-$ has broad bands at 15.6 and 16.3 kK which can be ascribed to $a^4\Gamma_4$ and $a^4\Gamma_5$ of $\gamma_3{}^3\gamma_5{}^2$ and a narrow peak at 18.8 kK caused by $^4\Gamma_1$ and/or $a^4\Gamma_3$ of $\gamma_3{}^2\gamma_5{}^3$. Two further, weak bands are observed at 20.1 and 22.4 kK. Δ is roughly -5 kK and $\beta = 0.58$. The strong bands at 27.3, 31.9, and 41.1 kK must be caused by electron transfer from filled MO to the half-filled sub-shells, but have not been identified in detail.

Low-spin d^5 complexes. $RuCl_6{}^{---}$, when pure, has a weak band at 19.0 kK which must be one of the many possible $\gamma_5{}^5\ {}^2\Gamma_5 \rightarrow \gamma_5{}^4\gamma_3\ {}^2\Gamma_n$ transitions. The shoulder at 25.6 kK and the two strong peaks at 28.7 and 32.4 kK are electron transfer bands, identified by Jørgensen (1959) as $\pi^{24}\gamma_5^5 \to \pi^{23}\gamma_5^6$ transitions. The symmetry types of the three sets of MO involved seem to be even γ_4, odd γ_5, and odd γ_4, respectively [cf. eq. (4.10)]. The broad, much stronger band at 43.6 kK must be caused by odd γ_4 (π+some σ character)$\to\gamma_3$, being a transition from 2 odd γ_4 to 2 even γ_3 in eq. (4.10).

$Ru(NH_3)_5Cl^{++}$ was reported by Hartmann and Buschbeck (1957). It is very interesting that the first strong band, at 30.5 kK, occurs at nearly the same wavenumber as of $RuCl_6^{---}$, showing the nearly constant difference in optical electronegativity between the π electrons of Cl and the γ_5 subshell of Ru(III) in the two cases. The weaker band at 38.5 kK may be one of the $\gamma_5^5 \to \gamma_5^4\gamma_3$ transitions. Similar behaviour is observed by Cady and Connick (1958) of $Ru(H_2O)_5 Cl^{++}$ and the two isomers of $Ru(H_2O)_4Cl_2^+$.

$OsCl_6^{---}$ (which is only stable in strong HCl, Jørgensen, 1959) has the electron transfer bands in exactly the same pattern as $RuCl_6^{---}$, but at 7 kK higher wavenumber, i.e. the optical electronegativity of the γ_5 subshell of Os(III) is 0.23 unit lower than of Ru(III) (if the spin-pairing energy correction, $-4/3\ D$, is the same in the two cases). The weak shoulder at 22.2 kK is presumably a $\gamma_5^5 \to \gamma_5^4\gamma_3$ transition.

$IrCl_6^{--}$ has again the same pattern of electron transfer bands, but at 8 kK *lower* energy than of $RuCl_6^{---}$, indicating an optical electronegativity 0.27 unit higher of Ir(IV). The electron transfer bands are particularly easy to understand in low-spin d^5 systems, where the excited states have a closed subshell γ_5^6, but actually the same pattern is found in $5d^4$ systems such as $OsCl_6^{--}$ (Jørgensen, 1959; also an observation by Garner, 1954) and in the $5d^3$ system IrF_6 mentioned above. One might imagine, as pointed out by Dr. R. Englman, that dynamic Jahn-Teller effects are important for the structure of the $\pi^{23}\gamma_5^6$ group, as well as relativistic effects originating in the 6p shell of symmetry type odd γ_4 in the central atom. However, the main feature seems to be the three different MO sets mentioned above. High-pressure effects (producing a red shift of all the bands) have been measured by Balchan and Drickamer (1961), and solvent effects and shifts by formation of solid salts by Jørgensen (1961, 1962). The isoelectronic, dark-green $RhCl_6^{--}$ has been studied in Cs_2RhCl_6. The weak band of $IrCl_6^{--}$ at 27.8 kK is possibly a $\gamma_5^5 \to \gamma_5^4\gamma_3$ transition, whereas the band at 32.7 kK seems a little too strong for such an explanation and probably is the σ (odd γ_4)$\to\gamma_5$ transition expected there. The strong, broad band at 43.1 kK is the π (odd γ_4)$\to\gamma_3$ as discussed above for $RuCl_6^{---}$, the energy difference Δ between the subshells γ_5 and γ_3 being larger in $IrCl_6^{--}$.

$IrBr_6^{--}$ has a very complicated structure of seven electron transfer bands in the visible. It is necessary to take relativistic effects of intermediate coupling in the $\pi^{23}\gamma_5^6$ group into account (Jørgensen, 1959). Solvent effects have also been studied (1962). The weak shoulder $\sim$24 kK may be $\gamma_5 \to \gamma_3$ or $\sigma \to \gamma_5$. The two broad bands at 31.5 and 37.0 kK represent the $\pi \to \gamma_3$ transitions. The reason for the splitting in two components is relativistic effects in the bromine ligands, splitting the original energy levels and also redistributing the character of odd γ_4 on two different orbital energies. Dr. J. S. Brinen has recently measured the $\sigma \to \gamma_3$ band at 47.9 kK.

Low-spin d^6 complexes. $Co(NH_3)_6^{+++}$ has two spin-allowed, Laporte-forbidden, rather broad bands at 21.2 and 29.6 kK, corresponding to transitions from the ground state $^1\Gamma_1$ (predominantly γ_5^6) to the two levels $^1\Gamma_4$ and $^1\Gamma_5$ (mainly of $\gamma_5^5\gamma_3$), separated by the energy difference $16B - 84B^2/\Delta$, whereas the energy difference between $^1\Gamma_1$ and $^1\Gamma_4$ is $\Delta - 4B + 86B^2/\Delta$, assuming $C = 4B$. The calculations by Schäffer have actually given the empirical parameters $\Delta = 22.9$ kK and $B = 615$ K (extrapolated for gaseous Co^{+3} 1100 K). The spin-forbidden transition to $^3\Gamma_4$ of $\gamma_5^5\gamma_3$ was reported by Jørgensen (1954), as a broad band at 13.0 kK which is 250 times less intense than the spin-allowed transitions. The broad, very intense band ~ 50 kK is caused by electron transfer $\sigma NH_3 \to \gamma_3$. Linhard and Weigel (1951) studied these electron transfer bands and reported the "tunnelling" effect in ion pairs such as $Co(NH_3)_6^{+++}, I^-$ having a broad band already at 37 kK due to electron transfer from the iodide ion at larger distance. The separation effect results in the wavenumber not being as low as in the complex $Co(NH_3)_5 I^{++}$ discussed below. $Co(NH_3)_5 Cl^{++}$ has a very weak, spin-forbidden band to $^3\Gamma_4$ at 11.4 kK studied by Linhard and Weigel (1957). The transition to $^1\Gamma_4$ is split into two, a maximum at 18.7 kK (doubly degenerate, according to dichroitic experiments) and a shoulder at 21.4 kK. This is caused by the deviation from octahedral symmetry. On the other hand, the transition to $^1\Gamma_5$ at 27.5 kK is not markedly split. Griffith and Orgel (1956) and Yamatera (1958) pointed out that this behaviour is not compatible with any electrostatic ligand field model, but can be easily understood by means of the σ- and π-antibonding effects of the ligands. The comparatively weak electron transfer band at 37.1 kK and the thirty times stronger band at 43.9 kK were discussed by Linhard and Weigel (1951) and were given their theoretical interpretation by Orgel (1956) and Yamatera (1960) as being caused by the transfer of a π and a σ electron, respectively, from the halogen atom at the z axis to the empty $(2z^2 - x^2 - y^2)$ orbital of the central atom.

$Co(NH_3)_5 I^{++}$ has spin-forbidden bands at 10.7 and 13.8 kK which are about a third as strong as the spin-allowed band at 17.2 kK (Linhard and Weigel, 1957). This is caused by relativistic effects in the heavy iodine atom. The rest of the $\gamma_5^5\gamma_3$ levels are covered by the electron transfer bands at 26.1 and 34.9 kK. The relative intensity distribution between these two bands, 1 to 6, is higher than in the chloro-pentammine, again due to relativistic effects explained by Yamatera (1960).

$Rh(NH_3)_6^{+++}$ has a larger Δ, 34.1 kK, than the Co(III) complex, and a smaller $B = 430$ K, though the nephelauxetic ratio $\beta = 0.60$ (Rh^{+3} extrapol. 720 K) is slightly larger. The transitions from $^1\Gamma_1$ to $^1\Gamma_4$ and $^1\Gamma_5$ occur at 32.7

and 39.1 kK. The electron transfer bands must occur outside the measured range well above 50 kK (Jørgensen, 1956).

$RhCl_6^{---}$ has a smaller Δ, 20.4 kK, than the hexammine, and a smaller $B=350$ K ($\beta=0.49$). The transitions to $^1\Gamma_4$ and $^1\Gamma_5$ occur at 19.3 and 24.3 kK. The spin-forbidden transition to $^3\Gamma_4$ can be observed as a very weak shoulder at 14.7 kK, some forty times weaker than the transition to $^1\Gamma_4$. The electron transfer band at 39.2 kK is the $\pi(+$ a little σ) odd $\gamma_4 \rightarrow \gamma_3$ found at 43.6 kK in $RuCl_6^{---}$, whereas, by analogy to $PtBr_6^{--}$, the even stronger σ(odd γ_4)$\rightarrow \gamma_3$ can be expected around 55 kK. The ion slowly aquates if held at lower HCl concentrations than some 6 Molar.

$RhBr_6^{---}$ is even more unstable and can only be measured in very strong alkali metal bromide solutions. $\Delta=19.0$ kK and $B=290$ K ($\beta=0.40$) can be found from the spin-allowed transitions to $^1\Gamma_4$ and $^1\Gamma_5$ at 18.1 and 22.2 (a shoulder) kK. The two electron transfer bands at 30.1 and 33.9 kK are both caused by $\pi \rightarrow \gamma_3$ as discussed above for $IrBr_6^{---}$. Contrary to the situation in Ru(III) complexes, the electron transfer band in halidepentammine Rh(III) occurs at much higher wavenumber than in the hexahalides (the π band in $Rh(NH_3)_5Br^{++}$ at 40.6 kK, the σ around 50 kK; the π band in $Rh(NH_3)_5I^{++}$ at 36.0 and the σ band at 44.3 kK) since the accepting, empty orbital increases in energy as a function of increasing Δ in the mixed ammonia complexes.

$Rh\,dtp_3=Rh(S_2P(OC_2H_5)_2)_3$ has $\Delta=22.2$ kK and $B=210$ K, corresponding to the unusual low nephelauxetic ratio $\beta=0.29$. The transitions to $^1\Gamma_4$ and $^1\Gamma_5$ occur at 21.3 and 24.4 kK. The strong band at 31.2 kK is presumably due to $\pi \rightarrow \gamma_3$ electron transfer, whereas the other bands such as a shoulder at 36.6 kK and a maximum at 38.8 kK may be caused by internal transitions in the ligands. It is a quite common phenomenon that such transitions are somewhat shifted by the presence of the central ion, and they are observed in most ligands having bond orders differing from 1, such as NO_2^-, SO_3^{--}, acetylacetonate, aromatic compounds, etc.

$IrCl_6^{---}$ has $\Delta=25.0$ kK (larger than of $RhCl_6^{---}$) and $B=300$ K (B is extrapolated to be 660 K in gaseous Ir^{+3}), though relativistic effects may make the direct determination of B difficult, as pointed out by Griffith (1960). The spin-forbidden band at 17.9 kK (shoulder at 16.3 kK) is only eight times weaker than the spin-allowed transitions to $^1\Gamma_4$ at 24.1 and $^1\Gamma_5$ at 28.1 kK (Jørgensen, 1956). The broad, strong electron transfer band at 48.5 is caused by $\pi(+$ a little σ) odd $\gamma_4 \rightarrow \gamma_3$.

$IrBr_6^{---}$ has $\Delta=23.1$ kK and $B=250$ K. The spin-forbidden band at 16.8 kK has $^3\Gamma_4$ as excited level, whereas 22.4 and 25.8 kK have $^1\Gamma_4$ and $^1\Gamma_5$. The electron transfer transition $\pi \rightarrow \gamma_3$ gives rise to two bands, at 36.8 and 41.1 kK, as explained above in the analogous case of $RhBr_6^{---}$.

$Ir\,dtp_3$ has $\Delta=26.6$ kK and $B=160$ K. The spin-forbidden band is observed at 21.2 kK, only four times weaker than the two spin-allowed bands at 26.2 and 28.6 kK. The high band at 37.4 kK is presumably caused by electron transfer, and with regard to the shoulder at 43.1 and maximum at 45.7 kK, similar remarks may be made as in the case of Rhdtp$_3$.

PtF$_6^{--}$ has $\Delta=33.0$ kK and $B=380$ K (estimated B for gaseous Pt^{+4} 720 K). Professor T. Perros was so kind as to inform me about the spectrum, showing a spin-forbidden transition at 24.4 kK (shoulder at 22.5 kK) and $^1\Gamma_4$ at 31.4 and $^1\Gamma_5$ at 36.4 kK with no trace of electron transfer bands in the measured range below 45 kK. Consequently, the Laporte-forbidden transitions are much weaker than is usual for low-spin d^6 complexes.

PtCl$_6^{--}$ has the spin-forbidden transition at 22.1 kK and the transition to $^1\Gamma_4$ is represented by a shoulder at 28.3 kK. The very strong, broad band at 38.2 kK is caused by $\pi(+$ a little $\sigma)$ odd $\gamma_4 \to \gamma_3$ and is followed by a $\sigma \to \gamma_3$ band now observed by Brinen at 49.7 kK.

PtBr$_6^{--}$ has a more complicated electron transfer spectrum with bands at 27.5, 31.8, and 33.3 kK, corresponding to the structure found in the Rh(III) and Ir(III) hexabromides, and an unusually strong band at 44.2 kK which must be ascribed to σ(odd $\gamma_4) \to \gamma_3$. This type of transition has only been identified in OsI$_6^{--}$, PdCl$_6^{--}$, PtBr$_6^{--}$, and PtI$_6^{--}$ (Jørgensen, 1959) and in OsBr$_6^{--}$, IrBr$_6^{--}$, and PtCl$_6^{--}$ (Brinen and Jørgensen), but can probably be found in other complexes when the measurements are extended to the vacuo ultraviolet above 50 kK.

High-spin d^8 complexes. Ni(H$_2$O)$_6^{++}$ is one of the most studied transition group ions. The energy level scheme is the inverted image of the octahedral d^2 systems. $^3\Gamma_2$ of $\gamma_5^6\gamma_3^2$ is the ground state, followed by $^3\Gamma_5$ of $\gamma_5^5\gamma_3^3$ at exactly the distance Δ in the expanded radial function model. The two terms a$^3\Gamma_4$ and b$^3\Gamma_4$ have not the pure subshell configurations $\gamma_5^5\gamma_3^3$ and $\gamma_5^4\gamma_3^4$, but interact with a nondiagonal element equivalent to $6B$. Actually, $B=940$ K indicate $\beta=0.89$ since gaseous Ni^{++} has $B=1060$ K. In the nickel (II) hexaaquo ion, there is no doubt that the first band at 8.5 kK has $^3\Gamma_5$ as excited level and the third spin-allowed band at 25.3 kK has b$^3\Gamma_4$. The situation is a little more complicated in the case of the maximum at 13.8 kK and the narrow secondary maximum at 15.2 kK. There has been a long controversy between authors who believe that the structure can be explained by first-order relativistic effects in a$^3\Gamma_4$ alone, and authors, like the present one, who believe that the spin-forbidden transition to $^1\Gamma_3$, belonging approximately to the same subshell configuration $\gamma_5^6\gamma_3^2$ as the ground state, must be very close to a$^3\Gamma_4$ and cause the narrow maximum. However, as pointed out recently by Griffith and other workers, there is no doubt that the final result, when $^1\Gamma_3$ and a$^3\Gamma_4$ coincide neglecting relativistic effects, is a superposition of two narrow components on a broad third band, and showing a separation twice the nondiagonal element of intermediate coupling. Low-temperature and crystalline-solid effects have been observed (Bostrup and Jørgensen, 1957, Holmes and McClure, 1957) which are remarkably large and might possibly be related to changes of the oxygen co-ordination from tetrahedral to trigonal. The weak band at 22.0 kK can be ascribed to $^1\Gamma_5$ of $\gamma_5{}^5\gamma_3{}^3$, whereas Piper and Koertge (1960) have shown that the very weak band at 18.4 kK is caused by co-excitation of O−H stretching frequencies on the $^1\Gamma_3$ at 15.2 kK.

$Ni(NH_3)_6{}^{++}$ has $^3\Gamma_5$ at 10.8 kK, which hence illustrates Δ. The two other spin-allowed transitions at 17.5 and 28.2 kK are ascribed to $a^3\Gamma_4$ and $b^3\Gamma_4$, indicating $B=890$ K and $\beta=0.84$. The spin-forbidden transition to $^1\Gamma_3$ is distinct as a narrow, weak band at 13.15 kK, indicating 2 K(1, 3) of eq. (4.24). No electron transfer bands are known of this ion, and in general the optical electronegativity of high-spin Ni(II) is only known from tetrahedral complexes such as $NiI_4{}^{--}$ and $NiCl_4{}^{--}$. The hexammine ion is only stable in concentrated aqueous ammonia; or in solid salts such as $Ni(NH_3)_6Br_2$ measured by Bostrup and Jørgensen (1957). High-pressure measurements, indicating highly increasing Δ at some 100,000 atmospheres and slightly decreasing B have been made by Stephens and Drickamer (1961).

Ni $gly_3{}^-$ containing the glycinate ion $NH_2CH_2COO^-$ has not octahedral symmetry, strictly speaking. However, the absorption spectrum is hardly distinguishable from an octahedral environment N_3O_3, having $^3\Gamma_5$ (and hence Δ) at 10.1 kK, the weak, narrow band $^1\Gamma_3$ at 13.1, and the two spin-allowed $a^3\Gamma_4$ and $b^3\Gamma_4$ at 16.6 and 27.6 kK. A long series of amine and amino-acid complexes of nickel (II) were discussed by Jørgensen (1955, 1956) and the variation of $^1\Gamma_3$ and of B was included in the original evidence for the nephelauxetic series.

$KNiF_3$ is an example of Ni(II) in octahedral microsymmetry in a crystal. Among other examples which have been frequently studied in the literature may be mentioned NiO, Ni(II) substituting in MgO, or in $MgTiO_3$. Pappalardo, Wood, and Linares (1961) make comparisons between these cases and tetrahedral microsymmetry (occurring in ZnO or $MgAl_2O_4$) as also, on a more empirical basis, Schmitz-DuMont, Gössling, and Brokopf (1959), whereas Schmitz-DuMont and Reinen (1959) studied synthetic compounds containing Cr_2O_3 and Neuhaus (1960) Cr(III) in minerals. The hexafluoride environment produces $^3\Gamma_5$ at 7.2 kK, $a^3\Gamma_4$ at 12.5 kK, and $b^3\Gamma_4$ at 23.7 kK, corresponding to a very weak nephelauxetic effect ($B=960$ K). The first spin-forbidden transition $^1\Gamma_3$ is very clearly separated at 15.3 kK, but here on the *blue* side of $a^3\Gamma_4$. Another weak band at 21.0 kK belongs to $^1\Gamma_5$ of $\gamma_5{}^5\gamma_3{}^3$.

$RbNiCl_3$ is a perovskite like the preceding compound and was studied by Asmussen and Bostrup (1957). The first band has not been observed, but Δ can be calculated from the other band positions to be approximately 7.2 kK. The spin-forbidden transitions to $^1\Gamma_3$ (at 11.5 kK) and to $^1\Gamma_5$ (at 18.6 kK) are close to the spin-allowed transitions to $a^3\Gamma_4$(11.5 kK) and $b^3\Gamma_4$(21.6 kK) and are therefore relatively intense due to intermixing from relativistic effects, The nephelauxetic effect is very pronounced; B is only 760 K ($\beta=0.72$). Comparable features appear in the bromides $MNiBr_3$ with $NiBr_6$ environment.

Low-spin d^8 *systems.* Square-planar $Nidtp_2 = Ni(S_2P(OC_2H_5)_2)_2$ is a good example of the tetragonal symmetry $\gamma_{t1}^2\gamma_{t5}^4\gamma_{t4}^2$ [cf. eq. (4.20)]. The band at 14.5 kK is presumably caused by a jump of a γ_{t4} electron to the empty γ_{t3} orbital and the band at 19.1 kK to $\gamma_{t5} \rightarrow \gamma_{t3}$. However, as Dr. D. Leussing has pointed out to me, the π-antibonding effects may be stronger on γ_{t5}, rather producing the first absorption band. The much stronger band at 26.1 kK may or may not be due to $\gamma_{t1} \rightarrow \gamma_{t3}$. On the other hand, the even much higher band at 31.6 kK is presumably electron transfer (ligands)$\rightarrow \gamma_{t3}$. The band at 43.9 kK may be caused by internal ligand transitions. The spectrum was discussed by the present writer (1962).

$PdCl_4^{--}$ has a similar spectrum; the broad and somewhat irregular band at 21.1 kK is known from dichroitic experiments to consist of at least two transitions, $\gamma_{t4} \rightarrow \gamma_{t3}$ and $\gamma_{t5} \rightarrow \gamma_{t3}$. The corresponding spin-forbidden, thirty times weaker, band is observed at 16.2 kK. The shoulder at 29.8 kK may possibly be the $\gamma_{t1} \rightarrow \gamma_{t3}$, whereas the two very strong bands at 35.8 and 44.9 kK probably are $\pi \rightarrow \gamma_{t3}$ and $\sigma \rightarrow \gamma_{t3}$ electron transfer. (They occur at 30.1 and 40.5 kK in $PdBr_4^{--}$.)

$Pd(NH_3)_4^{++}$ has a spin-forbidden band at 26.8 kK and a single spin-allowed band at 33.8 kK. If only σ-antibonding effects are taken into account in MO theory, the other, occupied, four orbitals of the 4d shell should remain nearly degenerate, and hence, only one band is expected. On the other hand, in tetrahalides or in sulphur-containing complexes, γ_{t5} is weakly and γ_{t4} strongly (about twice as much) π-antibonding.

$PtCl_4^{--}$ was interpreted along these lines by Chatt, Gamlen, and Orgel (1958). Two spin-forbidden transitions are represented by a shoulder at 18.2 and a maximum at 21.15 kK and are now only four times weaker than the corresponding spin-allowed transitions at 25.7 kK ($\gamma_{t4} \rightarrow \gamma_{t3}$) and 30.3 kK ($\gamma_{t5} \rightarrow \gamma_{t3}$). The shoulder at 37.6 kK is the last internal transition, $\gamma_{t1} \rightarrow \gamma_{t3}$. The two strong bands at 43.1 and 46.1 kK may either be electron transfer $\pi \rightarrow \gamma_{t3}$ or $5d \rightarrow 6p(\gamma_{t2})$ transitions to the empty p orbital which is not σ-antibonding.

$AuCl_4^-$ has a very dubious shoulder at 26.0 kK which might indicate a spin-forbidden transition. Anyhow, the MO energy differences in the partly filled shell must be rather large. The two strong bands at 31.8 and 44.1 kK seem to be $\pi \rightarrow \gamma_{t3}$ and $\sigma \rightarrow \gamma_{t3}$ electron transfer.

It is seen from the previous sections that identifications of absorption bands frequently are uncertain, and in a few cases have been much disputed. A quite general impression remains: the utility of the MO classification is not that it is possible to start a description *a priori* for a definite individual complex, say $RhCl_6^{---}$. The great advantage is that a unified description is obtained by comparison and analogy, *by induction from experimental values in a large series of related molecules.* This was already the general tendency in

MO description of the energy levels of cyclic molecules (see a review by Mason, 1961), but the theory of transition group compounds has a much wider scope: all the intermediate cases between nearly pure ionic bonding in $KMnF_3$ and $Mn(H_2O)_6^{++}$ on one side to quite pronounced covalent character in IrF_6 and $PtBr_6^{--}$ are covered by the same description, and the energy levels develop according to a continuous scheme in this range, not according to a black and white separation in ionic and covalent complexes.

The general MO theory (or possibly its approximation in LCAO, if qualitative understanding rather than a fictive numerical agreement is desired) is capable of such a classification. This is not true for the two special cases: the electrostatic model, where Δ cannot be determined and where the nephelauxetic effect is neglected, but which, of course, is isomorphous or more exactly homomorphous with general MO theory and therefore yields several valid results of this group-theoretical reason; and the hybridization theory which is entirely in disagreement with the excited levels observed. The fall of the latter theory has indeed been so loud that a general, and it seems well-founded, suspicion can be raised against valence-bond descriptions of excited states.

It may be asked whether the classification of energy levels of transition group complexes also involves some evidence about the symmetry types S, Γ_n of the excited levels. It must be answered that, at present, by far the most important evidence is built on order of energy alone, as expressed, for instance, in the Tanabe-Sugano diagrams given in Fig. 4.3. Measurements of crystals which are not cubic, i.e. which are anisotropic, can reveal important effects of dichroism in polarized light. The interpretation of such phenomena have been reviewed by McClure (reference in Chapter 4). However, they have only been of decisive influence in a very few cases as yet. The reason is the same as with application of selection rules for symmetry-forbidden transitions: one always finds an excuse for the unexpected exceptions.

However, one should not feel that arguments based on distribution of energy levels alone are necessarily extremely weak. The spectroscopy of transition group complexes, and, in general, of simpler polyatomic molecules, is today much in the same situation as was atomic spectroscopy in the years 1920 to 1930: it is possible to find the number of low-lying energy levels, having different symmetry types, from a consideration of well-defined configurations; and on the other hand, it is evident that calculations *a priori* are practically impossible at present, and that the actual wavefunctions are *not* well-defined configurations.

Atomic spectroscopists found the main structure of atomic energy levels by induction from empirical facts and really were not helped very much by the new quantum mechanics which then offered a rationalization of the data already known. Molecular physicists may very well today harvest the same experience.

REFERENCES

Asmussen, R. W., and Bostrup, O. (1957), *Acta Chem. Scand.*, **11**, 745.
Balchan, A. S., and Drickamer, H. G. (1961), *J. Chem. Phys.*, **35**, 356.
Bostrup, O., and Jørgensen, C. K. (1957), *Acta Chem. Scand.*, **11**, 1223.
Cady, H. H., and Connick, R. E. (1958), *J. Am. Chem. Soc.*, **80**, 2646.
Chatt, J., Gamlen, G. A., and Orgel, L. E. (1958), *J. Chem. Soc.*, 486.
Cotton, F. A., Goodgame, D. M. L., and Goodgame, M. (1962), *J. Am. Chem. Soc.* **84**, 167.
Finkelstein, R., and Van Vleck, J. H. (1940), *J. Chem. Phys.*, **8**, 790.
Furlani, C., and Furlani, A. (1961), *J. Inorg. Nucl. Chem.*, **19**, 51.
Gill, N. S., and Nyholm, R. S. (1959), *J. Chem. Soc.*, 3997.
Griffith, J. S., and Orgel, L. E. (1956), *J. Chem. Soc.*, 4981.
Griffith, J. S. (1960), *Trans. Faraday Soc.*, **56**, 193.
Hartmann, H., and Buschbeck, C. (1957), *Z. physik. Chem.*, **11**, 120.
Hartmann, H., and Schmidt, H. J. (1957), *Z. physik. Chem.*, **11**, 234.
Heidt, L. J., Koster, G. F., and Johnson, A. M. (1958), *J. Am. Chem. Soc.*, **80**, 6471.
Holmes, O. G., and McClure, D. S. (1957), *J. Chem. Phys.*, **26**, 1686.
Jørgensen, C. K. (1954), *Acta Chem. Scand.*, **8**, 1502, (Cr(III), Mn(II), Co(III).)
Jørgensen, C. K. (1955), *Acta Chem. Scand.*, **9**, 1362; (1956), **10**, 887, (Ni(II), Cu(II)).
Jørgensen, C. K. (1956), *Acta Chem. Scand.*, **10**, 500; 518. (Rh(III), Ir(III), Ru(III), Pt(IV)).
Jørgensen, C. K. (1957), *Acta Chem. Scand.*, **11**, 53. (Mn(II)).
Jørgensen, C. K. (1958), *Discuss. Faraday Soc.*, **26**, 110. (Mn(II), Fe(III)).
Jørgensen, C. K. (1958), *Acta Chem. Scand.*, **12**, 1539. (Mn(IV)).
Jørgensen, C. K. (1959), *Mol. Phys.*, **2**. 309. (Ru(III), Rh(III), Pd(IV), Os(III), Os(IV), Ir(III), Ir(IV), Pt(IV), Pb(IV)).
Jørgensen, C. K. (1960), *Mol. Phys.*, **3**, 201. (Os(VI), Ir(VI), Pt(VI)).
Jørgensen, C. K. (1961), *Mol. Phys.*, **4**, 231; 235. (Rh(IV), Ir(IV)).
Jørgensen, C. K. (1962), *J. Inorg. Nucl. Chem.*, (Ir(IV) solvent effects).
Jørgensen, C. K. (1962), *J. Inorg. Nucl. Chem.*, (Ni(II), Pd(II), Cr(III), Rh(III), Ir(III) dtp-complexes).
Jørgensen, C. K., and Brinen, J. S. (1962), *Mol. Phys.*, **5**.
Larson, L. L., and Garner, C. S. (1954), *J. Am. Chem. Soc.*, **76**, 2180.
Linhard, M., and Weigel, M. (1951), *Z. anorg. Chem.*, **266**, 73; (1952), **271**, 101.
Linhard, M., and Weigel, M. (1957), *Z. physik. Chem.*, **11**, 308.
Mason, S. F. (1961), *Quart. Rev.*, **15**, 287.
Moffitt, W., Goodman, G. L., Fred, M., and Weinstock, B. (1959), *Mol. Phys.*, **2**, 109.
Neuhaus, A. (1960), *Z. Kristallogr.*, **113**, 195.
Orgel, L. E. (1955), *J. Chem. Phys.*, **23**, 1824.
Orgel, L. E. (1956), "Quelques Problèmes de Chimie Minérale. X. Conseil Solvay", p. 289, Stoops, Bruxelles.
Pappalardo, R., Wood, D. L., and Linares, R. C. (1961), *J. Chem. Phys.*, **35**, 1460.
Piper, T. S., and Koertge, N. (1960), *J. Chem. Phys.*, **32**, 559.
Pratt, G. W., and Coelho, R. (1959), *Phys. Rev.*, **116**, 281.
Schmitz-DuMont, O., Gössling, H., and Brokopf, H. (1959), *Z. anorg, Chem.*, **300**, 159.
Schmitz-DuMont, O., and Reinen, D. (1959), *Z. Elektrochem.*, **63**, 978.
Stephens, D. R., and Drickamer, H. G. (1961), *J. Chem. Phys.*, **34**, 937; (1961), **35**, 429.
Stout, J. W. (1959), *J. Chem. Phys.*, **31**, 709; (1960), **33**, 303.
Yamatera, H. (1958), *Bull. Chem. Soc. Japan.*, **31**, 95.
Yamatera, H. (1960), *J. Inorg. Nucl. Chem.*, **15**, 50.

9. Energy Levels of Crystals

The distribution of energy levels predicted by MO theory for a system containing a few hundred nuclei tends to be excessively complicated. This is the main reason why we have only considered relatively simple molecules such as $RhCl_6^{---}$ and $Ni(NH_3)_6^{++}$ and not polyatomic species common in organic chemistry such as azobenzene or phenanthroline. The number of states of a system constructed from even identical atoms is very large; if we consider a model of q sodium atoms each having zero, one or two electrons in the orbital 3s, the total number of states is much larger than 2^q (the number of states produced by neutral sodium atoms with each one 3s electron) and is the binomial expression in eq. (2.22) for the distribution of q electrons on 2q positions. There is no doubt, however, that, in a small piece of sodium metal, the consideration of one orbital per sodium atom is a rather bad approximation, and one might with larger success consider the infinite number of orbitals available for an electron in free space, perturbed by relatively small, positively charged cores Na^+.

As exposed, among other places, in Seitz's book, the infinite repetition of unit cells in perfect crystals (and not in more or less disordered or amorphous substances) make a very great mathematical simplification possible. It is then feasible to construct the wavefunctions of the system, and also of the orbitals ψ, as products of characteristic functions of each unit cell and of an infinite set of functions related to the translational symmetry of the infinitely extended crystal. In this book, we have restricted ourselves to time-independent solutions of Schrödinger's equation, i.e. the stationary states, and we shall not consider the complications arising from time dependence, the mechanism of radiation and in general, dynamic problems in chemical physics. Hence, we cannot here give a complete discussion of the nature of the wave vector k, which is the (continuously variable) quantum number of the translation group and which essentially describes the wavenumber of the process by which the excitation (i.e. one rather than zero or two electrons in the orbital considered) would move from one unit cell to the next unit cell. For so-called direct optical transitions, the selection rule is that k is the same in the ground and the excited orbital, whereas indirect transitions can be observed in cases where k is changed. The necessary change of momentum is supplied by the vibrational motion of the nuclei of the system, and, in this special case, the quanta of the motion are called "phonons". There is a close analogy between the occurrence of indirect transitions and the beginning breakdown of Laporte's rule and other selection rules in isolated molecules, due to vibronic interaction. If more than one molecule of a given type occurs in the unit cell, the factor group, i.e. the symmetry properties of the unit cell, already induces differences and splitting into more components of the energy levels appropriate to each isolated molecule. This phenomenon is very pronounced in certain organic compounds, such as anthracene, and is called "Davydov splitting". (See McClure's review.) The splitting is usually proportional to the oscillator strength of the transition and strongly dependent on the distance and relative position of the molecules in the unit cell.

If the internuclear distances are much larger than usually occur in the crystal, the interaction between the individual atoms is very weak, and one has essentially an antiferromagnetic coupling, as discussed in Chapter 5, splitting the energy levels to a small extent. The smooth change to the *energy band description*, as outlined above, occurs at smaller internuclear distances, where each atomic orbital energy is smeared out to a broad band, the energy within a band being a fairly complicated function of the wavenumber vector k and determined by the actual potential in the crystal lattice. The Bloch plane-wave functions (later supplemented by orthogonalization on cores close to the nuclei) were obviously tried as a model for metallic crystals, where the electrons form a rather mobile republic, not attached to the individual atomic cores. Obviously, the energy band method, considering the one-electron eigenfunctions in the core field of an infinitely extended, perfect crystal, has the same relation to a more localized description of the energy levels, say, in the unit cell, as the MO theory of a polyatomic molecule has to a localized Heitler-London valency-bond treatment of the constituent atoms.

Hence, it might seem to be inconsistent when the present writer usually prefers a more localized description in crystals rather than the energy band method, i.e. MO theory for translational symmetry; and at the same time defends MO theory in simpler polyatomic molecules against the assumptions of the valency-bond model. We shall shortly see that this is again a question of equivalent orbitals and microsymmetry, of large or small internuclear distances, that is finally of the importance of nondiagonal elements of two-electron operators between different configurations. We may note, as we did in Chapter 6, that the situation of molecules having entirely closed-shell configurations (and hence $S=0$) is special. For such systems, if Ψ can be written as an antisymmetrized determinant, the expressions in localized orbitals ψ or in their linear combinations in the completely filled energy bands are exactly equivalent. This remark has no great practical importance; there is no doubt that a system with as very many excited configurations is not very close to a well-defined configuration.

Experimental confirmation or disagreement with the energy band model can be studied in excited states, where an electron is lacking in an otherwise fully occupied "valency band" and occurs in an otherwise empty "conduction band"; and also in general in systems having positive S such as transition group compounds.

As a qualitative description of electric conductance, the energy band model has had a great success in textbooks. Metals are characterized by having their highest band roughly half occupied (or having two bands overlapping and partly occupied such as 3s and 3p in magnesium metal), whereas typical semi-conductors have a few electrons in the lowest conduction band or a few "holes" left in the highest valency band. Typical isolators such as NaCl have so large a distance between the valency and conduction bands that the former is completely filled and the latter empty. This explanation is also well adapted to another time-dependent process, the energy transfer from one unit cell to another in the crystal. Such a transfer occurs in anthracene crystals, where minute traces of other molecules, say tetracene, may take over energy originally absorbed by the numerous anthracene molecules and radiate their own fluorescence spectrum. It is a very doubtful question at present whether a similar energy transfer occurs in cadmium sulphide; and Varsanyi and Dieke (1959) demonstrated that coloured ions such as Nd(III) or U(III) dispersed in anhydrous $LaCl_3$ only fluoresce in radiation corresponding to their own absorption bands and do not take energy from other ions. On the other hand, Van Uitert (1960), has firmly established that in lanthanide compounds such as the hexa(antipyrine) iodides $[M(C_{11}H_{12}N_2O)_6]I_3$ or in mixed wolframates such as $Ca_{1-2x}Na_xM_xWO_4$, energy absorbed in the main constituents of the lattice, i.e. antipyrine molecules or WO_4 groups "belonging" to a definite, major rare earth, say Gd(III), can be transferred to very minor constituents, say Eu(III) or Tb(III), and radiated in their characteristic emission lines. Quantum mechanics opens rather surprising possibilities for such energy transfer at distance without direct contact between the molecules involved. However, most of these processes have a probability strongly decreasing as a function of increasing distance, and it is not very easy to show that they are indeed realized. One difficulty in the case of strong resonance in fluorescence (as is frequently found in gaseous atoms) is the distinction between scattering of actual light quanta and the more "metachemical diffusion" in the time-dependent wavefunction.

Returning to the case of light absorption in ordered crystals, our thesis is that the excited orbitals frequently, and perhaps in a majority of the cases studied, are fairly localized in a cluster consisting of a few atoms. A closer analysis of this statement from the quantum-chemical point of view shows that here we are talking about second-order density matrices, of the position of the excited orbital *relative* to the hole created in the original orbital. Obviously, we cannot irradiate parts of large samples smaller than the order of magnitude of the wavelength of the light. Hence the part has a radius of some 1,000 atomic radii and a volume corresponding to some 10^9 atoms. Within this small volume, we cannot excite the atoms of a given species selectively, and our wavefunction of the excited state must in all cases be a linear combination of all 10^8 possible excitations, if our atomic species is a tenth of all atoms in the sample. Since the excitation always occurs one or another place in the sample, we may place the origin of our co-ordinate system in one definite unit cell and talk about the extension of the excited orbital inside and outside this particular unit cell. It is recalled that though for our purposes we do not usually need to think of electrons as very small particles (and for reasons to be explained in Chapter 10, we would then ascribe them a radius 137^2 times smaller than a Bohr unit a_0), but only of the square of the wavefunction expressing an electric charge distribution, it is still true that quantum mechanics *may be interpreted* as the theory of probability densities of the behaviour of such very small particles, and hence an optical excitation always produces a change in the electronic density from one point to another. The results of a very great number of such experiments are different, and constitute the difference in electronic (first-order and second-order) densities between the two states.

The alkali metal halides are among the simplest typically ionic crystals and have a series of strong absorption bands in the far ultraviolet which have been much studied in the last thirty-five years. A recent study was made by Eby, Teegarden, and Dutton (1959). Originally, Von Hippel (1936) interpreted the first of these bands in each compound (let us take NaCl) as the electron transfer from a chloride ion to its nearest sodium neighbour, forming two neutral atoms in the configurations $Cl(3p^5)$ and $Na(3s)$. This reaction would take place spontaneously at very large internuclear distances, because the electron affinity A_{Cl} of gaseous Cl atoms is 11 kK smaller than the ionization energy I_{Na} of gaseous Na atoms. At decreasing internuclear distances r, the Madelung potential [assuming nonoverlapping ions, cf. eq. (7.8)] for negative charges $-\alpha/r$ at the chloride positions in the lattice and $+\alpha/r$ at the sodium positions strongly increases the energy of the excited state because the electron is transferred against the intrinsic tendency to charge distribution in the crystal. This positive energy is cancelled to a small extent by the attraction between the hole and the electron, *viz.* $-1/r$ (with energies measured in units of 2 rydbergs) and the final result is

$$A_{Cl} - I_{Na} + (2\alpha - 1)/r \qquad (9.1)$$

giving 92 kK for the actual NaCl crystal. This is not qualitatively out of order, the experimental value being 62 kK, which can be explained away by various polarization effects. The presence of more than one absorption band might be explained by the possibility of electron transfer to next-nearest, third-nearest sodium neighbours, and so on, giving a series with a continuum limit 41 kK higher than indicated by eq. (9.1). However, there is no doubt that this is stressing the electrostatic model too much, and further on, incredibly high wavenumbers for electron transfer are calculated for crystals such as CaF_2 and ThO_2.

Other elements for the understanding of the optical excitation process in halides come from the fact that isolated halide ions in aqueous solution show similar absorption bands at nearly identical wavenumbers. Franck and Scheibe already suggested in 1929 that the reaction here is electron transfer to one acceptor orbital of the solvent, leaving the neutral halogen atom dissolved. As we shall see in Chapter 10, the term ^2P of $5p^5$ of iodine is split some 7.5 kK by relativistic effects, and indeed, I^- in solution or in alkali halide crystals exhibit two bands with this separation.

However, the unique nature of the acceptor orbital in solution, and the fact that, in all cases, the wavenumbers of the first band of a given halide are nearly invariant (contrary to the somewhat lower wavenumbers in gaseous diatomic alkali halide molecules) might indicate that electron transfer is not the whole truth. From the point of view of MO theory, the explanation is fairly simple: the empty 3s orbital of sodium and empty 4s orbital of chlorine have roughly the same energy, when first put into the lattice. Hence, restricted by the conditions of group theory of the same symmetry type γ_n, these orbitals mix. Since the electron originate in a 3p shell of chlorine, we may expand eq. (4.8) around this chlorine atom, and hence we expect the lowest empty MO to have the following symmetry types and approximate composition:

$$
\begin{aligned}
&1 \text{ Even } \gamma_1: \quad (4\text{sCl}) + (3\text{sNa}_6) \\
& \text{Odd } \gamma_4: \quad (4\text{pCl}) + (3\text{sNa}_6) \\
& \text{Even } \gamma_3: \quad (3\text{dCl}) + (3\text{sNa}_6) \\
&2 \text{ Even } \gamma_1: \quad (3\text{sNa}_6) - (4\text{sCl})
\end{aligned}
\tag{9.2}
$$

taking only the six closest sodium neighbours into account. As discussed by Knox and Inchauspé (1959), Griffiths and Symons (1960), and the present writer (1962), we expect the first transition $(3\text{pCl}) \rightarrow (1 \text{ even } \gamma_1)$ to be a mixture of $3\text{p} \rightarrow 4\text{s}$ excitation of the halogen and electron transfer to the sodium neighbours. Obviously, if the neighbour ions are strongly reducing (i.e. transition group ions with high oxidation number), or the solvent has low-lying acceptor orbitals, the transition is predominantly electron transfer, as demonstrated by Kosower, Martin, and Meloche (1957) in the case of substituted pyridinium iodides.

On the other hand, the Mg, Ca, Sr, Ba oxides, sulphides, and selenides crystallizing in the NaCl lattice have first absorption bands (studied by Saum and Hensley, 1959) which seem rather weakly dependent on the chalkogen and hence might be suspected to be $(n\text{p}) \rightarrow (n+1)\text{s}$ excitations of the metalloid atom to a larger extent than electron transfer.

This leads us to the class of typical semiconductors crystallizing in wurtzite or zincblende structures, such as ZnO(27 kK), ZnS(31), ZnSe(22), ZnTe(19), CdS(21), CdSe(15), CdTe(12), GaAs(11), GaSb(5), InAs(3), InSb(1.3), Si(10), and Ge(6). The wavenumbers in parentheses indicate the position of the first strong absorption band, the so-called fundamental absorption band. This is experimentally rather conspicuous, because these materials are usually entirely transparent in the infrared and then, in an interval of a few kK, increase their molar extinction coefficient to above 3000. Since many solid materials are roughly 30 molar, this means that a layer thickness of some 0.0005 mm. is practically opaque. However, there is little doubt that, in analogy to the alkali halides, there are several such strong absorption bands, and the fundamental band (or "absorption edge") is only the first among these.

Semiconductors are characterized by two quantities: the "energy gap" and the mobility (measured in cm^2/v sec) of the positive and negative carriers. The "energy gap" can be determined experimentally rather independently of the theoretical interpretation as the distance between the higher limit of the valence energy band and the lower limit of the first conduction band. In an intrinsically conducting crystal (without too many electron donors or acceptors, traces of other elements), the variation of the conductivity as a function of the absolute temperature T can be described by the Arrhenius equation for activation energies, the conductivity being

$$\sigma = \sigma_0 \exp(-E_a/2kT). \tag{9.3}$$

The thermally determined activation energy E_a for conductivity usually agrees within some 10 per cent with the optically determined energy gap. The mobility which is the main factor determining σ_0 in eq. (9.3) is highly dependent on imperfections (traces of impurities; crystalline defects) and frequently can be increased very strongly by careful preparation of single crystals, whereas the position of the first strong absorption band is much less sensitive to imperfections. (cf. Welker, 1956.)

The agreement between thermally and optically determined E_a values in semiconductors makes it a too simple interpretation to think about the first absorption band solely as a $4p \rightarrow 5s$ excitation in selenium atoms (in ZnSe and CdSe) or possibly as $4p \rightarrow \gamma_3 4d$ excitation in germanium. On the other hand, the simple energy band model is not necessarily an instructive one, as we shall see below.

One must distinguish between an *internal* and an *external* ionization energy in a large crystal. In a crystal, the Einstein photoemission of electrons has a threshold wavenumber, the energy (the "work function") necessary to remove the loosest bound electron to a remote place in empty space with no kinetic energy left. This is strictly comparable to the ionization energy of a smaller molecule. However, in a very large crystal, one may also talk about a lower, internal ionization energy, which can be determined (with some modification, as discussed below) from the threshold wavenumber of *photoconductivity*. This has no direct analogy in a small molecule.

In a molecule consisting of a finite number of atoms, the MO energies form a discrete set having positive values of the external ionization energy, obeying the virial theorem, and a continuous set above the energy of a remote electron outside the molecule having no kinetic energy. The latter state is taken as the zero point of the orbital energy scale. The discrete set is dense just before the ionization limit, due to the existence of the "Rydberg states". This is comparable to the fact mentioned on page 10 that all neutral atoms or positive ions have an infinite number of discrete states, whereas negative monatomic entities may not have it. However, in a very large molecule, such as a crystal, the set of discrete states may become dense in a wide interval below the zero point of energy, as suggested in Fig. 9.1, forming a sort of "conduction band". The reason is the following: if we neglect the one or two atomic layers forming the surface of the crystal, the effective core field $U(x, y, z)$ may be more negative than a given upper limit—U_0 everywhere in the crystal. Consequently, the Schrödinger equation allows solutions in the range of energy between $-U_0$ and 0, *as if* the electrons were free to move inside a box, i.e. in the inner part of the crystal, but of course not allowed to move out in empty space. Assuming that the virial theorem still is valid for this quasi-continuous set of internally ionized states, their energy is distributed in the range $-\frac{1}{2}U_0$ and 0, whereas the discrete set of MO continue below $-\frac{1}{2}U_0$. It might be questioned whether $U(x, y, z)$ is always negative in all crystals. In strongly ionic crystals, such as NaCl or CaF_2, one might expect that the strongly positive (for electrons) Madelung potential at the positions of the positive ions might cancel or exceed the negative potential from the general core attraction at some distance from the nuclei of the positive ions. However, numerical examples seem to show that U usually indeed has a negative, higher limit $-U_0$.

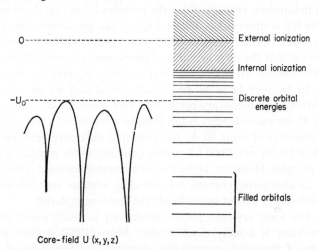

FIG. 9.1. Qualitative representation of the difference between external and internal ionization in solid substances in the case where the core field has an upper limit which is negative, $-U_0$.

Anyhow, it is an experimental fact that the thermal or optical "energy gap" of many semiconductors is some 25 kK lower than their "work function", their external ionization energy. The same is true for a metal such as cadmium, where the internal ionization energy per definition is zero and the external ionization energy some 32 kK. It might possibly be easier understood that a heteroatomic compound has this large difference between the two ionization energies than an element such as germanium has—what is the exact mechanism by which such a neutral crystal can attract electrons with zero energy in empty space? At least, it suggests strongly that the "conduction band" is not built of antibonding MO as frequently implied in textbooks, but rather of nonbonding MO of such symmetry types not participating in the chemical bonding to a large extent. This might explain why carbon in diamond, lacking a low-lying empty 3d shell or other high l values, has a much larger energy gap than germanium or grey tin.

In alkali halides, Taft and Philipp (1957) and Eby, Teegarden, and Dutton (1959) observed both photoemission and photoconductivity above a wavenumber somewhat higher than the first absorption band, and actually in RbI accompanied by a weak absorption peak. One might suspect that the next-lowest empty MO set of each XM_6 unit, the odd γ_4 of eq. (9.2) to which the transition from the halogen p shell is Laporte-forbidden, might in some way contribute to the photoconductivity observed. One might think that it "dissociated" to a very extended, internally ionized MO by a process comparable to auto-ionization of pseudo-discrete states in atoms above the first ionization energy. The experiments on alkali halides are not very easy to interpret; on one hand, the lifetime of the charge carriers created by the far ultraviolet radiation is very short, i.e. the mobility is low; on the other hand, a certain time lag is observed in the buildup of the photoemission, suggesting some destruction of the regular crystal, some atomic rearrangements. It must be emphasized that the identification of photoconductivity with the presence of internally ionized MO otherwise has much to be said for it; an excited entity has to be very large to be directly influenced by an external field gradient. Most experiments are performed with gradients amounting to some 1000 v/cm. If the excited entity is localized in a cluster of a few atoms, it has at most a diameter of some 10 Å. The potential difference between two such points is then 10^{-4}ev or 0.0008 kK and is quite negligible compared to optical excitation energies. However, in the case of electroluminescent semiconductors excited by an alternating current, it is not clear whether very inhomogeneous potential differences do not occur inside the emitting material.

Taking less ionic crystals, photoconductivity is much easier to observe, and the mobility is usually much higher. Moss (1952) studied the photoconductivity of the solid, nonmetallic elements and found in all cases the phenomenon accompanying the absorption bands in the region 8–20 kK. A quite interesting question remains: energy cannot be transferred to the crystal if no absorption occurs. Hence, the threshold limit of internal ionization energy might already be reached before the absorption bands occur. Is the photoconductivity equally probable down in the beginning of the bands, i.e. is the quantum yield constant? Considering the relative uncertainty of the experimental material, the answer is essentially affirmative. Nearly all light absorption in these non-ionic materials induce photoconductivity. This is also true for strongly coloured organic materials, such as crystalline dyes or phthalocyanine complexes. However, the absolute size of the photoconductivity here is very small, and can be compared to the very weak mobilities found in the organic semiconductors (Terenin, 1961). Significant mobilities of organic compounds are at present only known in addition compounds with the photoconductive, nonmetallic elements such as iodine.

One might imagine that the excited states of inorganic semiconductors such as CdS just after the light absorption are still predominantly localized and then dissociate to completely delocalized states due to some mechanism, i.e. slight rearrangements of internuclear distances. It is usually assumed among solid-state physicists that the charge separation effects expressed in eq. (7.25) are very small in typical semiconductors with a large dielectric constant ε because the attraction $-J(a, b)$ between the electron in the orbital b and the hole left in the orbital a is assumed to be divided by ε. The theory of *hydrogenic excitons* assumes that the semiconducting material can be considered as a homogeneous dielectric, and Schrödinger's equation is applied to the exciton, the pair of an electron b and a hole a. One then gets a hydrogenic type of energy levels, proportional to $-1/n^2$ where n is the "principal quantum number", a positive integer, but where the Rydberg constant has the effective value $(1ry)\mu_*/\varepsilon^2$ with the effective mass μ_* in the unit of electron masses. This is usually a rather small quantity, and fine structure within some 2 kK before the fundamental absorption band has been interpreted as such hydrogenic exciton series. Particularly Cu_2O has been very much studied (Gross, 1959; Nikitine, 1959, 1962) and four different exciton series have been found (Grun, Sieskind, and Nikitine, 1961). Whereas in each series, transitions to $n=2, 3, 4, 5$ represent the strongest lines, $n=1$ has been identified as a much weaker electric quadrupole transition. (cf. Elliott, 1961.)

The average radii of the hydrogenic excitons are enormous $n^2\varepsilon\mu_*^{-1}a_0$, and there is indeed evidence found by the Russian physicists that the excitons in Cu_2O may have radii of some 2000 Å. Recently, the far infrared spectra of donor atoms with one loosely bound electron, such as arsenic in germanium crystals, have been interpreted as hydrogenic spectra of the appropriate exciton, again with an effective Rydberg constant below 1 kK.

Remembering the success of this interpretation in these special cases, one may look with some hesitation on a model describing a chemical compound as a homogeneous dielectric and thus neglecting both the variations in the core field $U(x, y, z)$ and the need of orthogonalization on the occupied orbitals.

O.A.M.–E*

Many dangers are let out of Pandora's box when one begins tampering with Coulomb's law, and the assumption of a well-defined, local dielectric constant ε may be a rather dubious one. It may be a good treatment when nearly macroscopic distances are considered, but the formal difficulty remains that one would expect a great number, and probably an infinity, of other, more closely localized, excited states to occur even at lower energy than the first hydrogenic exciton state at $n=1$. The hydrogenic exciton treatment obviously reduces itself *ad absurdum* in a case like NaCl, where the exciton radii would be of the same order of magnitude as the unit cell parameter, but it may be useful in highly polarizable materials, in particular in semiconducting elements. The high polarizability, the high value of ε, and high charge carrier mobility usually are combined in the same materials.

Several of these materials have another, most intriguing property: *phosphorescence*. The distinction between this phenomenon and the fluorescence (where H. Becquerel has already measured the short half-lives in milliseconds or shorter) is not so much a question of length of time as of the detailed mechanism. Though most optical excitations rapidly decay to heat (and possibly infrared radiation, which then is quickly reabsorbed), direct return to the ground state under light emission may be observed. The wavenumber may either be the same, when the potential surface of the excited state has a minimum at nearly the same internuclear distances as the ground state [e.g. the excited $4f^7$ energy levels of Gd(III), or $^2\Gamma_3$ of γ_5^3 of Cr(III) in ruby and other compounds]; or the wavenumber may be smaller (Stokes's rule) if the vibrational energy of the excited electronic state has decayed by "radiationless processes" to values of the internuclear distances where the ground electronic state is vibrationally quite excited [such as the electron transfer to the empty 5f orbital in UO_2^{++}, or $^4\Gamma_4$ of $\gamma_3^3\gamma_5^2$ of $MnBr_4^{--}$ and many other tetrahedral Mn(II) compounds, or $4f \rightarrow 5d$ of Ce(III), or $6s \rightarrow 6p$ of Tl(I) and Pb(II) complexes]. In addition, a smaller wavenumber may be emitted when less excited states rather than the ground state are arrived at by the fluorescence [e.g. $4f^6$ levels of Sm(II) and Eu(III) and $4f^8$ levels of Tb(III)]. In most cases, only one excited state is able to fluoresce; it is well above the other states below and usually has a lower value of the total spin S than the ground state (the latter situation is less common in organic compounds, where triplet $\rightarrow$ singlet transitions only occur under special circumstances and usually have so long half-lives that they are named phosphorescence). Very frequently, higher states can take up the energy and decay without radiation to the fluorescent state. There is not a clear-cut difference between fluorescence (a given atom or at least a given complex taking up radiation and then radiating) and the phosphorescence mechanism discussed below. Thus, an organic ligand bound to a transition group ion may take up energy which is then radiated as the characteristic internal transitions in the partly filled d or f shell. Quite generally, low temperatures and high viscosity of the solvent (or crystalline state) favours the fluorescence. This can be explained by the competing reaction mechanisms without radiation which become less probable when the vibrational motion is less violent and when collisions with other molecules are less frequent. This is also the reason why fluorescence may be quenched by a high concentration of the fluorescent compound itself in solution. It may be mentioned that the radiationless decays can be divided in cases of directly crossing potential curves (at "anomalous" internuclear distances) and by quantum-mechanical "tunnel effects" comparable to the conversion of a localized to a completely delocalized excitation discussed above.

One of the best studied, but by far not completely understood, groups of phosphorescent semiconductors are ZnS, CdS, and isomorphous mixtures of these two compounds, containing other elements as small traces. One of the best reviews was written by Kröger (1956); a previous one was written by Birus (1942). The characteristic behaviour of the phosphorescent materials involves not only a relatively long time of radiation, but also mostly a non-exponential decay and a very complicated behaviour of enhanced radiation and strongly decreasing lifetime as function of increased temperature. This suggests a bimolecular reaction where light is emitted after the collision of two different entities which is made more probable by increasing kT. We shall as an example consider ZnS in the following, but all our remarks are leisurely translated into the analogous statements about similar compounds.

Absorption of near ultraviolet radiation in the first strong absorption band of ZnS is accompanied by formation of electrons in the "conduction band" e^-_{con} and holes in sulphide ions, S^-. However, the natural lifetime of the recombination of these holes and electrons is very short and gives rise to the so-called edge fluorescence in very pure materials. Kröger showed that a vibrational structure of this edge fluorescence occurs. Incidentally, it is often difficult to distinguish vibrational and exciton series frequencies, and, even in the case of Cu_2O, the energy differences between subsequent "exciton series" might be taken for Cu–O stretching frequencies.

If ZnS contains traces of other elements, the recombination becomes in part much slower. This may be ascribed to one of two reasons: that the electrons for a time are kept in electron traps Y and the slow, subsequent reaction is a reduction by Y^- of the fluorescent ion M^{+z+1} in a higher oxidation number than that (z) emitting the light; or that holes are kept in the form of S^- reacting slowly with M^{+z-1}:

$$\begin{array}{llll}
& & : & \text{slow process} \qquad (9.4)\\
& S^- + M^{+z} \rightarrow S^{--} + M^{+z+1} & : & M^{+z+1} + Y^- \rightarrow \\
& e^-_{con} + Y \rightarrow Y^- & : & Y + M^{+z}_{exc} \searrow \\
h\nu + S^{--} \rightarrow e^-_{con} + S^- \nearrow & & : & \qquad\qquad M^{+z} + h\nu_{lum}. \\
\uparrow_____| \searrow & & : & \\
\text{edge luminescence} & e^-_{con} + M^{+z} \rightarrow M^{+z-1} & : & M^{+z-1} + S^- \rightarrow M^{+z}_{exc} + S^{--}
\end{array}$$

One can get a qualitative picture of the relative energies by considering the electron transfer spectra $M^{+z}+S^{--}\rightarrow M^{+z-1}+S^{-}$ such as are known of Ni(II) in ZnS. Figure 9.2 illustrates such a series of estimated orbital (ionization) energies. We are deliberatedly deviating from the energy band picture in ascribing a definite number of electrons to each metal atom. This is justified according to Pappalardo and Dietz's measurements (1961), showing discrete energy levels of Ni(II), Co(II), etc. in semiconducting sulphides which can be interpreted by ligand field, i.e. the microsymmetry principle and MO theory.* We also note a consequent change of ionization energy as a function of the oxidation number of M, i.e. an effective value of the Coulomb integral J(3d, 3d).

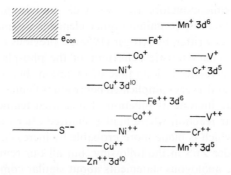

FIG. 9.2. Plausible ionization energies for various ions in zinc sulphide. Remark that the wavenumber of the electron transfer band of a given ion, say Ni^{++}, is given as the difference between the wavenumber of the fundamental absorption band $(S^{--}\rightarrow S^{-}+e^{-}_{con})$ and the ionization energy of $Ni^{+}(\rightarrow Ni^{++}+e^{-}_{con})$, since the process roughly can be described as $(Ni^{++}\ S^{--})\rightarrow(Ni^{+}S^{-})$.

It is easily explained why some ions, such as Ni(II), Co(II), or Fe(III) are "quenchers" or "killers" of phosphorescence, even at extremely low concentrations, taking over energy and phosphorescing in the infrared or not radiating at all. From stoichiometric considerations, it is also understood why Kröger found that Cu(I) at low concentration can be incorporated in ZnS only if accompanied by monovalent anions (such as Cl^{-} substituting S^{--}) or by an equivalent amount of trivalent cations (such as Al^{+3} or Ga^{+3}). However, many details are not understood: the copper form at low concentration fluoresces green. At higher concentration, a dimer is formed, where the second copper atom is close to the first and not substituting a zinc atom in the lattice. This blue-fluorescing dimer has the total oxidation number Cu_{2}^{+} (Kröger, 1952). Recent studies (Blicks, Riehl, and Sizmann, 1961) suggest

---

* The (actually very feeble) delocalization of the partly filled shell of Mn(II) in CdS, not only on the four S neighbours but on the nearest Cd atoms, can be estimated from the Cd "super-hyperfine structure" effects on electron spin resonance (Dorain, 1958; Lambe and Kikuchi, 1960).

$Cu_2{}^{++}$. It is also known that zinc metal is soluble in ZnO and forms inter-stitial neutral zinc atoms (Mohanty and Azaroff, 1961). Only about a thou-sandth of these atoms contribute to the conductivity. The explanation in eq. (9.4) seems also a little too radical in cases such as Dy(III) in ZnS (Ford and Williams, 1960) where one would not expect Dy(II) or Dy(IV) to occur as intermediates. Here again, it is a question as to what extent one shall consider a local dielectric constant ε well above one seriously; the deviations from usual oxidation numbers become more probable the higher the ε.

The typical behaviour of semiconducting materials is not necessarily con-nected with their crystallinity, and the idealization of an infinitely large, perfect crystal may be rather a mathematical device for simplification in the energy band method than expressing something physically significant. Thus, Dr. E. Mooser has pointed out to me that amorphous and liquid selenium as well as the crystalline form is semiconducting. A very characteristic effect of microsymmetry and local order is found in the absorption spectra of glasses which frequently are of exactly the same type as the isolated entities in solu-tion or the regular crystalline substances. Thus Brode (1933) compared the absorption spectra of the violet, blue, and dark green tetrahedral CoO_4, CoS_4, $CoCl_4$, $CoBr_4$, CoI_4 compounds of Co(II) and the much weaker coloured, pink CoO_6 and studied the equilibria in glasses.

Weyl wrote a most interesting book, "Coloured Glasses", compiling the varying and often surprising experimental data on absorption spectra of glasses. In some cases, the mononuclear entities, such as green $V(III)O_6$, green $Cr(III)O_6$, yellow $Cr(VI)O_4$, nearly colourless $Mn(II)O_6$, purple $Mn(III)O_6$ (or square-planar O_4), blue-grey $Fe(II)O_4$, blue-green $Fe(II)O_6$, brown $Fe(III)O_4$, nearly colourless $Fe(III)O_6$, purple $Ni(II)O_4$ and yellow $Ni(II)O_6$ can be clearly distinguished and compared to similar complexes in aqueous solution and in crystals. In other cases, polymerization reactions seem to take place. Copper is a particularly interesting and complicated element, though silver and gold make similar effects. According to Weyl, neutral copper atoms can occur completely dispersed and are then colourless. It is somewhat unexpected that the electron configuration $[Ar]3d^{10}4s$ with the very bulky and σ-antibonding 4s electron should occur in silicate glasses. However, the copper atoms have a great tendency to polymerize. Their dimer is compared with $Hg_2{}^{++}$ containing a σ-bonding electron pair besides the closed shells. At a given cluster size of some hundred atoms, copper forms a beautifully dark red coloured, colloidal solution in glass. At higher grain size a livery brown, metallic reflecting material is seen dispersed in the glass. In addition Cu(I) and monomeric blue-green Cu(II) occur in glasses. It is possible to draw interesting analogies to the confusing situation of knowledge regarding copper in phosphorescent materials.

The description given in eq. (9.2) of the lowest empty MO in alkali halides can only be easily extended to crystals containing one "excitable" species such as S^{--} in BaS (which, incidentally, also forms the Lenard phosphorescent materials with Mn(II), Ce(III), Pb(II), etc., as activators). The situation is much more complicated in cases like AgCl and AgBr crystallizing in NaCl lattice and CuCl, CuBr, CuI, and AgI crystallizing in zincblende, a four-co-ordinated structure. The empty s orbitals of metal and halogen atoms might as well receive electrons from the filled d shell of the metal as from the filled p shell of the halogen. Actually, in AgCl and AgBr, the first absorption bands seem to be caused by p halogen→5sAg, whereas Ag(I) aquo ions and the crystalline fluoride have 4d→5s transitions at somewhat higher wavenumber, about 50 kK. The transitions, about 25 kK in the three Cu(I) halides, can be described in local MO theory (now having a copper nucleus as centre!) as the transition from the highest filled set of MO of symmetry γ_5 consisting partly of a 3d subshell of Cu and partly of σ- and π-bonding combinations with the ligands, to the lowest empty MO of symmetry γ_1 consisting predominantly of 4s of Cu and σ-antibonding to the four halogen neighbours. This is in agreement with some relativistic effects found to vary in an otherwise unexpected way with the halogen, being comparatively small in the bromide [cf. eq. (10.17)]. The principal argument for the electron transfer character of a definite transition is the regular decrease of wavenumber $F > H_2O > Cl > Br > I$ in eq. (7.22) when the ligands are varied around a definite central ion. This is, however, no absolutely certain argument, as we shall see below in the case of Bi(III) complexes.

Seitz was the first, in 1938, to suggest that Tl(I) substitutionally built-in alkali halide crystals have a weaker and a strong transition in the ultraviolet which in spherical symmetry would correspond to $6s^2(^1S_0) \rightarrow 6s6p(^3P_1)$ and $6s6p(^1P_1)$, respectively. The subscripts correspond to the quantum number J to be defined in the next chapter. Similar transitions can be observed of Tl(I), Pb(II), Bi(III), and with smaller intensities of the spin-forbidden transition to $^3P_1$ also In(I), Sn(II), Sb(III) in halide crystals (a review, Eppler, 1961) and in aqueous solution of a variety of ligands (Jørgensen, 1962). The fluorescence in solution was reported by Pringsheim and Vogels (1940). Actually, these bands shift to lower wavenumber with decreasing electronegativity of the ligand, as if they were electron transfer bands (though they have much too low a wavenumber in that respect, when the oxidizing character of the central ion is considered). In MO formulation, the 6s orbital is σ-antibonding with respect to the ligands and the 6p orbital σ- and π- antibonding (in most symmetries), and the central atom contributions to both are expected to be somewhat more than half the total electron density. Crystals containing easily "excitable" metalloid atoms together with the $6s^2$ family metals (such as PbS, PbSe, PbTe, all with the energy gap 2 kK) have a very complicated description, approaching the energy band behaviour.

Closely analogous to the 6s→6p energy differences are the 4f→5d transitions observed in Ce(III), Sm(II), Eu(II), Tb(III), Yb(II) and 5f→6d in

Pa(IV), U(III), Np(III), Pu(III) (in Chapter 11 we shall see reasons exactly why these central ions are particularly apt to show these transitions in the accessible range below 50 kK). They move to somewhat smaller wavenumbers when less electronegative ligands are substituted for F^- or H_2O; and on the other hand, the aquo ion already has a smaller energy difference than the corresponding gaseous ion in the only case, where both are known, Ce(III).

These transitions are obviously localized in the central ion and its nearest ligand atoms. This is also the case in the internal transitions in the partly filled 3d, 4d, or 5d shell of transition group complexes, as discussed in Chapter 8. Actually, the breakdown of the energy band model in compounds such as MnO and NiO (both crystallizing in NaCl lattice and having half-filled subshells $\gamma_5{}^3\gamma_3{}^2$ and $\gamma_5{}^6\gamma_3{}^2$ in each transition group atom) was foreseen in Chapter 5, the allocation of almost exactly five electrons to the partly filled shell of Mn and eight in Ni being a consequence of the large charge separation effects. In other words, the energy band method would more or less suggest that MnO or NiO already in their ground state would find themselves internally ionized, i.e. electrons readily moving from one metal atom to the next. However, the large difference between the ionization energy and the electron affinity of a definite transition group ion, i.e. J(d, d), is the reason why this argument is not valid; in weakly antiferromagnetic compounds of transition group elements, the situation is that of "large internuclear distances".

Dr. M. Tobin, Cyanamid Laboratories, Stamford, Connecticut, was so kind as to point out to me the close analogy between the concept of site groups (which are subgroups of factor groups) in Winston and Halford's description (1949) of lattice modes and molecular modes, the ligand field theory being a site group orbital theory. However, the problem has two different aspects: not only are the conditions for the one-electron wavefunctions subject to the hierarchy of subgroups appropriate to the compound, but the presence of nondiagonal elements of two-electron operators introduce another type of difficulty at what we call "large internuclear distances", i.e. at situations where the $\langle r_{12}{}^{-1}\rangle$ integrals are comparable to or larger than the splitting of MO energies in a given set which would be degenerate in a lower micro-symmetry.

Another example of the role of microsymmetry may be given in this context of Orgel's elaboration (1955) of Weyl's idea that tetrahedrally co-ordinated Mn(II) shows green and octahedral Mn(II) shows orange lumine-scence in fluorescent and phosphorescent materials. This is not to be con-founded with the dark red $^2\Gamma_3 \rightarrow {}^4\Gamma_2$ fluorescence found by Kröger of Mn(IV) in other materials. We see again how it is a meaningful approximation to ascribe a definite number of electrons to each transition group atom. This can be done in a great variety of solid compounds, such as $CoAl_2O_4$ or Ni_2SiO_4, but not in Fe_3O_4 or Mn_3O_4, and possibly not in $LaCoO_3$.

REFERENCES

Birus, K. (1942), *Ergeb. Exakt. Naturwiss.*, **20**, 183.
Blicks, H., Riehl, N., and Sizmann, R. (1961), *Z. Physik.*, **163**, 594.
Brode, W. R. (1933), *J. Am. Chem. Soc.*, **55**, 939.
Dorain, P. B. (1958), *Phys. Rev.*, **112**, 1058.
Eby, J. E., Teegarden, K. J., and Dutton, D. B. (1959), *Phys. Rev.*, **116**, 1099.
Elliott, R. J. (1961), *Phys. Rev.*, **124**, 340.
Eppler, R. A. (1961), *Chem. Rev.*, **61**, 523.
Ford, R. A., and Williams, M. M. R. (1960), *Spectrochimica Acta*, **16**, 721.
Griffiths, T. R., and Symons, M. C. R. (1960), *Mol. Phys.*, **3**, 90; (1960), *Trans. Faraday Soc.*, **56**, 1125.
Grun, J. B., Sieskind, M., and Nikitine, S. (1961), *J. Phys. Chem. Solids*, **21**, 119.
Gross, E. F. (1959), *J. Phys. Chem. Solids*, **8**, 172.
Jørgensen, C. K. (1962), "Solid State Physics", **13**.
Knox, R. S., and Inchauspe, N. (1959), *Phys. Rev.*, **116**, 1093.
Kosower, E. M., Martin, R. L., and Meloche, V. W. (1957), *J. Chem. Phys.*, **26**, 1353.
Kröger, F. A. (1952), *J. Chem. Phys.*, **20**, 345.
Kröger, F. A. (1956), *Ergeb. Exakt. Naturwiss.*, **29**, 61.
Lambe, J., and Kikuchi, C. (1960), *Phys. Rev.*, **119**, 1256.
McClure, D. S. (1959), "Solid State Physics", **8**, 1.
Mohanty, G. P., and Azaroff, L. V. (1961), *J. Chem. Phys.*, **35**, 1268.
Moss, T. S. (1952), "Photoconductivity in the Elements", Butterworths, London.
Nikitine, S. (1959), *Phil. Mag.*, **4**, 1.
Nikitine, S. (1962), *Prog. in Semiconductors*, **6**, 233; **6**, 269.
Orgel, L. E. (1955), *J. Chem. Phys.*, **23**, 1958.
Pappalardo, R., and Dietz, R. E. (1961), *Phys. Rev.*, **123**, 1188.
Pringsheim, P., and Vogels, H. (1940), *Physica*, **7**, 225.
Saum, G. A., and Hensley, E. B. (1959), *Phys. Rev.*, **113**, 1019.
Scheibe, G. (1929), *Z. physik. Chem.*, **B5**, 355.
Seitz, F. (1940), "The Modern Theory of Solids", McGraw-Hill, New York.
Taft, E. A., and Philipp, H. R. (1957), *J. Phys. Chem. Solids*, **3**, 1.
Terenin, A. (1961), *Proc. Chem. Soc.*, 321.
Varsanyi, F., and Dieke, G. H. (1959), *J. Chem. Phys.*, **31**, 1066.
Van Uitert, L. G. (1960), *J. Electrochem. Soc.*, **107**, 803.
Von Hippel, A. (1936), *Z. Physik.*, **101**, 680.
Welker, H. (1956), *Ergeb. Exakt. Naturwiss.*, **29**, 275.
Weyl, W. A. (1959), "Coloured Glasses", Dawson's of Pall Mall, London.
Winston, H., and Halford, R. S. (1949), *J. Chem. Phys.*, **17**, 607.

10. Electrodynamic (Relativistic) Effects

In spherical symmetry, an electron with a definite l obtains one of two different energies corresponding to the quantum number $j=l\pm1/2$, if l is positive, whereas an s electron always has $j=1/2$. The energy difference between $j=l+1/2$ (of higher energy) and $j=l-1/2$ can be expressed by the Landé parameter ζ_{nl}, being to the first approximation $(l+1/2)\,\zeta_{nl}$ where

$$\zeta_{nl}=\frac{1\text{ry}}{137^2}\int_0^\infty \frac{d(U)}{dr}\cdot\frac{R^2}{r}dr \tag{10.1}$$

is strongly dependent on the behaviour of the squared radial function R^2 close to the nucleus (r small) where the gradient $d(U)/dr$ of the central field is largest. The integral in eq. (10.1) is indeterminate for $l=0$ because it becomes divergent at $r=0$, but it can be shown in a hydrogen atom that the relativistic effect on the ns shell is a shift comparable to the effect on the np states with $j=1/2$, i.e. an energy decrease $-\zeta_{np}$.

The numerical constant $(1\text{ry})/137^2$ is rather small, 0.0058 kK. In a one-electron system with the atomic number Z, eq. (10.1) gives by comparison with eq. (2.14)

$$\zeta_{nl}=Z<r^{-3}>\cdot\frac{1\text{ry}}{137^2}=\frac{Z^4}{n^3l(l+1/2)(l+1)}\cdot\frac{1\text{ry}}{137^2} \tag{10.2}$$

showing a strong dependence on Z, n, and l. As previously discussed by the present writer (1955), attempts to introduce "effective charges" Z_* and "effective principal quantum numbers" n_* in eq. (10.2) for the description of systems containing more than one electron are rather unsuccessful. There remains only Landé's empirical rule (1924):

$$\zeta_{nl}=Z^2Z_0^2k \tag{10.3}$$

where Z_0 is the ionic charge plus one, k is nearly invariant in an isoelectronic series and has the values in 10^{-6} kK :

$$
\begin{array}{ll}
3d & 20 \\
3d^2 & 24 \\
4d & 20 \\
5d & \sim18 \\
6d & 16.
\end{array}
\tag{10.4}
$$

Many authors assume the left-hand part of eq. (10.2) with the weaker assumption that ζ_{nl} is proportional to the product of $<r^{-3}>$ and an effective charge Z_* not much below Z (Foglio and Pryce, 1961, suggests Z_* about 60 in the actinides) and hence estimate values of $<r^{-3}>$ from observed Landé parameters. This is an interesting problem, though not entirely solved.

It has been possible to calculate relativistic HFSCF, where each of the two j values of a shell with positive l have an individual radial function. Thus, Mayers (1957) found considerable differences in the mercury atom and, of course, much larger than found by Williams (1940) in the gaseous Cu⁺. Table 10.1 gives the relativistic and nonrelativistic HF and experimental (from X-ray spectra to be discussed in Chapter 12) ionization energies of these two species. It is remarkable that in particular the energy difference between the two j values of a given nl shell is very well predicted by the relativistic calculations.

The number 137 occurring in eqs. (10.1)–(10.3) is probably not an integer, but is, according to the newest measurements 137.030 ± 0.016, called the reciprocal hyperfine structure constant. It has a very fundamental significance as already seen by the fact that the rest mass mc^2 of an electron is 4.12 million kK, i.e. 2×137^2 rydbergs. One may consider the energy of formation of atoms, loosely speaking with the effective charge Z_*, from free electrons as a small perturbation of the order of magnitude $(Z_*/137)^2 mc^2$. The electrodynamic and relativistic effects mentioned above are proportional to $(v/c)^2$ where v is the velocity of the electron, and hence proportional to $(Z_*/137)^4 mc^2$. As expected, higher members of this Taylor series occur, such as the Lamb shift, separating the two levels with $j=1/2$ of 2s and 2p (which otherwise are degenerate in the first-order relativistic treatment) and which also operate a shift to more negative energy of 1s, amounting to $Z^4 mc^2/137^5$ or some 4000 kK in mercury, as pointed out by Brown and Mayers (1959). One should not conclude that these enormous relativistic corrections of various orders,

TABLE 10.1. Ionization energies for nonrelativistic and relativistic Hartree-Fock wavefunctions for Cu⁺ and Hg compared to experimental ionization energies, all in kK

	Cu⁺(Z=29)			Hg(Z=80)		
	nonrel.	rel.	exp.	nonrel.	rel.	exp.
1s	72200	72940	72580	609100	674200	670460
2s	8608	8727	8860	101500	118700	119730
2p$_{1/2}$	7666	{ 7754	7700	97870	{ 114300	114655
2p$_{3/2}$		7588	7540		97530	99110
3s	984	985	990	23800	28050	28745
3p$_{1/2}$	667	{ 659	620	22010	{ 25910	26470
3p$_{3/2}$		638	600		22460	22975
3d$_{3/2}$	123	{ 112	166	18710	{ 19010	19270
3d$_{5/2}$		110	164		18260	18540

frequently thousands of times larger than the chemical bonding energies, change our qualitative electrostatic picture of an atom very much. We must remember that in the classical electromagnetic theory, all atoms and molecules immediately would collapse, and hence one cannot talk about relativistic corrections as changing an otherwise simpler and consistent model. Our description is simply not consistent if not developed to a certain degree of complication and sophistication. One has, of course, the final problem to what extent the separation into various orders of relativistic effects becomes divergent as the atomic number approaches 137. Anyhow, the relativistic effects become very large in the inner shells of heavy atoms, as demonstrated by HFSCF calculations (Cohen, 1959, and Winocur, 1960) on the uranium atom, and the measurements by Nordling and Hagström (1959) of the ionization energies in U:

$$
\begin{array}{ll}
1s & 932610 \text{ kK} \\
2s & 175516 \\
2p_{1/2} & 168986 \\
2p_{3/2} & 138483.
\end{array}
\tag{10.5}
$$

If only the first-order relativistic effect occurred in this case, ζ_{2p} of eq. (10.1) would be 20,336 kK, which is, however, some 10,000 times larger than ζ_{5f} and ζ_{6d} of the loosest bound, partly filled shells of this atom. Cauchois and Hulubei compiled tables of orbital energies from X-ray absorption and emission spectra, from which Table 10.2 is a short selection. Ionization energies below 200 kK, however, are frequently estimated from atomic spectroscopy. The inner shells at very high atomic number Z have energies which become hydrogen-like and conveniently can be written $-(Z-s)^2/n^2$ ry, where s is a small "screening constant". Hence, it is useful in Moseley diagrams to consider the square root of the ionization energy in rydbergs, which then is interpreted as $(Z-s)/n$. Cauchois gives the following values for $(Z-s)$:

Z=	20	30	40	50	60	70	80	90	
1s	17.24	26.67	36.41	46.37	56.65	67.20	78.22	89.92	
2s	—	—	27.39	36.27	45.88	55.59	66.13	77.65	(10.6)
$2p_{1/2}$	10.19	17.55	26.06	35.00	44.52	54.21	64.71	76.15	
$2p_{3/2}$	10.13	17.35	25.58	34.02	42.79	51.33	60.17	69.29	

illustrating the phenomenological utility of the concept s. In the region Z=30 to Z=60, s is roughly constant ∼3.5 for the 1s orbital. The relativistic effects are responsible for the apparent decrease of s in the very heavy elements. It may be remarked in Table 10.1 that the nonrelativistic HFSCF of mercury corresponds to $(Z-s)=74.5$, i.e. the effects of external screening; that is the repulsion from the outer shells have increased s to about twice the value in calcium.

TABLE 10.2. Ionization energies in kK estimated by Cauchois (1952 and 1955) and, in a few cases, from atomic spectroscopy. It is worth noting the distinction between the kilo X-unit-rydberg and the "international rydberg", the former being 0.2 per cent smaller and frequently leading to slightly different estimates in literature

	Ne(Z=10)	Ca(20)	Zn(30)	Zr(40)	Sn(50)	Nd(60)	Yb(70)	Hg(80)	Th(90)
1s	7000	32570	77920	145160	235540	351450	494560	670460	884440
2s	390	3544	9655	20400	36010	57500	84600	119730	165060
$2p_{1/2}$	175	2824	8430	18595	33520	54230	80490	114655	158830
$2p_{3/2}$	174	2791	8245	17910	31690	50080	72150	99110	131470
3s	—	355	1130	3460	7125	12715	19345	28745	41800
$3p_{1/2}$	—	203	730	2760	6100	11335	17540	26470	38890
$3p_{3/2}$	—	200	710	2645	5760	10470	15740	22975	32575
$3d_{3/2}$	—	—	141	1460	3980	8075	12715	19270	28140
$3d_{5/2}$	—	—	138	1440	3905	7890	12335	18540	26865
4s	—	49	76	400	1105	2550	3930	6495	10670
$4p_{1/2}$	—	—	—	210	730	1960	3210	5495	9360
$4p_{3/2}$	—	—	—	200	700	1815	2775	4680	7735
$4d_{3/2}$	—	—	—	70	200	970	1600	3100	5735
$4d_{5/2}$	—	—	—	70	190	950	1490	2920	5450
$4f_{5/2}$	—	—	—	—	—	100	143	855	2700
$4f_{7/2}$	—	—	—	—	—	100	140	760	2645
5s	—	—	—	56	110	315	650	1010	2340
$5p_{1/2}$	—	—	—	—	63	170	—	660	1810
$5p_{3/2}$	—	—	—	—	59	160	—	500	1395
$5d_{1/2}$	—	—	—	—	—	—	—	135	—
$5d_{3/2}$	—	—	—	—	—	—	—	120	700
6s	—	—	—	—	—	50	57	84	485
$6p_{1/2}$	—	—	—	—	—	—	—	—	—
$6p_{3/2}$	—	—	—	—	—	—	—	—	330

Fröman (1960) studied the influence of relativistic effects on the total energy of atoms. As mentioned in Chapter 3, whereas the nonrelativistic energy of an atom can be written as Z^2 times a Taylor series in Z^{-1}, the first term in the first-order relativistic correction is $Z^4 ry/2 \times 137^2$ in the two-electron series He, Li$^+$, Be^{++}, . . ., or in other words, the relativistic correction is roughly proportional to the square of the total nonrelativistic energy with the proportionality constant $1 ry/8 \times 137^2$. This is by no means negligible for high atomic numbers, and Fröman actually calculates that the relativistic correction is *larger* than the total interelectronic repulsion energy $\langle r_{12}^{-1} \rangle$ in the two-electron series for Z above 40 and in the ten-electron series (Ne, Na$^+$, . . .) for Z above 65. However, for medium values of Z, nearly all the relativistic correction is concentrated in the two 1s electrons.

After this excursion into the X-ray region where the relativistic effects produce splittings between the two j values of the same shell (such as 2p) amounting to thousands of kK, we return to the outer shells studied by visible and near-ultraviolet spectra and find obviously much smaller effects.

Table 10.3 gives the values of ζ_{nl} of eq. (10.1) estimated from gaseous atoms and ions [and for compounds of Yb(III)] having one electron in the n, l shell, or one hole, i.e. $4l+1$ electrons. In the latter case, the doublet term is *inverted*, the energy level with $J=l+1/2$ has lower energy (corresponding to the absence of an electron with $j=l+1/2$ of higher energy) than the other level with $J=l-1/2$.

The energy difference 0.0172 kK between the two spectral lines in the sodium doublet in the yellow (at 16.96 kK) has the same origin as the parameter given in Table 10.3, since $\frac{3}{2}\zeta_{3p}$ represents the splitting of [Ne]3p, the excited configuration of the two lines. Rydberg already observed how this kind of splitting becomes much more pronounced in alkali metals as a function of increasing Z, and how it decreases rapidly as a function of increasing l.

A certain decrease with increasing l is indeed observed in Table 10.3, but much smaller than suggested by hydrogenic formulae such as eq. (10.2). It is interesting to compare the beginning and the end of a given transition group, such as Sc++ and Cu++, or Zr+3 and Cd+3, and find the strongly increased ζ_{nd}. It is also instructive to compare ζ_{5d} of La++ and Lu++. Though Z has increased by 14 units between these two elements, the Landé parameter has increased rather little, because an even more internal shell has been filled, the 4f shell, screening the nucleus away from the main part of the 5d shell.

TABLE 10.3. The Landé parameter ζ_{nl} in various gaseous atoms and ions and in Yb(H$_2$O)$_9$+++

2p B 0.01	C+ 0.04	N++ 0.12	2p⁵ F 0.27	Ne+ 0.52	Na++ 0.91
3p Al 0.07	Si+ 0.19	P++ 0.37	3p⁵ Cl 0.59	Ar+ 0.95	K++ 1.44
3d Sc++ 0.08	Ti+3 0.15	V+4 0.25	3d⁹ Ni+ 0.60	Cu++ 0.83	—
4p Ga 0.55	Ge+ 1.18	As++ 1.96	4p⁵ Br 2.46	Kr+ 3.58	Rb++ 4.92
4d Y++ 0.29	Zr+3 0.50	Nb+4 0.75	4d⁹ Ag++ 1.81	Cd+3 2.33	In+4 2.87
5p In 1.48	Sn+ 2.83	Sb++ 4.38	5p⁵ I 5.07	Xe+ 7.02	—
4f —	Ce+3 0.64	—	4f¹³ —	Yb(III) 2.95	—
5d La++ 0.64	Ce+3 1.00	Lu++ 0.80	5d⁹ Au++ ~5	—	—
6p Tl 5.20	Pb+ 9.39	Bi++ 13.86	6p⁵ —	Em+ ~20	—
6d Ac++ 1.36	Th+3 2.12	—			
5f Ac++ 0.75	Th+3 1.24	—			

In the systems with between 2 and $4l$ electrons in the partly filled shell, *intermediate coupling* covers all the range of intermediate cases between the Russell-Saunders coupling where the Landé parameters are negligible compared to the term distances in the configuration, and the pure j, j *coupling* where the parameters of interelectronic repulsion are negligible compared to the relativistic effects. The latter situation is rarely realized in atomic spectroscopy; on the other hand, it is appropriate for the description of X-ray spectra. This difference is caused by the fact that the interelectronic repulsion parameters, the J and K integrals, are proportional to the effective charge Z_*, whereas the relativistic effects are more or less related to Z_*^4.

Figure 10.1 shows the energy diagram of intermediate coupling for the configurations p^2, p^3, and p^4 in spherical symmetry. Only for very large values of ζ_{np}/F^2 do the configurations $(1/2)^a(3/2)^b$ become pure, but the slopes of the lines in the diagrams indicate a final tendency to separate into three groups with $a=2$, 1, and 0, respectively.

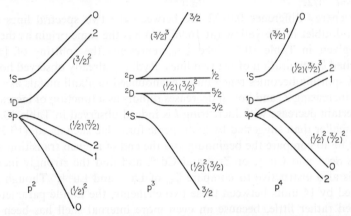

FIG. 10.1. The energy levels of p^2, p^3, and p^4 in intermediate coupling as functions of ζ_{np}/F^2, the parameter of interelectronic repulsion representing the distances between the three multiplet terms in the left-hand side of each diagram. The numbers indicate the values of J of the individual levels and the configurations $(1/2)^a(3/2)^b$ the j,j-coupling configurations asymptotically approached for large values of the variable. As seen in "Absorption Spectra and Chemical Bonding in Complexes", page 179, the same diagrams are valid for γ_5^4, γ_5^3, and γ_5^2, respectively, and the corresponding energy levels can be identified with the intra-subshell transitions in octahedral $5d^q$ complexes.

We shall not discuss here the question of how the diagonal elements of interelectronic repulsion are determined in the extreme case of j, j coupling; Condon and Shortley give a method in principle. The opposite situation, the diagonal elements of the first-order relativistic effect (i.e. the effect expressed by the one-electron quantity ζ_{nl}) by small deviations from Russell-Saunders coupling is of great practical interest to atomic spectroscopy, because, in the majority of atoms, the multiplet terms characterized by S and L can still be recognized, but their energy levels with definite values of J are separated (hence the name "multiplet") and frequently occur in the order:

$$J=(L+S), (L+S-1), (L+S-2), \ldots (|L-S|). \tag{10.7}$$

The diagonal elements mentioned above can be expressed as a multiple of a quantity ζ characteristic for each multiplet, the deviation of the energy levels from the baricentre of the multiplet being given by

$$[J(J+1)-L(L+1)-S(S+1)]\zeta/2 \tag{10.8}$$

corresponding to *Landé's interval rule* that the distance between two adjacent levels in a multiplet having the values J and $J-1$ is $J\zeta$. If ζ is negative, the multiplet is said to be inverted. This is usually the case in the second half of a transition group (l^q with $q>2l+1$) but may occur in special cases already for $q=3$.

If only one term of l^q has the combination of L and S considered, ζ is a rational fraction multiplied by ζ_{nl}, whereas implicit functions of term distances may produce irrational factors in other cases. In the special case of the maximum value of S, the factor relating ζ to ζ_{nl} is particularly simple:

$$\zeta=\zeta_{nl}/q \text{ for } q<2l+1 \text{ and } \zeta=-\zeta_{nl}/(4l+2-q) \text{ for } q>2l+1. \quad (10.9)$$

Since the total width of a multiplet going from $J=L+S$ to $J=L-S$ in the case of $L\geq S$ is $S(L+1/2)\zeta$ according to eq. (10.8), the total width in the special case of eq. (10.9) is $(L+1/2)\zeta_{nl}$ if $L\geq S$. If $L<S$, the total width in eq. (10.8) is $L(S+1/2)\zeta$.

One may also determine multiplet splitting parameters ζ in systems containing more than one partly filled shell. These are ordinarily functions of all the ζ_{nl} involved, but since the Landé parameter produces no splitting in a s shell, the situation is relatively simple in a configuration sl^q. In the cases $q=1$ or $4l+1$, ζ of the triplet is $\pm\frac{1}{2}\zeta_{nl}$ and hence the width of the triplet is $(l+\frac{1}{2})\zeta_{nl}$, the same as the doublet of the configuration without s electron. It can be seen in general for the ground term of l^q, having the width $(L+\frac{1}{2})\zeta_{nl}$ that the term with the same L and having S half a unit larger of sl^q must have the same width (because the two extreme J values are coupled with the s electron to give the two extreme J values of sl^q) and hence $\zeta=\zeta_{nl}/(q+1)$ for $q<2l+1$. One can also prove in the case of d^5p that, if the d^5 part of the wavefunction exactly corresponds to ^6S, then the total width of ^7P is $\frac{7}{6}\zeta_{np}$ and of $^5P-\frac{5}{6}\zeta_{np}$, an inverted multiplet. From Charlotte Moore's tables, one may make the following comparisons:

$\zeta_{np}=$		Width of ^7P:		Width of ^5P:		$\zeta_{np}=$	
4p Ca$^+$	0.15	3d^{5}4p Mn$^+$	0.44	-0.19	3d^{10}4p Zn$^+$	0.58	
Sc^{++}	0.32	Fe^{++}	0.84	-0.41	Ga^{++}	1.14	(10.10)
5p Sr$^+$	0.53	4d^{5}5p Tc$^+$	1.54	-0.41	4d^{10}5p Cd$^+$	1.65	
Y^{++}	1.04	Ru^{++}	2.62	-0.82	In^{++}	2.90	
6s^{2}6p Lu	2.23	5d^{5}6p Re$^+$	6.74	-4.36	5d^{10}6p Hg$^+$	6.08.	

It seems that the assumption of pure fractional parentage $d^5(^6S)p$ is better for ^7P than for ^5P. This is also expected because $d^5(^4P)p$, $d^5(^4D)p$, and $d^5(^4F)p$ all may participate in the ^5P term, but not in ^7P. A quantity such as ζ_{np} in eq. (10.10) is, of course, a quite sensitive measure of how deep into the region close to the nucleus an excited (i.e. empty in the ground state) orbital such as np reaches. According to eq. (10.10), ζ_{np} in the middle of the transition group is already relatively closer to the high value at the end.

Jørgensen (1955) and Dunn (1961) have compiled values of ζ_{3d} and ζ_{4d} as functions of the atomic number and the ionic charge. Dunn emphasizes that s electrons have almost no screening influence on the d shell, $3d^q$, $3d^q4s$, and $3d^q4s^2$ presenting the same value of ζ_{3d} though belonging to three different ionic charges of the same element.

There is a large calculational programme going on, directed by G. Racah and by R. E. Trees, where energy levels of the 5d and (6d, 5f) groups are interpreted with interelectronic repulsion and Landé parameters as semi-empirical quantities, and very interesting results have been obtained for W, W^+, Re, Th^+, Th^{++}, and similar species. Unfortunately, the experimental material is usually only available for neutral atoms and ions with the charge $+1$. Analogous remarks apply to the lanthanide and actinide groups to which we shall return in the next chapter.

Before considering relativistic effects in lower symmetries, it is worth noting that with j and the parity as good quantum numbers, different values of l are not mixed in spherical symmetry though the radial functions are changed and hence in a certain sense the values of n intermixed. The well-defined l values follow from the series:

$$
\begin{array}{llllll}
j= & 1/2 & 3/2 & 5/2 & 7/2 & 9/2 & \cdots \\
\text{even parity} & s & d & d & g & g & \cdots \\
\text{odd parity} & p & p & f & f & h & \cdots
\end{array}
\tag{10.11}
$$

In octahedral symmetry, the possible values of γ_j are:

$$
\gamma_6(e') \qquad \gamma_7(e'') \qquad \gamma_8(u') \tag{10.12}
$$

combined with even or odd parity. The names in parentheses are suggested by Griffith in analogy to Mulliken's names for the orbitals. Griffith uses dashes only for the double groups, i.e. the quantum numbers introduced by the relativistic effects, whereas many authors use dashes in orbital names in various low symmetries, e.g. the trigonal one.

Degeneracy of orbitals discussed in Chapter 2 remains to a smaller extent in the high symmetries when relativistic effects are taken into account. Thus, the doubly degenerate γ_{t5} set in tetragonal symmetry D_{4h} is split by relativistic effects into γ_{t6} and γ_{t7}, the other nondegenerate γ_{tn} not being affected. Actually, *all γ_j represent an even number of spin orbitals*, two (γ_6 and γ_7 in O_h and T_d) or four (γ_8) or six (as encountered in icosahedral and spherical symmetry) and all the following even integers only known $(2j+1)$ from spherical symmetry. In the two linear symmetries $D_{\infty h}$ and $C_{\infty v}$, all degeneracies (except the spin orbitals taken two and two) are gone. Here, γ_j is called ω and has the value 1/2 for the σ orbital and the two values $\lambda - 1/2$ and $\lambda + 1/2$ for all the sets of orbitals with positive λ. If both l and λ happen to be well defined, the separation between these two ω values, i.e. the difference in diagonal elements of the one-electron operator representing the first-order relativistic effect, is $\lambda\zeta_{nl}$.

It is not always realized that if magnetic effects are neglected, it is still possible to talk about orbitals consisting of two degenerate spin orbitals in the relativistic theory in the same sense as the orbitals in the Russell-Saunders approximation. However, the angular extension in our three-dimensional space is no longer characterizing the orbitals in the same way as in the non-relativistic theory. Thus, in linear symmetry, the two degenerate spin orbitals from a p shell with well-defined $l=1$ and having $\omega=3/2$ must necessarily be π orbitals, i.e. have angular functions taken from the set (x/r) and (y/r) if the z axis is the axis of linear symmetry. If ζ_{np} is much larger than the energy difference between σ and π orbitals, the two sets of two spin orbitals $\omega=1/2$ have mixed σ and π character. Actually, the lowest one with $j=1/2$ has a spherically symmetrical spatial function, consisting of $\frac{1}{3}\sigma$ and $\frac{2}{3}\pi$ in the squares, and consequently, the $j=3/2$, $\omega=1/2$ set consists of $\frac{2}{3}\sigma$ and $\frac{1}{3}\pi$, i.e. is predominantly concentrated on the z axis.

We define Γ_J for more-electron system states in the same way as Γ_n for the nonrelativistic quantum numbers. Bethe found that the Γ_J values in octahedral symmetry for J being an integer are the same as the Γ_n values given in eq. (4.4) for the same L value. For J being a half-number, the following values of Γ_J obtain:

$$J= \quad 1/2 \quad 3/2 \quad 5/2 \quad\quad 7/2 \quad\quad \cdots$$
$$\quad\quad \Gamma_6 \quad \Gamma_8 \quad \Gamma_7+\Gamma_8 \quad \Gamma_6+\Gamma_7+\Gamma_8 \quad \cdots \quad\quad (10.13)$$

It is seen that a p shell in octahedral symmetry divides into γ_6 and γ_8 (as in spherical symmetry) and a d shell into γ_7 and two γ_8. It is possible to make a multiplication table, as reproduced in Table 4.1. The γ_j values of a set of orbitals having a definite γ_n can be found by multiplication with the Γ_J value appropriate for $S=1/2$, i.e. Γ_6, and hence, the subshells of a d and f shell have the following relativistic components:

d shell: $\quad \gamma_3=\gamma_8 \quad\quad$ f shell: $\quad \gamma_2=\gamma_7$
$$\gamma_5=\gamma_7+\gamma_8 \quad\quad\quad\quad \gamma_4=\gamma_6+\gamma_8 \quad\quad (10.14)$$
$$\gamma_5=\gamma_7+\gamma_8.$$

Obviously, one finds the same set of γ_j as given in eq. (10.13). The levels Γ_J of a term $^{2S+1}\Gamma_n$ can be found by multiplication of $\Gamma_J(S)$ and $\Gamma_n(L)$ both taken from eq. (4.4) in systems with an even number of electrons and otherwise $\Gamma_J(S)$ taken from eq. (10.13). Thus, the terms $^3\Gamma_4$ and $^4\Gamma_4$ divide into Γ_J components, similar to eq. (10.7):

$$^3\Gamma_4=\Gamma_1+\Gamma_3+\Gamma_4+\Gamma_5$$
$$^4\Gamma_4=\Gamma_6+\Gamma_7+2\Gamma_8. \quad\quad (10.15)$$

In pure subshell configurations $\gamma_5{}^q$, Kotani and Stevens pointed out that the energy levels Γ_J develop as functions of ζ_{nd} (if $l=2$) in exactly the same way as p^{6-q} develops as functions of ζ_{np}, illustrated in Fig. 10.1. For $q=1$, the four spin orbitals γ_8 have the lowest energy, $-\frac{1}{2}\zeta_{nd}$ and are comparable to $j=3/2$ in the p-shell case, and the two γ_7 have the higher energy, $+\zeta_{nd}$. Incidentally, the two γ_7 have exactly $j=5/2$ in the case of a d shell, as seen from eq. (10.13).

In the particular case of $\gamma_5{}^q$ with $l=2$, the terms show the same degeneracies and splitting ratios as the p^{6-q} terms. Indeed, Griffith has shown in the more general case of well-defined subshell configurations $\gamma_5{}^a\gamma_3{}^b$ with $l=2$ that the $^{2S+1}\Gamma_n$ ($n=1, 2, 3$) terms do not split at all, whereas $^{2S+1}\Gamma_4$ split in exactly the same way as ^{2S+1}P in spherical symmetry, i.e. according to eq. (10.8) with an appropriate value of ζ. Thus, the two components Γ_3 and Γ_5 of eq. (10.15) remain degenerate and imitate the level $J=2$ of ^3P in spherical symmetry, whereas the component Γ_4 with respect to energy represent $J=1$ and Γ_1 the level $J=0$. Hence it is possible to characterize $^{2S+1}\Gamma_4$ terms by their total width (reckoned negative if the term is inverted with Γ_J values representing $J=S-1$ at the highest energy) and Griffith and Tanabe independently calculated such widths, in units of ζ_{nd}:

$$
\begin{array}{lll}
^3\Gamma_5(\gamma_5\gamma_3)+3/4 & ^3\Gamma_4(^3Fd^8)+9/4 & ^4\Gamma_4(^4Fd^7)+2 \\
^3\Gamma_4(\gamma_5\gamma_3)+3/4 & ^3\Gamma_4(\gamma_5{}^4\gamma_3{}^4)+3/2 & ^4\Gamma_5(\gamma_5{}^4\gamma_3{}^3)-2/3 \\
^3\Gamma_5(\gamma_5{}^5\gamma_3{}^3)-3/4 & ^3\Gamma_4(^3Pd^8)-3/2 & ^4\Gamma_4(\gamma_5{}^4\gamma_3{}^3)-2/3 \\
^3\Gamma_4(\gamma_5{}^5\gamma_3{}^3)-3/4 & ^4\Gamma_4(\gamma_5{}^5\gamma_3{}^2)+4/3 & ^4\Gamma_4(^4Pd^7)-4/3.
\end{array}
\qquad (10.16)
$$

In the case of $^{2S+1}\Gamma_5$ terms, in the Γ_J values, Γ_1 and Γ_2 are everywhere to be exchanged, as well as Γ_4 and Γ_5. Equation (10.16) is also valid for tetrahedral symmetry.

One of the most conspicuous consequences of relativistic effects in complexes of octahedral symmetry is the breakdown of the selection rule of spin-allowed transitions that transitions between states with different S are forbidden. It is well known in atomic spectroscopy that this rule is very strict in lighter atoms, at least with Z below 20, but becomes less and less important in the heavier atoms. This is not connected with the diagonal elements of intermediate coupling discussed above, but with the nondiagonal elements which are complicated multiples of ζ_{nl} and mix together various terms, also having different values of S, and finally produce the pure j,j coupling, where S is only defined for exceptional levels (such as $J=1$ of p^2 which can only belong to ^3P).

Before Griffith and Tanabe actually calculated these nondiagonal elements in octahedral symmetry, it was possible to get an idea of the size of ζ_{nd} by putting the ratio between the intensities of the spin-forbidden and spin-allowed transitions roughly equal to $(\zeta_{nd}/\Delta E)^2$, where ΔE is the distance to the closest spin-allowed transition. It became clear that the Landé parameters estimated in this way are rather small compared to ζ_{nd} of the corresponding gaseous ions, for instance some 0.8 kK in the 4d group [Mo(III) and Rh(III) complexes] and some 2 kK in the 5d group [Ir(III), Pt(IV) and Pt(II) complexes]. This is actually the reason why the MO treatment in Chapter 4 succeeds without much consideration of relativistic effects; if ζ_{nd} were as large as in the gaseous ion, the terms characterized by Γ_n and S would hardly be recognizable in 5d group complexes.

There exists hence a *nephelauxetic effect on the relativistic parameters.* If the decription in eq. (4.14) is adapted, we expect a *relativistic nephelauxetic ratio* β_*

$$\beta_* = \frac{(\zeta_{nl})\,\text{complex}}{(\zeta_{nl})\,\text{gaseous}} = a^2 \zeta_M(Z_*) \pm b^2 \zeta_X \tag{10.17}$$

where the sign of the ligand contribution $b^2 \zeta_X$ can be obtained in each individual case by group-theoretical considerations. Since the atoms X frequently are rather light (of the 2p and 3p groups), it is often possible completely to neglect the ligand contribution. It is worth noting that the dependence on Stevens's delocalization coefficient a^2 and the effective charge Z_* in eq. (10.17), *viz.* $a^2 Z_*^2$, is quite different from the behaviour of the nephelauxetic ratio β in eq. (4.30) proportional to $a^4 Z_*$. Hence it is possible to draw some conclusion on the relative variation of a^2 and Z_* if both β_* and β can be estimated in a given complex. For instance, β_* seems to be so much higher in the gaseous IrF_6 and PtF_6 than β (more exactly, β_{55}) that Z_* must be rather large and a^2 relatively small in the γ_5 subshell.

It must be admitted that only in relatively few cases can the value ζ_{nd} be determined from absorption spectra. By far the best examples are found in the intra subshell transitions in $\gamma_5{}^q$ of octahedral 5d group complexes such as ReF_6, OsF_6, IrF_6, and PtF_6 studied by Moffitt, Goodman, Fred, and Weinstock, and $ReCl_6{}^{--}$, $ReBr_6{}^{--}$, $OsCl_6{}^{--}$, and $OsBr_6{}^{--}$ measured by the present writer. Usually, spin-allowed transitions do not exhibit the first-order splitting predicted in eq. (10.15). Schäffer indicated the reason why: the broad bands, having many co-excited vibrations, cannot be distinguished at room temperature in solution, if their centres are not at least one half-width away from each other; and this is rarely the case. The fine structure observed in crystals, particularly at low temperature, can sometimes be related to intermediate coupling effects. However, the structure is often caused also by static or dynamic distortions. The only well-authenticated cases of first-order relativistic splitting of spin-allowed bands occur in tetrahedral cobalt (II) and nickel (II) complexes studied by Cotton, Goodgame, and Goodgame (1961). In these compounds, as well as in the octahedral ones, it is necessary to take into account the effects of near-lying, spin-forbidden transitions. This can be done by Liehr and Ballhausen's determinants for d^2 and d^8 (1959) and by Eisenstein's determinants for d^3 and d^7 (1961) also given by Runciman and Schroeder (1962), and in general by Griffith, Tanabe, and Kamimura's theory.

In the first transition group, the effective value of ζ_{3d} in complexes is some 0.2 to 0.7 kK, and consequently, spin-forbidden transitions are only easily observable (except in high-spin d^5 where no spin-allowed transition occurs in the partly filled shell) if they occur not more than some 2 kK away from the spin-allowed transitions. However, if the spin-forbidden transitions occur approximately inside the same subshell configuration as the ground state, they are rather narrow. They may retain the small half-width and at the same time gain some 10 or 20 per cent of the intensity of the spin-allowed transitions. Then, Schäffer's argument no longer applies, and the narrow peaks can be easily observed, superposed on the broad bands, though the total area of the peak, proportional to the oscillator strength, is not very large. Very conspicuous effects occur in chromium (III) complexes when the first spin-allowed transition to $^4\Gamma_5$ (of $\gamma_5{}^2\gamma_3$) occurs at nearly the same wavenumber as the two spin-forbidden transitions to $^2\Gamma_3$ and $^2\Gamma_4$ (predominantly of $\gamma_5{}^3$). In the same way, the singlet $^1\Gamma_3$ (corresponding to the Γ_J component Γ_3) of $\gamma_5{}^6\gamma_3{}^2$ in octahedral nickel (II) complexes may come very close to, and actually cross, the two first spin-allowed transitions to $^3\Gamma_5$ and $a^3\Gamma_4$ as described by the present writer in 1955. If the crossing point is close to $a^3\Gamma_4$, one actually observes two rather narrow bands roughly at the distance twice the nondiagonal element of intermediate coupling, and representing the transitions to the two Γ_3 components interacting, whereas the three other components of $^3\Gamma_4$ in eq. (10.15) form a much broader, though more intense background as discussed by Jørgensen (1958). A similar situation occurs in tetrahedral cobalt (II) complexes, where $^2\Gamma_3$ and $^2\Gamma_4$, among other doublet terms, are crossing $b^4\Gamma_4$ and hence making the third spin-allowed transition a very complicated band conture.

The ligand contribution to relativistic effects in complexes, eq. (10.17), explains Linhard and Weigel's phenomenon (1957), that the spin-forbidden transition to $^3\Gamma_4$ is stronger in $Co(NH_3)_5Br^{++}$ and much stronger in $Co(NH_3)_5I^{++}$ than in complexes where all the ligands are constituted of light atoms, such as $Co(NH_3)_6{}^{+++}$ and $Co(NH_3)_5Cl^{++}$ (cf. Fig. 8.4). This "contamination" of the partly filled shell is very good experimental evidence for the delocalization of MO. The phenomenon has been known for a long time in organic molecules (where ζ_{2p} is very small) where the exceedingly weak singlet→triplet transitions are intensified by iodine substitution or even by application of iodine-containing solvent.

The dramatic increase of ζ_{np} in direction of iodine in Table 10.3 is also of importance in electron transfer spectra of hexahalides MX_6, where the present writer studied (1959) the highly varying fine structure when $X=$ chloride, bromide, or iodide. This effect can be interpreted as a competition between the MO energy differences introduced by the octahedral symmetry in eq. (4.10) and the relativistic differences according to $\omega=3/2$ and $1/2$ in linear microsymmetry. In addition, the contribution of ζ_{np} of the central atom M may not be negligible [cf. eq. (10.10)] in the sets of MO of symmetry type odd γ_4.

Owen and Stevens have contributed much to the method of estimating ζ_{nl} in complexes from paramagnetic resonance experiments. Here again, as Dunn pointed out, it is necessary to take the variation of both a^2 and Z_* of eq. (10.17) into account. If this amplification is allowed for, the values obtained show qualitative agreement with those estimated from absorption spectra. We shall not enter into detail here on the results but, only refer to Griffith, "The Theory of Transition-Metal Ions", where the group-theoretical aspects of relativistic effects are treated much more thoroughly than here. The theory may look a little terrifying to a chemist, but it is useful for him to know the existence of the relativistic effects as one of the modifications of the simple orbital configuration picture.

REFERENCES

Brown, G. E., and Mayers, D. F. (1959), *Proc. Roy. Soc.* (*London*), **A251**, 105.
Cauchois, Y. (1952), *J. Phys. Rad.*, **13**, 113; (1955), **16**, 253.
Cauchois, Y., and Hulubei, H. (1947), "*Constantes selectionnées: Longueurs d'onde des émissions X et des discontinuités d'absorption X*", Hermann, Paris.
Cohen, S., "UCRL-8633", Berkeley, February 1959.
Cotton, F. A., Goodgame, D. M. L., Goodgame, M., and Sacco, A. (1961), *J. Am. Chem. Soc.*, **83**, 4157.
Cotton, F. A., Goodgame, D. M. L., and Goodgame, M. (1961), *J. Am. Chem. Soc.*, **83** 4690.
Dunn, T. M. (1961), *Trans. Faraday Soc.*, **57**, 1441.
Eisenstein, J. C. (1961), *J. Chem. Phys.*, **34**, 1628.
Foglio, M. E., and Pryce, M. H. L. (1961), *Mol. Phys.*, **4**, 287.
Fröman, A. (1960), "Relativistic Corrections in Many-Electron Systems", Preprint No. 38, Kvantkemiska Gruppen, Uppsala.
Goodgame, D. M. L., Goodgame, M., and Cotton, F. A. (1961), *J. Am. Chem. Soc.*, **83**, 4161.
Griffith, J. S. (1960), *Trans. Faraday Soc.*, **56**, 193.
Jørgensen, C. K. (1955), *J. Inorg. Nucl. Chem.*, **1**, 301.
Jørgensen, C. K. (1958), *Discuss. Faraday Soc.*, **26**, 90 and 175.
Landé, A. (1924), *Z. Physik*, **25**, 46.
Liehr, A. D., and Ballhausen, C. J. (1959), *Ann. Phys.*, (New York), **6**, 134.
Linhard, M., and Weigel, M. (1957), *Z. physik. Chem.*, **11**, 308.
Mayers, D. F. (1957), *Proc. Roy. Soc.* (*London*), **A241**, 93.
Nordling, C., and Hagstrom, S. (1959), *Arkiv för Fysik*, **15**, 431.
Runciman, W. A., and Schroeder, K. A. (1962), *Proc. Roy. Soc.* (*London*), **A265**, 489.
Tanabe, Y., and Kamimura, H. (1958), *J. Phys. Soc. Japan*, **13**, 394.
Tanabe, Y. (1960), *Progr. Theor. Phys*, *Suppl.*, No. 14, 17.
Williams, A. O. (1940), *Phys. Rev.*, **58**, 723.
Winocur, J., "UCRL-9174", Berkeley, April 1960.

11. Lanthanides and 5f Elements

The rare earths are a group of chemical elements, yttrium (with the atomic number Z=39) and lanthanum (Z=57) to lutetium (Z=71) which were very difficult and tedious to separate before 1945, when ion-exchange methods were industrially developed. Their chemical properties are to a very good precision unaffected by the presence of a partly filled 4f shell in some of them [in the most frequent oxidation number +3 between $4f^1$ cerium (III) (Z=58) and $4f^{13}$ ytterbium (III) (Z=70)]; they behave like the Be, Mg, Ca, Sr, Ba series as closed-shell ions with all appropriate qualities developing according to one parameter, say the monotonically decreasing ionic radius as a function of increasing atomic number (this is the reason why yttrium seems to have a pseudo-Z of some 66.5). Deviations from the oxidation number +3 are relatively rare and occur at rather characteristic electron configurations:

	Aquo ions	Ternary Oxides	Anhydrous Fluorides	Iodides	
$4f^0$	Ce(IV)	Ce(IV)	Ce(IV)	—	
$4f^1$	—	Pr(IV)	Pr(IV)	—	
$4f^2$	—	—	Nd(IV)	—	
$4f^4$	—	—	—	Nd(II)	(11.1)
$4f^6$	Sm(II)	—	—	Sm(II)	
$4f^7$	Eu(II)	Tb(IV)	Tb(IV)	Eu(II)	
$4f^8$	—	—	Dy(IV)	—	
$4f^{13}$	—	—	—	Tm(II)	
$4f^{14}$	Yb(II)	—	—	Yb(II).	

In other words, just after $4f^0$ and $4f^7$, +4 is a little bit stable, and just before $4f^7$ and $4f^{14}$, +2 may occur. This is explained below as closely related to the spin-pairing energy $-DS(S+1)$ and its jump $8D$ at $4f^7$. It has become customary to call the group of elements having Z from 57 to 71 for lanthanides, and we are obviously most interested in it in the cases involving a partly filled shell.

The absorption spectra of a definite lanthanide central ion with a partly filled 4f shell show groups of very narrow bands, frequently genuine spectral lines, which only show small variation with the ligands, quite in contrast to the d transition group complexes. Going from ligands of relatively higher to lower electronegativity, there is an overall shift of all the line groups to slightly lower wavenumber, corresponding to a nephelauxetic effect. This effect was discovered by Ephraim in 1926 and is particularly pronounced in the first among the lanthanides, such as Pr(III), Nd(III), and Sm(III) (Jørgensen, 1956). In addition, there is a marked dependence on the micro-symmetry of the number and positions of the components in each line group. This obviously has something to do with ligand field effects and will be discussed further below.

However, we may conclude that the main features of the lanthanide spectra are those of a system in spherical symmetry; i.e. each of the line groups corresponds ordinarily to one electronic level with well-defined J value and to some extent, though the relativistic deviations from Russell-Saunders coupling are rather strong, to well-defined L and S. Unfortunately, very few of the corresponding gaseous ions have been studied, except Ce^{+3} which was found by Lang (1936) to have the levels in kK:

$$[Xe]4f\ ^2F_{5/2}\ \ 0 \qquad [Xe]5d\ ^2D_{3/2}\ 49.74$$
$$^2F_{7/2}\ 2.25 \qquad\qquad ^2D_{5/2}\ 52.23. \qquad (11.2)$$

Recently, Trees and Sugar have found that the interelectronic repulsion and the Landé parameters in gaseous Pr^{++} in the configuration $4f^3$ all are 20 per cent smaller than in the isoelectronic $Nd(H_2O)_9^{+3}$, which is a very good indirect confirmation; but Pr^{+3}, Nd^{+3}, ... themselves have not yet been studied. Hence, we are in the unusual situation that a very great deal of material on lanthanides in $+3$ has been interpreted by methods of atomic spectroscopy, though the line spectra of the real gaseous ions are unknown.

It is seen from eq. 11.2 that ζ_{4f} is 0.64 kK in Ce^{+3}. Gobrecht (1938) studied the line groups in the near-infrared of lanthanide compounds and identified the width of the ground multiplet with $(L+1/2)\ \zeta_{4f}$ as seen in eq. (10.9) and found a regular increase with Z up to 2.95 kK in Yb(III). The values given in Table 11.1 were partly derived by Judd (1956) by somewhat more sophisticated methods.

Among the parameters of interelectronic repulsion, Racah's E^3 is particularly important [eq. (2.53)] because the distances between the baricentres of multiplet terms with maximum value of S are multiples of E^3 alone. Actually, the energy differences between ^3H, ^3F, and ^3P of f^{12} and of ^6H, ^6F, and ^6P of f^5 and f^9 are the same as given for f^2 in eq. (2.54) and the energy differences between ^4I, ^4F, ^4S, ^4G, ^4D of f^{11} and of ^5I, F^5, ^5S, ^5G, and ^5D of f^4 and f^{10} are identical with those given for f^3 in eq. (2.55). Bethe and Spedding previously treated $4f^2$ Pr(III) and $4f^{12}$ Tm(III), but the first great attack on the excited multiplet terms of lanthanides was made by Satten (1953) investigating $4f^3$ Nd(III) and identifying the various J levels of the quartet terms. Actually, (Jørgensen, 1957), Satten did not identify the doublet terms and hence the spin-forbidden bands of Nd(III). This was due to an inappropriate assumption of the relative ratios between E^1, E^2, and E^3. This situation is now completely clear, and recently many authors have made complete calculations

TABLE 11.1. The parameter of interelectronic repulsion E^3 and the Landé parameter of relativistic effects ζ_{4f} in lanthanide compounds. All values in kK, arranged according to the number q of electrons in the 4f shell

q		E^3	ζ_{4f}
2	Pr(III)	0.46	0.73
3	Nd(III)	0.49	0.91
5	Sm(III)	0.48	1.18
6	Sm(II)	0.42	1.1
	Eu(III)	0.55	1.36
7	Eu(II)	0.5	—
	Gd(III)	0.61	1.54
8	Tb(III)	—	1.72
9	Dy(III)	0.57	1.92
10	Ho(III)	0.61	2.16
11	Er(III)	0.64	2.47
12	Tm(III)	0.63	2.7
13	Yb(III)	—	2.94

TABLE 11.2. J levels identified in absorption (and fluorescence) spectra of lanthanide compounds with the oxidation number $+3$. For literature references, see page 150

		$M(H_2O)_9{}^{+++}$	M in LaCl$_3$			$M(H_2O)_9{}^{+++}$	M in LaCl$_3$
Pr(III)	$^3H_4$	—	0–0.20		$^2G_{7/2}$	19.14–.22	18.99–19.08
	$^3H_5$	—	2.13–.28		$^4G_{9/2}$	19.59–.66	19.43–.46
	$^3H_6$	—	4.23–.52		$^2D_{3/2}$	21.16–.20 $\left\{ \begin{array}{l} 21.16–.19 \\ 21.03–... \end{array} \right.$	
	$^3F_2$	—	4.92–.95		$^2G_{9/2}$		
	$^3F_3$	—	6.28–.34		$^4G_{11/2}$	21.55–.75	21.37–.46
	$^3F_4$	—	6.70–.80		$^2P_{1/2}$	23.399	23.215
	$^1G_4$	9.8	9.74–.81		$^2D_{5/2}$	23.9	23.76–.78
	$^1D_2$	16.71–.96	16.63–.78		$^2P_{3/2}$	26.29–.34	26.14–
	$^3P_0$	20.687	20.746		$^4D_{3/2}$	28.26–.29	27.97
	$^3P_1$	21.28–.29	21.07–.10		$^4D_{1/2}$	28.8	28.51
	$^1I_6$	21.40–.46	21.30–.50		. . .		. . .
	$^3P_2$	22.42–.45	22.21–.25	Sm(III)	$^6H_{5/2}$	0	—
Nd(III)	$^4I_{9/2}$	0–0.38	0–0.25		$^6H_{7/2}$	1.1	—
	$^4I_{11/2}$	—	1.97–2.06		$^6H_{9/2}$	2.3	—
	$^4I_{13/2}$	—	3.93–4.08		$^6H_{11/2}$	3.6	—
	$^4I_{15/2}$	5.88	—		$^6H_{13/2}$	5.0	—
	$^4F_{3/2}$	11.57–60	11.42–.45		$^6F_{1/2}$	6.2	—
	$^4F_{5/2}$	12.62	12.46–.49		$^6H_{15/2}$	6.5	—
	$^2H_{9/2}$	—	12.53–.56		$^6F_{3/2}$	6.7	—
	$^4F_{7/2}$	13.49–.68	13.40–.49		$^6F_{5/2}$	7.2	—
	$^4S_{3/2}$	—	13.53–.53		$^6F_{7/2}$	8.0	—
	$^4F_{9/2}$	14.77–.90	14.70–.72		$^6F_{9/2}$	9.2	—
	$^2H_{11/2}$	15.99–16.08	15.91–.96		$^6F_{11/2}$	10.5	—
	$\left. \begin{array}{l} ^2G_{7/2} \\ ^4G_{5/2} \end{array} \right\}$	17.15–.47	17.10–.30		$J={}^5/_2$	17.8	—
	$^2K_{13/2}$	—	18.55–. . .		$^4F_{3/2}$	19.88	—
					. . .	. . .	. . .

TABLE 11.2—*contd.*]   11. LANTHANIDES AND 5F ELEMENTS   149

		$M(H_2O)_9^{+++}$	M in $LaCl_3$		$M(H_2O)_9^{+++}$	M in $LaCl_3$
Eu(III)	$^7F_0$	0	—	^6P	28.34–.53	—
	$^7F_1$	0.31–.46	—	^6P	30.63–.72	—
	$^7F_2$	0.96	—	. . .	. . .	. . .
	$^7F_3$	2.0	—	Ho(III) $^5I_8$	0	—
	$^7F_4$	3.0	—	$^5I_7$	5.03	—
	$^7F_5$	4.0	—	$^5I_6$	8.53	—
	$^7F_6$	5.1	—	$^5I_5$	11.14	—
	$^5D_0$	17.26	—	$^5I_4$	13.25	—
	$^5D_1$	19.00–.02	—	$^5F_5$	15.42	—
	$^5D_2$	21.48–.50	—	$^5S_2$	18.37	—
	. . .	. . .	. . .	$^5F_4$	18.52	—
Gd(III)	$^8S_{7/2}$	0	—	$^5F_3$	20.56	—
	$^6P_{7/2}$	32.08–.16	—	$^5F_2$	21.03	—
	$^6P_{5/2}$	32.68–.75	—	$^3K_8$	21.30	—
	$^6P_{3/2}$	33.27–.31	—	$^3K_6$	22.2	—
	$^6I_{7/2}$	35.82–.86	—	$^5F_1$	22.30	—
	$^6I_{9/2}$	36.17	—	$^5G_5$	24.01–.06	—
	$^6I_{17/2}$	36.23–.27	—	$^5G_4$	26.0	—
	$^6I_{11/2}$	36.45–.50	—	$^3K_7$	26.2	. . .
	$^6I_{15/2}$ $^6I_{13/2}$ }	36.54–.64	—	. . .	. . .	. . .
	$^6D_{9/2}$	39.65	—	Er(III) $^4I_{15/2}$	0–0.30	0–
	$^6D_{1/2}$	40.63	—	$^4I_{13/2}$	6.87–7.00	6.55–.64
Tb(III)	$^7F_6$	0	—	$^4I_{11/2}$	10.53–.60	10.21–.24
	$^7F_5$	2.1	—	$^4F_{9/2}$	12.43–.64	12.40–.49
	$^7F_4$	3.4	—	$^4I_{9/2}$	15.30–.40	15.25–30
	$^7F_3$	4.4	—	$^4S_{3/2}$	18.46–.49	18.39–.41
	$^7F_2$	5.0	—	$^2H_{11/2}$	19.17–.29	19.13–.18
	$^7F_1$	5.5	—	$^4F_{7/2}$	20.55–.65	20.48–.55
	$^7F_0$	5.8	—	$^4F_{5/2}$	22.26–.28	22.17–.18
	$^5D_4$	20.5	—	$^4F_{3/2}$	22.59–.63	22.50–.53
	. . .	. . .	. . .	$^2H_{9/2}$	24.57–.69	24.50–.60
Dy(III)	$^6H_{15/2}$	—	0–0.14	$^4G_{11/2}$	26.42–.56	27.36
	$^6H_{13/2}$	—	3.46–.56	$^2K_{15/2}$	—	26.32–.41
	$^6H_{11/2}$	—	5.79–.86	$^4G_{9/2}$	27.4	27.99–
	$^6H_{9/12}$ $^6F_{11/2}$ }	—	7.59–.75	$^4G_{7/2}$	28.1	27.60–.63
	$^6H_{7/2}$ $^6F_{9/2}$ }	9.0	8.94–9.09	. . .	. . .	. . .
	$^6H_{5/2}$	10.2	10.12–	^4D	39.18	—
	$^6F_{7/2}$	10.9	10.91–.95	. . .	. . .	. . .
	$^6F_{5/2}$	12.3	12.31–.34	Tm(III) $^3H_6$	0–0.31	—
	$^6F_{3/2}$	13.2	13.11–.12	$^3H_4$	5.8	—
	$^6F_{1/2}$	—	—	$^3H_5$	8.2	—
	—	21.05	20.96	$^3F_4$	12.58–.76	—
	—	22.08–.17	21.95	$^3F_3$	14.41–.49	—
	—	23.42	23.30	$^3F_2$	15.08–.11	—
	—	25.35	24.94	$^1G_4$	21.17–.51	—
	—	25.92	25.58–26.10	$^1D_2$	27.91–.97	—
	^6P	27.31–.43	27.26–.29	$^1I_6$	—	—
				$^3P_0$	35.5	—
				$^3P_1$	36.5	—
				$^3P_2$	38.2	—

with intermediate coupling and identified the lowest ten to fifteen line groups of Pr(III) (Hellwege, 1951; Sayre, Sancier, and Fried, 1955; Margolis, 1961), Nd(III) (Carlson and Dieke, 1961; Wybourne, 1960; Wong, 1961), Pm(III) (Crozier and Runciman, 1961), Sm(III) (Lämmermann, 1958), Eu(III) (Hellwege and Kahle, 1951; Judd, 1955), Gd(III) (Dieke and Leopold, 1957; Lacroix, 1961) Tb(III) (Geisler and Hellwege, 1953), Dy(III) (Jørgensen, 1957; Crosswhite and Dieke, 1961), Ho(III) (Hüfner, 1961; Crozier and Runciman, 1961), Er(III) (Wybourne, 1960; Kahle, 1961; Erath, 1961; Dieke and Singh, 1961) and Tm(III) (Jørgensen, 1955; Johnson, 1958; Runciman and Wybourne, 1959; Gruber and Conway, 1960; Wong and Richman, 1961). Representative values of these parameters are given in Table 11.1. Though both Judd and the previous writer previously had started general calculations for $4f^q$ in spherical symmetry, the most extensive article is that by Elliott, Judd, and Runciman (1957).

To the same extent as in atomic spectra, E^1, E^2, E^3, and ζ_{4f} function as phenomenological parameters, the agreement with experiment being within a few tenths of a kK in average. There is no doubt, as suggested by Watson's and by Ridley's Hartree-Fock calculations, that considerable correlation effects have decreased the interelectronic repulsion parameters from the values they would have had for Slater antisymmetrized determinants.

The ligand field effects in lanthanides are two orders of magnitude weaker than in the d transition groups. A large experimental material of low-temperature spectra of crystals have been collected and the usual width of distribution of sublevels belonging to a definite J level is 0.05 to 0.15 kK. It decreases slightly, but not dramatically, as a function of increasing atomic number. Only in a few exceptional cases, the ground-level exhibits sublevel splittings up to 0.3 kK. The microsymmetry most frequently studied is trigonal D_{3h} in $M(H_2O)_9(C_2H_5SO_4)_3$ and $M(H_2O)_9(BrO_3)_3$ and also of M(III) substitutionally built into anhydrous $LaCl_3$, where again nine chlorides are bound to M, six in a trigonal prism and three in a triangle in the middle, parallel to the two other triangular faces but turned 60 deg. around the trigonal axis. Other crystals frequently studied, such as MCl_3, $6H_2O$, unfortunately contain $MCl_2(H_2O)_6$ groups not having much higher symmetry than a hedgehog, whereas $Mg_3M_2(H_2O)_{24}(NO_3)_{12}$ has a ligand field not very different from the vertigineously high icosahedral symmetry. Judd (1957) very prudently did not suggest that the microsymmetry is indeed icosahedral, but only that (possibly for accidental reasons) the ligand field parameters closely reproduce the degeneracy numbers e appropriate to icosahedral symmetry. Actually, γ_n can here attain one of five values, corresponding to $e = 1, 2, 3, 4,$ and 5. Except the spherical symmetry, it is the only symmetry with orbital degeneracies as high as 4 and 5, and the only symmetry besides the various octahedral and tetrahedral symmetries having several threefold axes.

Starting with a paper by Elliott and Stevens (1952; cf. also the paper on operator equivalents by Stevens, 1952) it has become customary to express the ligand field effects in terms of first-order electrostatic perturbation parameters $A_k^m \langle r^k \rangle$, which are multiples of the average value of r^k of the partly filled f shell and the individual components of the perturbing field arranged according to decreasing symmetry. The components with $m=0$ are cylindrically symmetrical around the highest symmetry axis of the system. In the general case, the first-order perturbation on a 4f shell can be expressed by six parameters, $A_2^0 \langle r^2 \rangle$, $A_4^0 \langle r^4 \rangle$, $A_4^3 \langle r^4 \rangle$, $A_6^0 \langle r^6 \rangle$, $A_6^3 \langle r^6 \rangle$, and $A_6^6 \langle r^6 \rangle$. In various higher symmetries, some of these parameters necessarily vanish; e.g. in the trigonal symmetry $A_4^3 \langle r^4 \rangle$ and $A_6^3 \langle r^6 \rangle$ are absent. In octahedral symmetry, only two independent parameters survive, namely $A_4^0 \langle r^4 \rangle$ and $A_6^0 \langle r^6 \rangle$.

These parameters are quite successful in one regard, that is that the structure of the individual line groups are predicted to within a few K, even for many-electron systems such as Er(III) and Tm(III) in trigonal symmetry. However, Judd has already pointed out that there must be something wrong with the ligand field model, no conceivable field originating at a distance R being able to produce, for instance, much larger values of $\langle r^6 \rangle / R^7$ than of $\langle r^2 \rangle / R^3$. Various authors attempt to explain these discrepancies in terms of special polarization and screening effects.

Taking our previous experience in d complexes into account, a much simpler explanation seems plausible: *though the effects of chemical bonding (MO formation) on the partly filled shell are small, they are still larger than the electrostatic first-order perturbation.* From an MO point of view, we are in the situation of very large internuclear distances (Chapter 5) with one fortunate condition, however: that only one of our atoms involves a partly filled shell. Consequently, we cannot expect well-defined MO configurations to form in any lower symmetry than the spherical (except in the extraordinary cases where only the sublevel of a given symmetry type Γ_j originates in the configuration f^q), but we can hope for orbital energies being physically significant parameters for describing the energy differences which occur. Since at most seven different one-electron energies are possible for a f shell, six independent MO energy differences can occur at most. They can uniquely be translated to the six ligand field parameters $A_k^m \langle r^k \rangle$, but it is evident that the reason for the MO energy differences occurring may be many other effects than a first-order electrostatic perturbation. Hence, the homomorphous relation between the electrostatic ligand field model and the more general MO theory has again secured a set of parameters which have much more physical significance in the form of one-electron energy differences than in the form of $\langle r^k \rangle$ contributions.

In trigonal symmetry, the trigonal axis introduces roughly a linear microsymmetry in the central ion orbitals. Thus, the f shell splits into odd $\sigma(a_2'')$, $\pi(e')$, and $\delta(e'')$. Only the two odd φ orbitals which can be separated by the ligand field angularly dependent with a period of 120 deg. around the trigonal axis do not imitate linear symmetry but split into $\varphi_1(a_1')$ and $\varphi_2(a_2')$, the symbols in parentheses indicating Mulliken's group-theoretical quantum numbers. Since two pairs of orbitals, π and δ, each remain degenerate, only four independent MO energy differences occur, which can be related to the four $A_k{}^m\langle r^k \rangle$ usually given in trigonal symmetry.

Eisenstein (1956) calculated the symmetry types γ_n of σ and π orbitals in a variety of symmetries. Since the three σ orbitals from the three ligands in the plane are $a_1'+e'$ and the six σ orbitals from the trigonal prism $a_1'+a_2''+e'+e''$ the only one of the seven f orbitals which is not σ-antibonding in the nine-co-ordinated lanthanide complexes is $\varphi_2(a_2')$. Hence, it is not evident what the actual order of the seven orbital energies will be, but the present writer still believes that it is a useful exercise to indicate the MO energy differences of the appropriate γ_n rather than the so-called ligand field parameters.

The transitions from 4f to 5d occur in Ce(III) complexes at lower wavenumbers than in Ce^{+3} [eq. (11.2)] as found by Freed (1931) for $Ce(H_2O)_9{}^{+3}$. In various anion complexes, the 4f→5d bands which are moderately strong (allowed by Laporte's rule) occur at somewhat lower wavenumbers than in the aquo ion (Jørgensen, 1956). Thus, in the bromo complexes in ethanol to be discussed below, the bands are observed at 31.9 kK in Ce(III), at 44.5 kK in Pr(III), and at 43.4 kK in Tb(III). The reappearance in the f^8 system is a half-filled shell effect, the excited state $4f^7 5d$ now being strongly stabilized. Actually, these wavenumbers correspond to $D=6.2$ kK and an increase of the 4f–5d orbital energy difference 4.7 kK for each new electron in the 4f shell. This is valid for the oxidation number $+3$; the 4f→5d transitions in $+2$ have about 50 kK lower wavenumbers according to this theory and give the strong red colour of Sm(II) compounds.

Electron transfer spectra have recently been observed (Jørgensen, 1962) of lanthanide perchlorate solutions in nearly anhydrous ethanol, to which small quantities of NH_4Br are added. The absorption bands of these bromo complexes show a remarkable variation with q, the number of electrons in the 4f shell [cf. the M(II) iodides in eq. (11.1)]:

$$
\begin{array}{lll}
q= & 3 \ \text{Nd(III)} & \sim 49 \ \text{kK} \\
& 5 \ \text{Sm(III)} & 40.2 \\
& 6 \ \text{Eu(III)} & 31.2 \ \text{and} \ 37.6 \qquad\qquad (11.3) \\
& 12 \ \text{Tm(III)} & 44.5 \\
& 13 \ \text{Yb(III)} & 35.5 \ \text{and} \ 42.0
\end{array}
$$

whereas for the other values of q, the corresponding bands are not observed and must be well beyond 49 kK. Good agreement can be obtained with a theory extracting its parameters from the well-known internal transitions in the 4f shell. The simplest version is to consider the one-electron energy difference between the highest filled MO (mainly concentrated on the bromide ligand) and the 4f shell to be $W - qQ$ and to consider the spin-pairing energy in eq. (2.58). Then

$$
\begin{array}{lll}
\text{Sm(III)} \quad q=5{\rightarrow}6{:} & 40.2 \text{ kK} = W - 5Q - 40D/13 & \\
\text{Eu(III)} \quad q=6{\rightarrow}7{:} & 31.2 \text{ kK} = W - 6Q - 48D/13 & (11.4) \\
\text{Yb(III)} \quad q=13{\rightarrow}14{:} & 35.5 \text{ kK} = W - 13Q &
\end{array}
$$

corresponding to $W=85.2$ kK, $Q=3.8$ kK, and $D=8.5$ kK. A somewhat more refined treatment, where the stabilization $-9E^3$ of H ground terms and $-21E^3$ of I ground terms, and the first-order relativistic effects expressed as multiples of ζ_{4f} also enter, give the better parameters $W=70$ kK, $Q=3$ kK, and $D=6.5$ kK. The latter value is in good agreement with the value of $\frac{9}{8}E^1$ otherwise known to increase regularly from 6 kK in Pr(III) to 8 kK in Tm(III). The refined theory predicts that the bands will occur at 49 kK in Nd(III), 46 kK in Tm(III), and above 50 kK in all the cases where no band has been observed.

The corresponding optical electronegativities are

	Before	After correction for spin-pairing energy	
Sm(III)	1.45	0.8	
Eu(III)	1.75	0.95	(11.5)
Tm(III)	1.3	1.45	
Yb(III)	1.6	1.6	

since Br has 2.8. This also agrees with the observation of electron transfer bands in the orange Eu(III) and lemon-yellow Yb(III) dialkyldithiocarbamates, assuming the ligand to have the optical electronegativity 2.5.

Dieke, Crosswhite, and Dunn (1961) reported the orbital energy differences in the gaseous ions M^{++} and M^{+3}, using the 6s energy as zero-reference:

	4f	5d	6p	
$4f^1$ La^{++}	-20	-15	$+30$	
$4f^{13}$ Tm^{++}	-40	$+5$	$+40$	(11.6)
$4f^1$ Ce^{+++}	-85	-40	$+35$	
$4f^{13}$ Yb^{+++}	-125	-25	$+50$.	

The actual ionization energy of 4f is some 150 kK of La^{++} and 300 kK of Ce^{+++}. The situation in the compounds is obviously quite different. In many respects, it is somewhat analogous to the ionic charge $+2$ of the gaseous ion, if the oxidation number is $+3$. We may look at various instances of this phenomenon:

1. The relative stabilization of the 4f shell, 12Q going from f^1 to f^{13}, is 36 kK in the electron transfer spectra mentioned above, interpolating to an ionic charge of 2.8 in eq. (11.6).

2. The energy difference 4f→5d in the bromide complexes is comparable to the ionic charge 2.65 by interpolation in eq. (11.6).

3. The nephelauxetic effect in bromide complexes would correspond to an ionic charge about 2.85.

4. However, the ionization energies in compounds are much smaller, and presumably comparable to those of the gaseous M^+.

We must not forget that the F^0 integral occurring in J(4f, 4f) is very large, of the order of magnitude 100 to 150 kK. Hence, there is a very serious difference between the electron affinity and the ionization energy of the 4f shell in a given compound, cf. eq. (7.25). The optical electronegativities given in eq. (11.5) correspond to the electron affinity M(III)→M(II). It is known from the studies of electron transfer spectra of Cs_3NdF_7 and Cs_3DyF_7 made by Asprey and Hoppe (1962) that, whereas the uncorrected optical electronegativity for the process M(IV)→M(III) in these two cases is 3.0, the values corrected for spin-pairing energy are 2.7 for Nd(IV) and 3.7 for Dy(IV), i.e. 2.6 units higher than in eq. (11.5) for isoelectronic species. This difference, 78 kK, is not much smaller than the integral J(4f, 4f) and is much larger than the difference in optical electronegativities for two isoelectronic 4d (or 5d) ions in the oxidation numbers +4 and +3, amounting to only 0.5 unit or 15 kK. This expresses a fundamental difference between the lanthanides, much more electrovalent bound and exhibiting a nearly invariant oxidation number +3; and the complexes of the ordinary transition groups.

From many points of view, the 5f elements take an intermediate position between the 4f lanthanides and the d transition elements (Katz and Seaborg, 1957). Thus, the oxidation numbers vary much more freely and are on average higher:

	Common	Rare	
Z=89	Ac(III)		
90	Th(IV)		
91	Pa(V)	Pa(IV)	
92	U(VI), U(IV)	U(III), U(V)	
93	Np(IV), Np(V), Np(VI)	Np(III)	
94	Pu(IV), Pu(III)	Pu(V), Pu(VI)	(11.7)
95	Am(III)	Am(IV), Am(V), Am(VI)	
96	Cm(III)	Cm(IV)	
97	Bk(III), Bk(IV)		
98	Cf(III)		
99	Es(III).		

The heavier elements, 100 Fm, 101 Mv, and 102 No, have only been prepared in exceedingly minute quantities; the two latter were identified in samples containing some twenty atoms. The identification was only possible because the ion-exchange techniques are so highly developed, and the predictions of where to find ions with the oxidation number $+3$ so well founded.

The spectroscopic studies made in the last ten years have shown most unequivocally that, in the cases where more than 86 electrons (the radon core) occur, and where the ionic charge is at least $+3$, the rest of the electrons belong to the 5f shell and not, for instance, to the 6d shell. This is true both for gaseous ions and for compounds of the isoelectronic series:

$$
\begin{aligned}
&5f \quad Pa(IV) \ U(V) \ Np(VI) \\
&5f^2 \ U(IV) \ Np(V) \ Pu(VI) \\
&5f^3 \ U(III) \ Np(IV) \ Pu(V) \ Am(VI) \\
&5f^4 \ Np(III) \ Pu(IV) \ Am(V) \\
&5f^5 \ Pu(III) \ Am(IV) \\
&5f^6 \ Am(III) \ Cm(IV) \\
&5f^7 \ Cm(III) \ Bk(IV).
\end{aligned}
\tag{11.8}
$$

This was somewhat of a surprise to many chemists who argued from the flourishing chemistry expressed in eq. (11.7) that Pa, U, Np, Pu could not possibly have anything to do with the rare earths. However, looking back on this complicated discussion, there may not have been too much reason to be surprised. The 3d transition group is also characterized by a certain austerity, keeping conservatively the oxidation numbers $+3$ and $+2$, as compared to the much more vividly changing 4d group with $+8, +7, +6, +5, +4, +3$, and $+2$. One would actually expect similar developments going from 4f to 5f as going from 3d to 4d. However, we will make one concession to this chemical attitude and call the elements in eq. (11.8) 5f elements rather than actinides, since we believe that the name of the partly filled shell involved says something much more essential than the tendency to oxidation number $+3$ which only becomes pronounced in the trans-uranium or more exactly, in the trans-neptunium elements in eq. (11.7).

The Landé parameter ζ_{5f} is some two to three times larger in the 5f elements than in the corresponding lanthanide ion. Consequently, the deviations from Russell-Saunders coupling are much more pronounced. For several years, there was no clear-cut evidence for the relative size of the interelectronic repulsion parameters. In gaseous Th^{++}, E^3 is 300 K, some three-quarters of what one would expect in Ce^{++}, but in the isoelectronic uranium (IV) aquo ion, the value does not seem to be much larger, as discussed by the present writer (1959). Also recent studies of the absorption spectra of curium (III) complexes suggest values of E^3 about half as large as in the corresponding Gd(III). The detailed identification of J levels, however, is at a much more preliminary stage at present in the 5f elements than in the lanthanides.

The most difficult question remains: what is the size of the ligand field effects in the 5f complexes? Rather extreme points have been taken. In the $5f^1$ system NpF_6, Goodman and Fred (1959) assumed that the orbital energy difference Δ between the lowest nonbonding odd γ_2 and the three degenerate π-antibonding orbitals odd γ_5 is 5.35 kK and that the difference Θ between these γ_5 and the three σ-antibonding odd γ_4 is 16 kK. However, we believe that this assumption is based on a misinterpretation of an electron transfer band as an internal transition in the 5f shell. On the other hand, Lammermann and Stapleton (1961) suggest that the sublevel splitting of the ground level $^6H_{5/2}$ of Pu(III) in $La(H_2O)_9(C_2H_5SO_4)_3$ and in $LaCl_3$ is not larger than of Sm(III) in the same environment. Gruber (1961) concluded that Am(III) in $LaCl_3$ exhibits slightly larger "ligand field" parameters than the corresponding Eu(III).

The situation is particularly interesting in octahedral 5f complexes. The $5f^2$ systems UCl_6^{--} and PuF_6 show rather unusual magnetochemical behaviour, the nearly temperature-independent paramagnetism demonstrating that the Γ_J component Γ_1 must be separated at least some 0.8 kK from the following component Γ_4 of the ground state $^3H_4$. Satten, Young, and Gruen (1960) originally assumed fairly large values of the ligand field parameters, i.e. MO energy differences, but their recent identification of the Γ_4 component mentioned as the excited level of a band at 0.91 kK suggests rather values of Δ and Θ close to 1.8 and 2.4 kK, respectively, and $\zeta_{5f}=1.8$ kK. This also corresponds well to Axe's estimate (1960) for the $5f^1$ system Pa(IV) in Cs_2ZrCl_6, viz. $\Delta=1.50$ kK, $\Theta=2.16$ kK, and $\zeta_{5f}=1.49$ kK. Satten and the present writer (1962) discuss the energy levels of UCl_6^{--} and the 4 per cent more nephelauxetic UBr_6^{--} and, in general, the relative influence of ligand field effects and central field effects in 5f compounds. Probably, in most of the lower symmetries, the MO energy differences are smaller than in the octahedral examples mentioned. The fact that the $5f^1$ system NpO_2^{++} has only narrow bands at 6.75 and 8.15 kK (Waggener, 1958) might suggest that even in the dioxo ions, the splitting into Ω sublevels of the J levels is not extremely large. Recently (Panzer and Suttle, 1961) a compound $PCl_4^+UCl_6^-$ has been reported, presenting narrow bands at 10.4 and 11.6 kK, presumably again being sublevels of the excited level $^2F_{7/2}$ of one 5f electron.

Laporte-allowed 5f→6d transitions are observed at kK:

$$\begin{array}{lll}
5f^1 \text{ Pa(IV)} & 36.3, 39.2, 44.8 & \\
5f^3 \text{ U(III)} & 25.5, 28.6, 31.2 & (11.9) \\
5f^4 \text{ Np(III)} & 34.5, 37.6, 43.5 & \\
5f^5 \text{ Pu(III)} & \sim 40, \ldots & \\
\end{array}$$

Similar to the situation in Ce(III), formation of chloride complexes shift the U(III) bands slightly to lower wavenumbers (Jørgensen, 1956). The shift to higher wavenumbers, going from the oxidation number $+3$ to the isoelectronic species in $+4$, can be extrapolated to some 25 kK, half the size of the shift of 4f→5d transitions going from $+2$ to $+3$ in the lanthanides.

It is not possible here to say much about electron transfer bands in the 5f complexes. Most definitely, they are observed in UCl_6, UF_6, and the other hexafluorides, UO_2^{++} and the other MO_2^{++} (but not with certainty in MO_2^+). However, the interpretation in terms of optical electronegativities is not yet easy (cf. page 95).

REFERENCES

Asprey, L. B., and Hoppe, R. (1962), *J. Am. Chem. Soc.*
Axe, J. D., Thesis, Berkeley, UCRL-9293, July 1960.
Carlson, E., and Dieke, G. H. (1961), *J. Chem. Phys.*, **34**, 1602.
Crosswhite, H. M., and Dieke, G. H. (1961), *J. Chem. Phys.*, **35**, 1535.
Crozier, M. H., and Runciman, W. A. (1961), *J. Chem. Phys.*, **35**, 1392.
Dieke, G. H., and Leopold, L. (1957), *J. Opt. Soc. Am.*, **47**, 944.
Dieke, G. H., and Singh, S. (1961), *J. Chem. Phys.*, **35**, 555.
Dieke, G. H., Crosswhite, H. M., and Dunn, B. (1961), *J. Opt. Soc. Am.*, **51**, 820.
Eisenstein, J. C. (1956), *J. Chem. Phys.*, **25**, 142.
Elliott, R. J., and Stevens, K. W. H. (1952), *Proc. Roy. Soc. (London)*, **A215**, 437;(1953), **A219**, 397.
Elliott, J. P., Judd, B. R., and Runciman, W. A. (1957), *Proc. Roy. Soc. (London)*, **A240**, 509.
Erath, E. H. (1961), *J. Chem. Phys.*, **34**, 1985.
Freed, S. (1931), *Phys. Rev.*, **38**, 2122.
Geisler, H. F., and Hellwege, K. H. (1953), *Z. Physik.*, **136**, 293.
Gobrecht, H. (1938), *Ann. Physik* [5], **31**, 755.
Goodman, G. L., and Fred, M. (1959), *J. Chem. Phys.*, **30**, 849.
Gruber, J. B., and Conway, J. G. (1960), *J. Chem. Phys.*, **32**, 1178 and 1531.
Gruber, J. B. (1961), *J. Chem. Phys.*, **35**, 2186.
Hellwege, K. H., and Kahle, H. G. (1951), *Z. Physik*, **129**, 62.
Hellwege, A. M., and Hellwege, K. H. (1951), *Z. Physik*, **130**, 549; (1953), **135**, 92.
Hüfner, S. (1961), *Z. Physik*, **164**, 269 and 456.
Judd, B. R. (1955), *Proc. Roy. Soc. (London)*, **A228**, 120.
Judd, B. R. (1956), *Proc. Phys. Soc.*, **A69**, 157.
Jørgensen, C. K. (1955), *Acta Chem. Scand.*, **9**, 540.
Jørgensen, C. K. (1956), *Mat. fys. Medd. Dan. Vid. Selsk.*, **30**, No. 22.
Jørgensen, C. K. (1956), *Acta Chem. Scand.*, **10**, 1503.
Jørgensen, C. K. (1957), "Energy Levels of Complexes and Gaseous Ions," Gjellerups Forlag, Copenhagen.
Jørgensen, C. K. (1957), *Acta Chem. Scand.*, **11**, 1981.
Jørgensen, C. K. (1959), *Mol. Phys.*, **2**, 96.
Jørgensen, C. K. (1962), *Mol. Phys.*, **5**, 271.
Kahle, H. G. (1961), *Z. Physik*, **161**, 486.
Katz, J. J., and Seaborg, G. T. (1957), "The Chemistry of the Actinide Elements", Methuen, London.
Lacroix, R. (1961), *Arch. Sci. (Geneva)*, **14**, 149.
Lämmermann, H., and Stapleton, H. J. (1961), *J. Chem. Phys.*, **35**, 1514.
Lämmermann, H. (1958), *Z. Physik.*, **150**, 551; (1960), **160**, 355.
Lang, R. J. (1936), *Can. J. Res.*, **14A**, 127.
Margolis, J. S. (1961), *J. Chem. Phys.*, **35**, 1367.
Panzer, R. E., and Suttle, J. F. (1961), *J. Inorg. Nucl. Chem.*, **20**, 229.
Ridley, E. C. (1960), *Proc. Camb. Phil. Soc.*, **56**, 41.
Runciman, W. A., and Wybourne, B. G. (1959), *J. Chem. Phys.*, **31**, 1149.
Satten, R. A. (1953), *J. Chem. Phys.*, **21**, 637.
Satten, R. A., Young, D., and Gruen, D. M. (1960), *J. Chem. Phys.*, **33**, 1140.
Satten, R. A., and Jørgensen, C. K. (1962).
Sayre, E. V., Sancier, K. M., and Fried, S. (1955), *J. Chem. Phys.*, **23**, 2060; 2066.
Stevens, K. W. H. (1952), *Proc. Phys. Soc.*, **A65**, 209.
Waggener, W. C. (1958), *J. Phys. Chem.*, **62**, 382.
Wong, E. Y., and Richman, I. (1961), *J. Chem. Phys.*, **34**, 1182.
Wong, E. Y. (1961), *J. Chem. Phys.*, **34**, 1989.
Wybourne, B. G. (1960), *J. Chem. Phys.*, **32**, 639; (1961), **34**, 279.

12. X-Ray Spectra

In Chapter 10 we discussed the X-ray absorption and emission spectra as examples of very large relativistic effects, separating the inner shells with positive l into the two j values $l \pm 1/2$. Taking these effects into account, we have some of the most convincing evidence for the utility of electron configurations (with the number of electrons in each shell being an integer) as classification of energy levels.

However, in Chapter 10 we talked as if the X-ray spectrum of a given element is independent of its chemical state. This is also true to a high approximation. Actually, very accurate measurements unveil small chemical shifts. Thus, Stelling (1928–34) studied sulphur compounds having the absorption edge corresponding to complete ionization of a 1s electron close to 20,000 kK. There is a small variation dependent on the oxidation number, $+6$ in SO_4^{--} having the edge at 90 kK higher wavenumber than -2 in sulphides, whereas 0 and $+4$ occupy intermediate positions. This was used as a criterion for the oxidation number in various phosphorus and chlorine compounds, and later in 3d transition elements. A much smaller variation could be found in the emission lines, e.g. a shift of the so-called $K\alpha_1$ and $K\alpha_2$ lines (transitions from $2p_{3/2}$ and $2p_{1/2}$ to 1s) amounting to 11 kK from SO_4^{--} to S^{--}.

It is quite evident that the ionization energy of internal shells is affected by the presence of the external electrons and hence apt to show weak chemical effects. An extreme case is the ionization of 1s electrons from very light elements, where the atomic spectral data are from Charlotte Moore's tables and the absorption edges from Cauchois's tables, all transformed into kK:

$$
\begin{array}{llll}
Li^+ \rightarrow Li^{+2} & 610 & Li\ edge & 440 \\
Be^{+2} \rightarrow Be^{+3} & 1240 & Be & 900 \\
B^{+3} \rightarrow B^{+4} & 2090 & B & 1520 \\
C^{+4} \rightarrow C^{+5} & 3160 & C & 2290 \\
N^{+5} \rightarrow N^{+6} & 4450 & N & 3220 \\
O^{+6} \rightarrow O^{+7} & 5950 & O & 4290.
\end{array} \tag{12.1}
$$

The difference between the two values is some 200 kK multiplied by the number of 2s and 2p electrons removed in the gaseous ions in the left-hand column. In general, it can be shown that the variation of the ionization energy of internal shells for a given element is of the same order of magnitude as the variation of the ionization energy of the external shells. This also explains why emission lines, involving the energy difference between two internal shells, show much smaller chemical shifts than the absorption edges.

Watson's HFSCF calculations show the effect clearly, as can be seen from Table 3.1 by a comparison of the ionization energies of an internal shell of a given element with different ionic charges. The chemical shifts actually observed are much smaller than the variation in ionization energy thus calculated for the gaseous ions. This probably reflects the fact that the actual MO ionization energies vary much less than in the corresponding ionic species in gaseous state.

We may give a somewhat qualitative justification of the chemical shift, $E_2 - E_1$ having about the same size as $E_5 - E_4$ in

$$
\begin{array}{ccc}
C(1s)^2 \ldots (a)^2 & \xrightarrow{\ E_1\ } & C(1s) \ldots (a)^2 \\
\downarrow E_4 & & \downarrow E_3 \\
C(1s)^2 \ldots (a) & \xrightarrow{\ E_2\ } & C(1s) \ldots (a) \\
\downarrow E_5 & & \\
C(1s)^2 \ldots & &
\end{array}
\tag{12.2}
$$

from eq. (1.12), neglecting K integrals. The contribution of J integrals to the chemical shift is

$$E_2 - E_1 = J(1s, a) \tag{12.3}$$

whereas

$$E_5 - E_4 = J(a, a) \text{ and } E_3 - E_4 = E_2 - E_1. \tag{12.4}$$

Actually, if the orbital a has a much larger average radius than the 1s shell, $J(1s, a)$ and $J(a, a)$ have the same order of magnitude, though the former integral usually is slightly larger. One may also remark that E_3 has approximately the size E_4 would have had in the element with the atomic number one unit higher.

Consequently, the relatively largest effects should occur for comparatively soft X-ray radiation such as absorption from the 3p levels in 3d complexes. However, for technical reasons, the very high wavenumbers from 1s absorption have been used, except the investigation by Collet (1959) of the $2p_{3/2}$ absorption edge in rhenium (IV), platinum (II), and platinum (IV) complexes. It is increasingly difficult to go below 15,000 kK, because very thin samples (though still uniform) are needed and because the spectrographs must be held *in vacuo*. It is seen in Table 10.2 that, for avoiding these difficulties and observing $2p_{3/2}$ edges, the element to be studied has to be heavier than zirconium, and for $3d_{5/2}$ of a higher atomic number than rhenium. However, there is no doubt that many interesting effects could be discovered in the softer region, such as coupling of partly filled shells with the X-ray created hole in lower shells. Thus, Horák (1960) compared Watson's calculations with the term differences between ^7P and ^5P of $3p^5(^6S3d^5)$ of manganese (II) and iron (III) compounds. Horák (1961) also studied the so-called satellite lines in the cases where more than one excitation subsists on the same atom.

This argumentation on the basis of spherical microsymmetry in compounds is clearly not complete. Already Stelling (1932) remarked that in some chloride complexes such as $Cr(NH_3)_5Cl^{++}$, the absorption edge has so low a wavenumber as to suggest an oxidation number more negative than -1. The explanation is, of course, that we did not speculate on the nature of the excited orbital accepting the electron in the absorption process. If we can use an MO description, we must ask for the distribution of available MO at energies just above the highest filled MO. It is quite conceivable that the partly filled 3d shell of Cr(III) in our example functions as a low-lying acceptor orbital.

This formulation suggests some interesting relations between visible and X-ray absorption spectra. Unfortunately, the monochromatic resolution in the X-ray region of interest is rarely better than 10 kK; we can hardly expect a greater accuracy by measurements around 50,000 kK. However, the studies by Mitchell and Beeman (1952) indicated with certainty very interesting effects of low-lying MO, for instance in strongly coloured compounds such as CrO_4^{--} and MnO_4^{-}. The same is true for $Ni(CN)_4^{--}$, and in general, for all low-spin nickel (II) complexes. Kauer (1956), Böke (1957), and Collet (1959), used the hybridization language for describing this phenomenon, but in a more general MO interpretation, it has something to do with the empty $4p_z$ orbital perpendicular to the plane of the four ligands which is not σ-antibonding as the three 4p orbitals are in octahedral symmetry. The strongest X-ray absorptions generally go $l \to l+1$, but weak bands $l \to l+2$, possibly due to electric quadrupole radiation, are also frequently found.

Very many problems remain to be solved in this area. Cotton and Hanson (1958) reported many unexplained phenomena, e.g. $Ni(NH_3)_6^{++}$ and $Co(NH_3)_6^{+3}$ as well as many zinc (II) complexes exhibit two adjacent $1s \to 4p$ transitions, presumably corresponding to two different MO sets of symmetry type odd γ_4.

REFERENCES

Böke, K. (1957), Z. physik. Chem., **10**, 45; 59; (1957), **11**, 326.
Collet, V., Thesis, Gauthier-Villars, Paris, 1959.
Cotton, F. A., and Hanson, H. P. (1958), J. Chem. Phys., **28**, 83.
Horák, Z. (1960), Czech. J. Phys., **B10**, 405.
Horák, Z. (1961), Proc. Phys. Soc., **77**, 980.
Kauer (1956), Z. physik. Chem., **6**, 105.
Mitchell, G., and Beeman, W. W. (1952), J. Chem. Phys., **20**, 1298.
Stelling, O. (1928), Z. Physik, **50**, 506.
Stelling, O. (1930), Z. physik. Chem., **B7**, 210; (1932), **B16**, 303; (1933), **B23**, 338; (1934), **B24**, 282.

Subject Index